‖‖‖‖‖‖‖‖‖‖‖‖‖‖‖‖‖‖
D1284712

CANCER 4   ME 5

After extra time

To ERICA,
LOVELY TO MEET YOU.
MAY YOU ALWAYS CLIMB
*   THE MOUNTAIN IN FRONT OF YOU.*
With very best wishes,

[signature]

ONE MAN AND HIS BATTLE WITH CANCER

First published in 2012
by Liam Ryan

ISBN 978-0-9573154-0-2

Printed by :
Guardian Print & Design, Nenagh
13 Summerhill, Nenagh, Co. Tipperary
Ireland

To my wife Pam
and my three boys Christy, Lowell and Abe
who made my life very easy to fight for

ACKNOWLEDGEMENT

This entire book is an acknowledgement in itself. It may have my name at the end of it but there are many people, without whom, neither it nor I would be here today. A huge part of my motivation to write it has been to allow me to express my gratitude to everyone. Everybody who sent a card, said a prayer, lit a candle or encouraged me in any way. You all played a role in this story. You all put a piece in the jigsaw without which I would not still be alive, ten years later.

This book is a testament to all of you. Every single gesture, from the smallest to the greatest, has been an essential element to me coming through this. I couldn't have done it without you.

Special mention must go to –

My wonderful wife Pam for all her dedication and devotion throughout my entire illness and recovery. I would simply not be here without her.

My three sisters Carol, Dolores and Eleanor who showed me what a great family really is.

All of my aunts, uncles, cousins and my treasured extended family

Carmel O'Sullivan for her wonderful care and compassion

Professor John Fenton and all of his team at the Mid West Regional Hospital in Limerick

Simon Rogers and his staff and everybody on wards 28 & 29 at the University Hospital, Aintree, Liverpool

David Husband, his team and all of the radiotherapy staff at Clatterbridge Hospital, Wirral

All of the staff at the Royal Hospital Liverpool and the Hospital de Gran Canaria

My 3 G.P.'s, Maureen Ryan and Blaithnaid McCurtain in Ballina and Joe O'Riordan in Liverpool

Michelle Lahart and Paul Denning. Two great friends who were not as lucky as I was.

Everybody in the wonderful community where I live in Ballina and Killaloe and all of the surrounding area

My running physiotherapist, Àine O'Meara

Michael and Irene Fenton

Paddy Hynes for showing me the difference between 5% and 0%

The people of Horseleap and the surrounding towns and villages of Rosemount, Streamstown, Clara, Moate, Kilbeggan and Athlone

All of my wonderful friends in Liverpool, Manchester and London

Everybody in Cloughjordan for giving me the chance to prove my second life had caught up with my first.

Padraic O'Maille in Galway for his assistance and encouragement to get this book published.

Roger Downer for his help with this book and his inspiration as a fellow cancer fighter.

Jane Tomlinson for being one of the most incredible people I have ever come across and the inspiration for where this story can go from here.

THANK YOU ALL

This story has been searching for a publisher to turn it into reality for quite a while. A few of the main book publishers in Ireland expressed good interest, recognising that it is an exceptional story, but in the economic climate of 2012, it proved impossible to convert that interest into an actual book.

Sometimes the further away you look for something the more you are always going to find it under your nose. I was in a bookshop in Nenagh one day, wondering where an author I knew had got her work published, when I found the solution to my problem. The place I was looking for was less than a hundred yards from where I stood.

I will always be eternally grateful to Paddy Brennan and his team at the Nenagh Guardian Print & Design Department for picking up my story from there and taking it to its conclusion. Within two short months, having just discovered that the offices of the Nenagh Guardian produce much more than just a weekly newspaper, my initial enquiry was converted into this finished book.

Paddy handed me over to a wonderful woman called Kathy Slattery who was simply a joy to work with as we turned the finalised scripts into the finished article.

This, in so many ways has been a fitting end to this story. The *Nenagh Guardian* was the first newspaper to print my original script in 2003. Without that happening the longer script may never have seen the light of day. They were there at the very beginning of the story and now they have closed that circle by printing the book itself.

Grateful thanks to Paddy, Kathy and all of the staff at the Guardian.

Places mentioned in this book - IRELAND

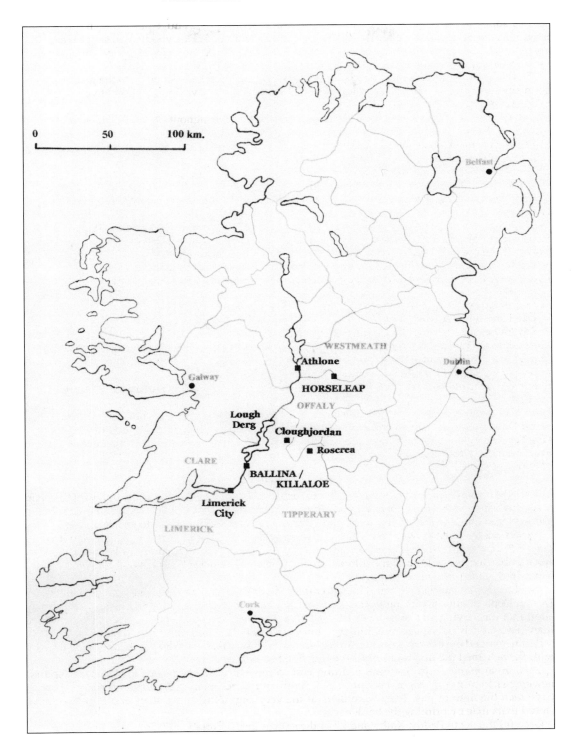

Places mentioned in this book – LIVERPOOL

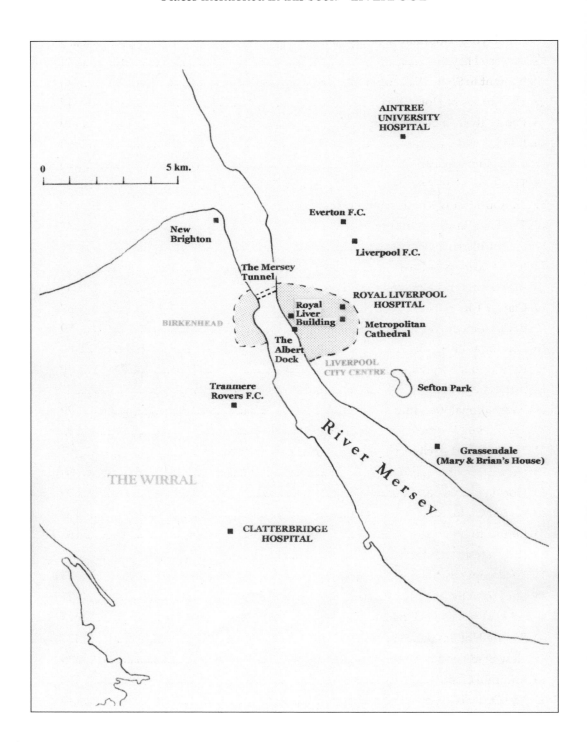

AINTREE
UNIVERSITY
HOSPITAL

0   5 km.

Everton F.C.

New
Brighton

Liverpool F.C.

The Mersey
Tunnel

ROYAL LIVERPOOL
HOSPITAL

Royal
Liver
Building

Metropolitan
Cathedral

BIRKENHEAD

The
Albert
Dock

LIVERPOOL
CITY CENTRE

Tranmere
Rovers F.C.

Sefton Park

River Mersey

Grassendale
(Mary & Brian's House)

THE WIRRAL

CLATTERBRIDGE
HOSPITAL

CONTENTS

1 - Climb your Mountain

In many ways it is ironic that I have written this book. I have never been a good reader. Most of the reading I have done has been through necessity rather than for pleasure. Books and I haven't exactly been great bedfellows ever since.

I would never have had cause to even consider writing a book unless something extraordinary happened to me. Ten years ago something extraordinary did happen to me. I have been through an experience that has enrolled me into a very rare species. There are very few people like me in the world today. I am one of the very lucky ones who should no longer be here.

I have a story now, a story I did not volunteer for. It is a story that I feel needs to be told. It is one of great encouragement to all others who will come after me. A story that is bigger than I am. It is a story that almost carries an obligation to be passed on.

I have been handed a light and I have always believed I have a sense of duty not to put that light under a bushel.

What I have endured and survived is a tremendous source of inspiration to people everywhere. It is a story that proves hope always exists, no matter what the prognosis. I should be dead but I am not. It is a story not just for cancer sufferers, but for everybody who believes there is no hope. Ten years later, against all the odds, I have written a book to tell that story.

The only qualification I have to be the writer and you to be the reader is that I was there. I did what many of you are now hoping to do. From my own experience I know how much more powerful the source of your inspiration is when it comes from somebody who has already achieved what you now need to do. Your friends and family will be busy saying and doing all the right things for you but nothing compares to the motivation that comes from somebody who has already done it. I am that person. I can say to you "I did it and if I did it there is no reason why you can't do it too." I am the proof that nothing is for certain. I am the living proof that the odds, no matter how great, can always be overturned.

My initial cancer diagnosis was one of the few occasions when I did go looking for a book. I had been given a mountain to climb and I needed my first foothold. I needed somebody to give me hope. A source of inspiration to encourage me to tackle something that appeared to be beyond me at that point in time. Somebody, somewhere, who could at least show me the route to the summit, even if I had to do the climbing myself.

The only book that appeared to be available to inspire newly diagnosed cancer sufferers at that time was Lance Armstrong's "It's not about the bike". It was given to me by a great friend of mine, Michelle Lahart, who had been diagnosed with breast cancer a few months earlier. I read some of this book but the only problem with Lance was that I already knew he went on to win the Tour de France seven times. What kind of a role model was that?

Even completing one Tour de France is well beyond most of us mere mortals. This guy won seven in a row!

So the more I read that book the more it actually worked against me. I just couldn't get past the achievements of its author. "How to beat cancer – Step 1, You need to be superhuman"! I would never underestimate any cancer diagnosis but I have a hunch that the seven Tours would put most of us in the grave long before the cancer gets us. Sorry Lance, not the best role model for the rest of us who prefer a cable car to a bicycle when it comes to going up a mountain.

At that time it did cross my mind that there was an opening for somebody ordinary to tell a cancer survival story. I had a long way to go before there was to be any likelihood that that person could be me. I had to survive first and then recover. Finally I had to appreciate how rare my case was and how lucky I was to still be here.

Six months after my treatment I wrote a short account of my story. I wrote it for myself, my own record of my disease. I wanted to have it so that I would not forget many of the finer details of my case. That transcript eventually got passed on and found its way into the hands of other cancer patients. Over time it got passed along by friends to friends. I have now had responses to that original script from all over the world. It was only then did I begin to realise the power it contained.

The greatest appeal of my story for many is that it is an ordinary story. There are no magic potions. No mythical diets. I was not an Olympic athlete or a multiple Tour de France winner. It is simply a story of mind over matter in the fight against greatest disease the world knows. One man and his cancer and how I channelled all my energies into taking the fight all the way. A mindset that in the end was my part in the equation that ensured the battle I had to face was won.

There are no promises in this book. Every personal challenge is unique, no matter how similar they may appear. We are all different. Every cancer is different. Unfortunately this particular story is just mine. It will take you through my life to the point of cancer, through my battle with the disease and then beyond. What I hope it will do is firstly inspire you. Inspire you to take on what you now need to do. Show you that if you are to succeed there is no room for doubt. You must take your fight to the end. If you do you have every chance of winning. If you don't, there will only be one winner. I hope it will then help you by giving you an insight into how I was thinking at certain times. How I dealt with my fears. How I always tried to find the strength of perspective. How I turned negatives into positives by using every single element of my life to assist my fight. How I was determined to fight to the very end.

Finally I hope it will encourage you that you now can be me. You need to take on whatever is in front of you without ever looking back. You must never lose sight of the winning line. Hope is never lost so don't ever give up on it. Nothing is for certain. Your life is your mountain and for some the peaks are higher than others. Go and climb it, step by step, inch by inch. Only if you believe can you reach the top. Only when you reach the top will you get to enjoy the view. I did it and you can too.

2 - Disease History

It won't be long after you are first diagnosed with cancer before somebody proclaims that there has to be a definite reason why. They will then completely unpack everything you did in your life up to that point just so that they can tell you where it came from. Their conclusions will range from, you got it because you fell off your bike 27 years ago to it must have been that dodgy cannelloni you had in your favourite Italian restaurant three weeks ago.

When it comes to cancer people seem to need the comfort of being able to pinpoint the reason why. We like to know our dangers. We seem to need to know where they come from. Perhaps all of this is more for their own benefit than for yours. They will promptly go home and take their kids off their bikes and vow never to eat pasta again.

For me, apart from some of the obvious links on certain occasions, such as smoking and lung cancer, cancer is very much an opportunistic predator. It doesn't tend to leave a trail before it strikes. If I had to give a reason why I got it, it would simply be because everything I had eaten and every breath I inhaled in the previous 40 years, had caused all my red immunity lights to go green for a split second. Cancer then just took its chance. It slipped in like a stealth bomber under the radar. So basically there was no definitive reason. It was just a moment in the middle of a lifetime when it was my turn for my numbers in the big C lottery to come up.

One of the best pieces of advice I feel I can offer through this book is to never look back. This was to become one of my major chips at the live or die roulette table. When you are told you have cancer it is the biggest news you will ever receive in your life. Nothing is bigger in life than the news that it might be about to end. You then have only one direction to go from there. Your focus only needs to be aimed at beating this disease and continuing to live. Everything that went before is irrelevant, including any speculation as to how you got cancer. You have it now so it is too late for that.

This is point zero. Any retrospective trawling back through the whys and wherefores is pointless. It will take you back into what I regard as minus territory. Your fight can only begin when you get yourself back to nought. That is where you must start. You must accept your disease from the very beginning. Your time on this earth has now clearly been divided into two distinct categories, life before-cancer and life after-cancer. There is no point in trying to spend time in the former when you have already been told you have enrolled in the latter.

Having said all that, when the "I'll find the reason" wizards had left the room I did give a cursory, but regardless, glance through my past. I wasn't looking for a reason. I suppose

I was already beginning to evaluate the life I had had. I would do a lot more of that in the years ahead. It would become a great source of strength. If I was contented with my life to that point in time I was automatically in a better frame of mind to take on what I needed to pro-long it. Perhaps I was also just checking if there was a clue, if not a reason, to have warned me about the oncoming predicament that I now found myself in.

3 - Nought to Sixty

I am the youngest and only boy in a family of four children. I grew up in the small village of Horseleap which straddles the border between Westmeath and Offaly in the middle of Ireland. My three sisters, Carol, Dolores, Eleanor and myself were blessed with a wonderful Mam and Dad, Carmel and Paddy. I can honestly say that I don't ever remember witnessing a cross word between them. As well as being husband and wife they were also genuine best friends. They simply lived for each other.

We owned the only pub and shop in the village that my grandfather, William, who I was called after, had bought in 1912. He died young at the age of 47, leaving my grandmother Ellen to raise six children and run the business. At that point my Dad, an only son like myself, had to leave his schooling and return home to give her a hand. My mother knew on marrying him years later that the package included not only a public house but also an in-house mother-in-law.

But the two women got on very well. We all have great memories of Granny Ryan being a seamless part of our parental care. She died in 1978 when I was in my teens and although I didn't realise it then, she was going to look after the ancestral inspiration piece of my cancer fight jigsaw many years later.

When you are diagnosed with cancer one of the unforeseen benefits it will grant you is time. You will have time waiting for treatment, time between treatments and time in recovery. Because you are ill you will either be unable to, or not expected to, do anything meaningful with this time by anybody else. Suddenly, right in the middle of busy lives, cancer sufferers are granted, without any obligation, as much free time as we have the strength for.

I have seen people use this time in many different ways. Some people only use it to worry. Others use it to get angry. Your cancer has brought your daily routine to a standstill. It has granted you a vacuum of time in the middle of your life. Everything you have been doing is now on hold before your cancer makes its next move or before you make a counter move.

So one of the first impacts your new disease has on you is unexpected time. Without your cancer it would not exist. You begin there. It is important to use this time wisely. It can be easy to only fill it with regret and despair. Cancer has cast a dark spell over you. Your instinct may be to begin to think of things that you haven't done and now may never get to do. To only use this vacuum of time to start having feelings of worry or regret is handing the advantage back to your disease.

As soon as I had accepted my cancer I felt I needed to use this time well. I wanted to turn it to my advantage as much as I could. It needed to become the very first weapon of my fight. My cancer had given me an interval in my life. I wanted to make it pay for giving me a chance to re-group. I wanted to be able to say "You made a mistake buddy. You shouldn't have given me time to come back and get you. Perhaps you need to have a word with you old friend Mr. Heart Attack. He doesn't mess around. He doesn't give anybody time for a second chance."

I used this time to look back at Granny Ryan. Now I didn't just see a doting grandmother anymore. I saw a great woman. Someone, who did a lot more than just make wonderful brown bread and knit you a new jumper every Christmas. I saw an inspirational individual. I saw a woman who stoically rose to the challenge of raising a family and being handed a business to run, in the same year that the Second World War broke out. It was Ireland in the thirties. It was a man's world, but her man was gone and her youngest child was just three years old.

This woman, my granny, just picked up the mantle that had been thrust upon her and carried it. She just got on with whatever needed to be done. Her life was suddenly transformed from being a housewife to now needing to be a business man and a single mother combined. She barely broke stride. She carried it so well that I have fond memories of people telling me that even when they had no money they could still come to our shop. My grandmother wouldn't see anybody go without. They could pay again when they had the money to do so.

Already laden down with the duties of raising a family of six, she now had the running of a pub and shop thrown in for good measure. From what all of the villagers told me, she performed both her roles impeccably well. She became a business woman and continued as a mother of six, without complaining. And yet my grandmother was no Lance Armstrong. She didn't win the Tour de France. Times were hard and people everywhere faced similar or even more difficult situations. They didn't shirk. They did whatever the job in hand required. We now must do the same. We all have a Granny Ryan in our past. That is your starting point. It is already in your blood!

My upbringing was typically rural Irish with the exception of living in a public house. Our village only had two places of interest, the pub and the church. The church only commanded attention for an hour once a week, when the village's only Mass took place at 10 o'clock on Sunday. For the rest of the week the village of Horseleap just about began and ended at Paddy Ryan's pub. There was no hall, or sports field or public space.

The shop and the pub ensured that some form of activity was taking place in our house all day long. Most of the mothers of the children in school with me would come to do their weekly shopping. We all worked in the shop as we grew up. We became very adept at the variety of tasks that each shopping order required. You needed to be able to fill a gallon of paraffin oil, slice up a side of bacon and weigh everything from sugar to smoked haddock.

Many of the menfolk would then return from the same homes later in the evening. Their destination however would be the other end of Paddy Ryans's, the pub. One of the disadvantages of having a shop and pub together was that many of these men would only remember on leaving that their wife had asked them to bring home some groceries. They would consider that as long as the pub was open then surely the shop was too. So in the early hours of the morning, just as you were contemplating locking the doors and getting to bed, you could be dispatched to fill a gallon of paraffin, or get a pound and a half of rashers, or a half pound of haddock, or worse, all three!

Apart from seeing the local people every day, another great advantage of our house was that it provided the opportunity to meet complete strangers. The main road between Dublin and Galway ran right through Horseleap. We already had a captive market with the locals for food and drink but we also had the one commodity that was of most interest to the passer-by, petrol.

We did not have a proper filling station as such, but our two kerb side Texaco petrol pumps ensured that up to a dozen strangers entered the shop every day. Self service pumps were still a few years away so their request was to ask you to fill petrol for them. No other house in the parish had this wonderful window to meet people from the rest of the world. This was the part of the job that most filled me with enthusiasm when it came to "minding the shop".

I always gave these callers a prompt and friendly service. I regarded myself an ambassador for our village. In return I usually garnered five minutes of warm conversation from them. This brief interlude would provide me with a fascinating glimpse into their lives. Why they were in my village at this point in time. Where were they going to and where had they come from. They could be working men returning to their families after a week away, Australian tourists heading for the scenery of the west of Ireland or a nervous trainee nurse on her way to a job interview.

With the long pub hours, the later it got, the more these callers were happier to see me rather than I to see them. In fact as we lived on the premises they were not even restricted to the pub closing time. Stranded motorists would often knock on our door at three or four in the morning desperate for the fuel to complete their journey home. On these calls their generosity would know no bounds. As you filled their tank in your dressing gown you could be handed a spontaneous gift of chocolates or wine or whatever was lying on the back seat of their car. Other times it would be an incontestable offer of a free meal in their pub or restaurant, on your next visit to Dublin.

As I lay on my hospital bed many years later I was scanning back over these early days of my life. I found I was magnifying many of the smallest everyday details of my youth to an exposure they had not been subjected to since they had actually happened. Many memories that had been dormant for years came flooding back.

This must be a natural reaction when news of a major illness or crisis is broken to most of us. It is only when it is confirmed to you that your glass is half empty, before you seriously begin to examine the portion that you now realise is the section that has been half full.

All of these freshly uncovered details of my past were an unexpected by-product of my new 'cancer time'. I was trawling back through my life to see if there were any hints to have foretold that I would now be lying in this bed, in this hospital, at this point in time and getting diverted into memories that I thought had been lost. The standout reference from my past however was that my mother died from cancer when I was twenty-two.

The "I told you so" merchants would have been quick to seize on this. "That's your link. You were always going to get it". But that had been eighteen years ago. She had already survived ten years at that point after undergoing a mastectomy in 1974. She had breast cancer, I now had head and neck cancer. What kind of a link is that? Furthermore all three of my sisters smoked and probably weren't as athletic as I was. If it was hereditary, why didn't they get it instead of me. Some people go to great lengths to insist that we all have cancer indicators in our past. The only qualifications they would appear to have for their declarations were obtained at the University of Hindsight.

Anyway, even if it was an indicator, what was I to do? Should I have stayed in bed for the rest of my life? I'd rather live an active, spirited life for as long as I can than just live for the sake of reaching a hundred. Give me a glass of champagne any day before a plate of raw Mongolian cabbage!

The only other possible link that I could identify was that having grown up in a pub I was probably a passive smoker for much of that time. But again, all my sisters were actual smokers. Why me and not them. And if that was the actual cause surely it should have been lung cancer rather than head and neck?

Cancer indicators from your past therefore, for me, are so tenuous and dubious that they are not worth the bother. Nothing that went before really matters. Even if it did, it's too late now. Your cancer starts here. Right here, right now. This is point zero. You begin at zero. There is only one direction to go from there. Everything that has happened to you up to this point is completely irrelevant now.

4 - The Stories of Horseleap

In many ways I feel I grew up in one of the best eras in rural Ireland. Perhaps everybody with fond memories of their childhood will say the same thing. The Ireland that was waiting for me seemed to be nicely located between the austerity of the lives that many of my ancestors had to endure and the fast paced world we live in today. I came into the world just shortly after many of the modern appliances, deemed essential today, only became commonly found in most homes. As a family we had electricity, central heating, an internal bathroom, a car, a television, a telephone and a record player. Country life however was still generally innocent and slow paced. People seemed to have a lot more time on their hands than they do today.

Behind our house we had eight acres of land. Much of this land was originally an old railway line that linked Clara to Mullingar. When the line was closed in the 50's the track was removed and the land divided out between the adjoining land owners.

The portion of this land that we received, to a small boy, was simply enchanting. Our land contained not only the ruins and platforms of the old station and goods shed that served Horseleap, but also a meandering river, a small wood and a series of hills.

The largest hill was known as the Hill of Horseleap. The ruins of an old drawbridge still stand beside this hill. It was here that the legendary incident that was to give the village its strange name, took place. In 1192 the ruling Norman baron for the area, Hugh De Lacy, was out riding one day. Unusually he was without the protective accompaniment of his henchmen. He was just about to return to his castle when he accidently stumbled upon a rabblerousing gang of the local Mac Geoghegan chieftain clan. The Mac Geoghegans greatly resented the Norman conquest of their land but rarely found themselves with an opportunity to do anything about it. They could not believe their luck when they encountered the unprotected baron and quickly gave chase. De Lacy's horse galloped as fast as it could in an attempt to reach the safety of the castle. It arrived at the drawbridge, just as the MacGeoghegans were about to capture their prize, only to find it raised. Nothing, it now seemed, could prevent a Mac Geoghegan feast of Norman blood.

De Lacy's horse however, had other ideas. From a standing position, just as the Mac Geoghegans were no more than a sword's length away, he majestically sprung across the 15 foot expanse that fell 30 feet to the moat below. A fall would have resulted in almost certain death. Incredibly he touched down on the other side and carried the baron to the safe confines of his castle. The frustrated Mac Geoghegans could only look on in amazement.

They had been thwarted by a magnificent horse. A horse, who singlehandedly would provide the name for the settlement that would evolve there, many years later.

The ruins of the two drawbridge embankments are still to be found beside the hill of Horseleap. It is said that the four hoof marks of De Lacy's horse are still to be seen on the western pillar to this day!

As an only son and youngest child, I was pretty much left to my own devices to explore every square inch of these fields as I grew up. This I did with unlimited enthusiasm, on a daily basis. I did it on my own or with my best friend from next door, Pat Carton. It was our own adventure playground before adventure playgrounds were even invented. The old station and goods shed would be a medieval castle on Monday, a city under siege on Tuesday, a spaceship landing on an alien planet on Wednesday. Pat and I would be the two astronauts who would save the world by killing all of the ferocious aliens.

The river was an endless challenge to be conquered by bridge, dam or an inspired collection of whacky, but ultimately unsuccessful, home-made floating devices. In the woods we were Robin Hood and on the hills Cù Chulainn or Brian Boru. Those fields were the wondrous backdrop that fired our imaginations. Yet we played in them without any awareness of their historical significance. On those very fields people caught a train for the last time to begin a journey to a new world in Australia or America. On those fields the Mac Geoghegan boys were the only witnesses to the finest jumping feat by a horse on these islands until Red Rum nearly a thousand years later.

In recent times Horseleap has also been attached to another delightful horse tale, when the village acquired a welcome piece of public art in 2000. The twelve foot high bronze horse statue that now stands on the village green is intended to represent the famous leap by De Lacy's horse. This horse however has an entirely different pedigree. This statue was actually made in Italy by the Ferrari motor racing corporation. It was shipped to Ireland in 1999. At that time, Ferrari had a tradition of giving each of their formula one racing drivers a large replica of their famous logo, the prancing horse. Eddie Irvine was driving for Ferrari at the time and this statue was to be given to him. It was to be a surprise gift at the end of the racing season.

The statue was stored in a farmyard in County Tyrone until the appointed presentation date. Just before this was to take place however Irvine announced to Ferrari that he was leaving the team to join Jaguar. They never told him about the statue and, now redundant, it remained in a barn whilst the bemused Ferrari officials worked out what to do with it.

About a year later a farmer from Horseleap happened to be in Tyrone buying cattle. He heard about the statue and returned to the village with the story of the horse that nobody knew what to do with. A committee was formed and a delegation was soon dispatched up north. Their mission was to make the case that our village green would make the perfect home for this horse. We had a village, with an unusual name, that badly needed a distinguishing feature. Horseleap would make an ideal permanent residence for the poor homeless bronze horse. A village, if you like, that already had his name on it.

Ferrari agreed to the request. The statue was bought for an agreed price. It was then brought back and erected in Horseleap in 2000 for the new millennium.

So the next time when you pass through the village of Horseleap you will see the Ferrari horse in all his magnificence in the middle of the green. You will also know that it took two men to get it there. Hugh De Lacy and Eddie Irvine!

5 – Paddy Ryan, A Soccer Man

Though we were probably a little better off than many of the farming based households in the village at that time, Mam and Dad were not wealthy by any means. We did have one of the few cars in the village when I was very young and the pub and shop would have brought in a regular, steady income but there were no holidays and very few luxuries beyond everyday living. My Dad within this quiet rural setting was progressive for his time. Back then television was just about the only source of entertainment and relaxation in all homes. Our house however, was the only one with a sixty foot aerial sticking out of it. This magical, slender skyscraper brought us B.B.C. It made our house appear as if it was a Christmas tree decoration dangling from the clouds.

It was not picture perfect, wide screen BBC as you know it today. It was black and white, often snowy BBC, but, poor reception or not, we all loved it. It gave us access to all kinds of programmes that were not available to our schoolmates. Every morning we relayed to them in great detail what we had seen on Crackerjack, Top of the Pops or Doctor Who. These were wonderful new programmes to us. We had nothing comparable to them on terrestrial Irish television.

This was also a time in Ireland when sport, at least in my part of the country, really meant only two things, hurling or football. The BBC started to bring me ice hockey, badminton, cricket, snooker, athletics and many more games and athletic pursuits that I had never seen before. These not only opened my eyes to the immense spectrum of the word "sport" but also conceived in me a love of all sports that I have retained to this day. The greatest new sport of all however, that our sky scraping, metal rod brought into our house, was soccer.

Paddy Ryan loved soccer. This was where my admiration for my dad and his lack of fear to be a non-conformist, was at its highest. The rural Irish midlands at that time were one of the least illuminated parts of the country. There were hardly any tourists or visitors and very little industry. Games like soccer and rugby were almost a secret compared to the interest they were generating in Dublin and the other urban centres. I was living in the middle of GAA only country. To express an affection for a different field game, particularly the queen's own garrison game, was likely to promote misunderstanding at best and ostracization at worst.

My dad, and I believe my grandfather before him, was unperturbed by any of this. He declared his admiration for the "beautiful game" from the outset. His one sacred weekly pleasure was Match of the Day on Saturday nights. His endless commitment to the pub ensured he was a father that we didn't get to see half enough of. So it was during this weekly hour that myself and my Dad formed our earliest bond. His knowledge of the game was immense but his tuition was always calm and understated. He would gently and reassuringly pass on his knowledge during the highlights of each game. He would tell me who was who and what was what.

As I got older the black and white television pictures turned into reality. He brought me to my first Irish international game in Dalymount Park in 1969 when I was eight. Poland came to Dublin and won 2-0. I missed very few home international games with him for about four years after that. I was still small enough to be lifted over the turnstiles and get a free seat on his knee.

1969 was also the year that Athlone Town joined the League of Ireland. My Dad had been involved with the club for the previous couple of years. When they became members of the league he was one of the first directors of the club. I still have the original programme from their very first home game against Shamrock Rovers and there, in the list of directors is his name, Paddy Ryan.

To a small boy league of Ireland games were light years away from being amongst forty five thousand people in Dublin watching Ireland play but, in his own way, he was showing me that without the little days at St. Mels Park there couldn't be the great nights at Dalymount Park. He passed on an appreciation of the game at all levels.

The older I got the more the smaller teams seemed to matter to me and the more disenfranchised I became with the bigger ones. Forty years later, having been to some of the finest stadia in Europe and having seen many of the great teams play, I have come full circle. The only team that can really set my pulse racing is "The Town". I have been to the temples of football in England and mainland Europe but I will never be happier than when I am shouting through the hardship of being an Athlone Town supporter. They are my team and your team is for life.

The big teams do little for me these days. Now it is the little ones who fascinate me. The loyal bands who support clubs that the mainstream barely acknowledges. They are the real supporters. I feel a true affinity with the fans of the Longford Town's, the Limerick City's, the Gillingham's and the Shrewsbury Town's.

As an Athlone Town fan I have a solidarity with every supporter of a downtrodden, underachieving team. Yet, at the start of every new season I refuse to have my dreams quashed. This will be our year. One year, success, no matter how small, will come. When it does the agony of the long wait will hugely magnify the pleasure it will bring. It is as if our morsel will taste far sweeter than the feast that a handful of bigger teams are gorging themselves on, at the top table of the game today.

As I lay on my cancerous bed all of my early football memories were freshly revived. I could remember the two Polish men chatting together before going in to that first international match in Dalymount Park. They were wrapped in warm overcoats with their red and white scarves just visible above the collar. I remember that they were the only Polish supporters I saw that night. Poland was a country then where people were not free to travel. The iron curtain was still drawn across the middle of Europe.

I remembered the sights and the smells of those earliest matches in Athlone. I could once again feel the sheer excitement of trips my Dad and I made to Dublin. We would be going up to see the Town play Drumcondra in the cup, hoping for a draw and to "get them back to our place". But most of all I started to remember my Dad.

Now, lying on my bed, with an uncertain future ahead of me, I brought everything back to the time of his death. I began to see all the things we didn't get to do. Wasn't it a pity he had just missed out on the glory years for the Irish soccer team. I remember the night he told me that Jack Charlton had been appointed as the new manager of Ireland. That was 24 hours before anybody beyond the F.A.I. knew, but my Dad knew. How I wished he could have lived just a little longer to enjoy the fruits of Big Jacks appointment. To have seen Ray Houghton score the goal to beat England in Stuttgart. He would have been there. He would then have gone to Italy and the U.S.A. for the World Cups. How I wished he could have lived long enough for me to return the favour and say "come on, let's go to Dublin tomorrow to see Athlone away to Pats. I'll drive and we'll get back to Kinnegad for closing time." How I regretted that he didn't live to see that the small eight year old he introduced to Athlone Town grow up to carry on his mantle. His boy would become just as big a fan as he was. He would then go on to become an architect and design the new stadium that the club moved in to in 2007. How I wished we could have stood there together on the opening night to see the fruits of the work that he had started with other great men like Peter Molloy and Seamus O'Brien.

And then I knew what I was doing was wrong. I was breaking my own rules. Everybody can look at their life after they have died and see things they would have loved to do. You will always want just a little bit more. So I started to look differently. I started to appreciate how lucky he was to have lived long enough to see Athlone Town win the league in 1982 & 1984. Nobody could have predicted that when they joined only 13 years earlier. None of the teams that joined then or since, like Finn Harps, Cobh Ramblers, Monaghan United and Longford Town, have come anywhere close to winning a title. He lived to see the mighty A.C. Milan come to Athlone and go home without scoring a goal. He had travelled on European adventures with Athlone in Norway, Italy, Denmark and Belgium. He had lived to marry a wonderful woman and share a relationship with her so perfect, that he really didn't have the heart to live on after she died. He had seen his four children grow up to the point where they were setting off on their own paths in life. He had done his job as their father remarkably well. He didn't have to worry about them anymore.

My mind had played a trick on me. It had sneakily tripped all the switches it needed to re-adjust my focus. As soon as I started seeing the portion of the glass that was half empty it shifted my viewpoint to show me that it was half full. Through my memories of my Dad it had shown me he had lived a good life. It was not what he had missed out on that prevailed in my thoughts but what he achieved and his good fortune. It was quietly instilling the thought process I was going to need to take on my disease. It was equipping me to be consummate about all of my life to that point of time, no matter when that point of time was to be. If the worst case scenario was going to prevail, that was the kind of mentality I was going to need to stay strong to the end.

6 – Friends and Cousins

For as long as I can remember we had a live-in barman in our house. When I was small my Mam and Dad kept my bed in their room for as long as they possibly could just so that the barman could have a room of his own. A curious array of characters came and went in these years. A job at our pub, for many of them, was just another sojourn along their colourful career path. Inevitably I grew to a point where I could just no longer be contained within the confines of my parents bedroom. For their sake and for mine I had to go.

Pat Grennan was just arriving as our new barman so his job description was altered to inform him that he was going to have to share his room with a seven year old. Pat was different from everybody before him. He was special right from the very start. We all liked him instantly. He must have liked us too because forty years later, long after we had all moved on, he was still to be found behind the counter at Paddy Ryan's. He was also very popular with all of the customers and became a great asset to the pub.

Pat and I got on great from the start. Sharing a bedroom was never going to be a problem. Over the next few years we became good friends and he effectively became the brother I never had.

Apart from Pat the barman and Pat Carton next door my other great friends at that time were three people from the one family. My Dads youngest sister Breda was the only member of the family to move away from the area when she got married in Dublin. She went on to have her own family of three great girls. My three Dublin cousins were all about my own age, Hazel a little older, Cora the same age and Miriam slightly younger. Family holidays were not common in Ireland at that time but our ample compensation was to swop visits with the Knowles girls. They would come down to Horseleap during the summer holidays and in return we would stay with them in Dublin.

This, town mouse country mouse, arrangement worked brilliantly. It gave me a wonderful opportunity to feel the pulse of big city life. An opportunity that again was not available to many of my school friends. It also gave me a regular platform, in two entirely different locations, to get to know my three great cousins.

Hazel, Cora and Miriam would each come down and spend three weeks immersed in rural life in Horseleap. They would join in with the hay making, try their hand at milking the cows and help out around the yard. We'd all go for long walks through the fields to all of the local landmarks, collecting blackberries or climbing trees as we went. At night time they loved to help out in the pub. Horseleap was a complete change of scene for them and they loved it.

When I returned with them to Dublin I was just as enthralled with my change of surroundings. I would explore wherever the double decker bus took me, mesmerised by the sights and sounds of bustling city life. We would go to the beach, play in the park, visit museums and galleries or just go in to town to browse around the busy shops. I would be transfixed by the scale and pace of everything I saw, compared to life in sleepy Horseleap.

I became very friendly with all three of the girls but because Cora and I were closest in age, we were perhaps always destined to become the closest friends of all. The earliest family photo albums show the two of us in prams, parked side by side, in our back yard. As we grew older, we never seemed to stray much further apart.

Every summer Cora and I became inseparable. We traded floating down the river in Horseleap on inner tubes with climbing trees in the Pheonix Park. Cora was a real tomboy. Her friendship would become invaluable to me. She could enlighten me on a girls perspective on many issues from an early age. Then, in later years, I had the benefit of a long established close female friend. That friendship, because she was my cousin, would remain constant. I had a wonderful girl friend and no matter how close we got, the words girl and friend would not attach.

So for those years the three main people in my life, beyond my immediate family, were Cora, Pat Carton and Pat Grennan.

When it came to secondary school our parents made the very altruistic decision to send us all to boarding school. It was very rare in those days for children from our village to be sent away to school. This decision however wasn't taken for grandiose reasons. Mam and Dad knew that now that we were all helping out in the pub and shop, they needed to remove the temptation of being able to ask us. If you were in the house when the pub got busy, you could not avoid being called into action. The three girls were sent off, one at a time, to the Loreto nuns in Mullingar. When it came to my turn several schools were considered. In the end I ended up only five miles down the road at the Carmelite College in Moate.

I was a bright student but, perhaps typical for an active boy of my age, I was easy to distract. I tended, as a result, to keep my studies to the minimum required. I always ensured that sufficient time was also allocated for my two great loves, sport and music. One teacher summed up my academic performance in these years quite succinctly. He claimed I was just like a good racehorse. I would just do enough to win. The margin would always be a short head when I could have won by a distance.

As the years went by Mam and Dad considered the short head margins were getting too slender. They needed to get more out of their horse. They knew he was capable of better. Moate was a relaxed school and because I lived so close, I was able to get home frequently. This didn't really give it the feel of a boarding school and my academic focus probably suffered as a result. All things considered, they felt I needed a change of school. After four years with the Carmelites in Moate I was to switch monastic orders. They were sending me to the Cistercians in Roscrea.

Cistercian College, Roscrea was a real boarding school! Firstly it was over an hour and a half from home. The emergency home comfort supplies that I had become used to were now gone. It was also remote, located in the middle of open countryside, miles from nowhere. As you drove through the gates the words "isolation" and "confinement" were flashing in front of you like an invisible sign. This was rubber stamped by the fact that the entire school grounds were surrounded by a ten foot high stone wall.

This was a proper, Colditz like, boarding school. The prison camp first impression was completed by the presence of the silent, stern looking, Cistercian monks that appeared to be on constant patrol throughout the grounds. They seemed to glide around, dalek like, in their brown and white habits. It was as if their stealth-like presence was there to remind you that any thoughts of escaping would indeed lead to your extermination. This was to be my home for the next two years. It looked as if the only thing the racehorse would have to worry about in all of that time would be how fast he could run.

I wasn't to know it then but the two main centres of my education, Roscrea, or more precisely North Tipperary, and Liverpool would both become major locations in the remainder of my life. My connection with both of them would extend well beyond the purpose of my original visit. Liverpool would give me a degree, a career, a wife and the two hospitals that would keep me alive. North Tipperary would just about cover everything else, a family, a home, a business and a wonderful community to live in.

Roscrea was a good school. It did bring the best out of me academically. Boarding schools can be tough but generally I found that most boys were able to find the niches within the school that suited them. The good all rounders thrived best of all. Their card tended to be in every hand, from the classroom, to the stage, to the sports field. The greatest concern were the boys who were a little bit vulnerable or isolated to begin with. Boarding school can become a very lonely place if you are cast adrift by the herd.

Because I was joining in late, I felt a little pressurized to fast track making acquaintances. I settled in quickly and after about a month I had identified an established group of friends that I felt suited me best.

Michael Dolan was not what he first appeared to be. When he first spoke to me he spoke with a broad Dublin accent. This immediately categorised him, in my mind, into the small group of Dublin lads in our year. This group were generally from well heeled south Dublin backgrounds and, if truth be told, considered themselves a little more sophisticated than the rest of us. I had known this divide to cause a clear distinction in other schools but in Roscrea, they were no more than a colourful offshoot within the student body.

Mick was definitely not part of this group. His father was a butcher from County Louth and his Dubliness began and ended with his accent. Behind the voice was a warm hearted character whose greatest love was the land and everything that grew and lived on it. He was friendly and an incessant talker from the off. He entertained us all, in ways we never thought possible, with vivid and humorous accounts of the world of butchery.

Mick and I became instant companions and I soon slotted in to his circle of friends. Some of the groups liked to meet up for a smoke, others got together to play records but the trademark activity of our group was to go for long walks by escaping beyond the school boundaries. As a relief to our daily incarceration these escapades almost became essential to the preservation of our sanity.

The route to the front gate and shop beyond was treacherous for any attempt to abscond. Food was always the greatest craving for every student and our preoccupation with getting our hands on a mars bar or a bag of crisps meant the shop was under constant supervision. The rural pastures behind the golf course were considered a much lesser security risk. They appeared to have little allure to a pack of starving inmates.

Every day in our free time, Mick, Pat Nichol, Gerry O'Rourke and myself simply headed for the back of the golf course. This was within the school bounds and gave no cause for suspicion to be aroused. As soon as we were out of sight of the school building we hopped over the ditch into the expanse of enchanting countryside that lay beyond. The clock was now ticking. We had ninety minutes of freedom before we would be missed.

The benefits of these escapes were both physical and psychological. This area of land contained an attractive sprawling woodland with a river running through it. We just enjoyed being out in the fresh air in this enchanting natural environment. It gave us all a great awareness of the fine rural landscape in which the school was set. It was as if we became part of it. It was there waiting for us every day. We got to know it and watched it change, season by season. It was our silent friend.

These escapes from school life were also important for our hearts and souls. We felt as if this was the only time in the day when we were truly free. We were beyond rule and regulation. We were out of range of bell and whistle. We were removed from somebody else telling us what we had to do.

We had no agenda for these escapades. We just walked and talked and savoured our window of freedom. Others had their cigarettes or their Led Zepplin L.P's but this was our haven. We could be individuals again. Our spirits temporarily freed from the chains of uniformity. Freed from the shackle of classroom and study hall and dormitory. Liberated from the confinement of the boundary wall.

If my daily walk was my physical getaway my minds escape to the world beyond was by writing and receiving a letter. We had four hours of compulsory study every evening. The only non academic activity you could conceal within this period was a letter disguised as written homework. I grabbed this secret opportunity to hoodwink my superiors with both hands. I wrote to as many people as I could. The letter became my television set. I relied on it totally for news of family, friends and everything that was happening beyond the ten foot high stone walls. I rejoiced every day when one arrived and despaired when one did not.

Cora and I began to turn our written exchanges into works of art in these years. We swopped a vast selection of all kinds of glorious, hand-written manuscripts. We kept trying to out-do each other by writing back an even more fantastic composition than the one that had just been received. Each letter got longer or was written on bigger sheets of paper or contained even more photos and illustrations than the one before.

Our woodland walks were confined to how far we could escape for ninety minutes but there were no restrictions to the escape potential of the letter. I usually had little of interest to report from within the school walls so the material that was needed to fill twenty pages often had to be invented. Cora and I had no limitations when it came to what was used to fill these compositions. We wrote plays, poems and scripts of all kinds of delightful fabricated nonsense to entertain each other. Generally these were constructed around a single fact or a modicum of truth and our imaginations just took over and did the rest. This wonderful period of correspondence only further cemented what was already an ardent friendship.

The reward for writing a letter was that you got one back in return. No sooner had you posted your latest composition when you began to eagerly await its response. To this day I don't think I have found a pleasure to match that of a letter being dropped in front of you on the refectory table of a boarding school.

My two years in Roscrea passed relatively smoothly. In the main I greatly enjoyed them. I would have had the usual grumbles about the quality of the food and the lack of home comforts but to balance the scales I made plenty of good friends and did well academically. For my Mam and Dad therefore, the decision to change schools was the correct one. From a personal development viewpoint these two years were the quintessence of my youth. They encompassed my transformation from boy to man. Boarding school throws you into a world of survival, beyond the sanctuary of family and home. It accelerates your maturing process by necessitating your requirement to be able to make wise character judgements from the outset.

You have just been dropped into a contained environment of 300 boys, all just the same as you. They can range from likeable and confident to insecure, scheming and even frenzied. You need to work out pretty quickly who is who and what is what. A good appraisement can result in finding yourself a new friend for life or steer you clear of somebody not as suited to you as they may want you to believe. A poor judgement can lead you into all sorts of trouble.

Boarding school can equip you with these essential skills of growing up, before you have fully grown up. Or it can destroy you. This speeded up metamorphose also extinguished the final remnants of our dependency on our parents. This must have been a little sad for our families. They dropped off a small child at the school only to return five years later and pick up a self contained young adult.

It was only in later years, with the benefit of a more mature reflection did I begin to see the monks themselves. When we were at school we just regarded them as law enforcers. We didn't see them as people. They were to be hidden from and not confronted at all costs.

On return visits, as a past pupil, I actually got to meet the men themselves. I was impressed with what I then found behind the habits. These men had given up many of the conventional goals of life that ironically we, as young adolescent men under their tuition, desperately sought. We were relying on their education to lead us to a life that they had passed up on. These men had chosen to live lives without wives, family, cars, careers, holidays and entertainment. Many of the things that the rest of us spend entire lives trying to attain. When I spoke to them, man to man, I found nothing to fear. They were gentle and kind, humorous and knowledgeable. They were wise. Most of them were able to pinpoint in a sentence what I would be babbling on about for an hour. They transmitted a sense of ease with life and everything they came across in it. They had found peace of mind. They seemed to know far more than I ever will. They were all great men.

Again, with the benefit of hindsight, I mused at the irony of what we put them through twenty five years earlier. They had declined the trappings of the modern world to enter a monastery and opt for a life of prayer, humility and tranquillity. But, as soon as they had signed up, they were suddenly handed riot shields and batons. They were then directed towards the exuberant collection of rampaging students streaming through the gates for the new academic year!

7 – The Shinrone 6

My last few days in Roscrea were memorable, if not even the stuff of legend. All through my teens I had been an avid fan of a band called Chips. They were a polished outfit, doing very good cover versions of likeable songs and were one of many bands playing the Irish dancehall circuit at that time. My devotion to them was best explained by the fact that I developed a teenage crush on one of their lead singers, Linda Martin. I got talking to her after one of my first nights to see them and was instantly smitten.

Ireland was a fairly barren place for quality original music at that time, especially for a heavy rock fan like myself. Rory Gallagher was my hero. Opportunities to see him however were limited to an annual gig every Christmas at the Stadium in Dublin. For the rest of the year I had to make do with finding the best of the touring showbands that played all over the country.

It was fashionable at that time to "follow" a band. Chips became my band. My selection somewhat influenced by my not so secret infatuation for Linda. She later went on to win the Eurovision Song Contest for Ireland in 1992 and I'm glad to be able to say my teenage crush matured into a genuine friendship. We are still in contact to this day.

It became my passion in those years to try and get to see Linda and the band as many times as I could. This crusade took me from little carnivals in villages that I had never been to before, to big ballrooms in some of Dublin's most glitzy hotels. I would have their poster on my bedroom wall and carefully record every night I saw them on the blank panel where the venue is normally written in. One year I had over 30 dates and venues written on it. That meant I had seen them more than once a fortnight that year.

Transport to all the various towns and villages for the shows, or dances as we called them, was my greatest problem. This was achieved through a variety of means. Sometimes I cajoled friends to drive me on the guarantee of seeing one of Irelands finest bands and the promise of a brief hello from Linda afterwards. On other occasions I hitch hiked, often setting out for home at three in the morning after the show. A few times, when this plan didn't work, I had to walk all the way home. Fifteen miles was the longest, just getting in the door in time for breakfast. The final method I also used once or twice was to take a bus and simply book in to a bed and breakfast in the town where they were playing.

When I eventually revealed my secret devotion to Mick and the lads in Roscrea the dilemma of deciding on an appropriate nickname for me was instantly solved. For my two years in Roscrea there were many who didn't know who Liam Ryan was, but everybody knew who "Chip" was. The night before the rest of the school went home for the summer in my final year, Chips were playing at a carnival in the village of Shinrone. Shinrone was about four miles from the school. The rest of us were staying on to sit our final exams.

This was just too close to pass up. How could Chips greatest fan not be there when they had come so close on his radar. I was too smart to risk my entire education on an escapade when, in a few weeks, I would be free to see them whenever I wanted. But I knew that even if we were caught we couldn't be prevented from sitting our exams. Then, when the exams were over, we were leaving the school anyway. Any punishment would be difficult to implement. The risk was worth taking. We also convinced ourselves that we were just not going to get caught. We were going to plan every detail of this operation with full military precision. Mick was on board immediately and we soon enlisted four others. Perhaps, in hindsight, six was too many. We were increasing the chances of the details of our mission falling into enemy hands.

After study that night we all retired to the dormitories as normal. We washed and got into bed. Half an hour after lights out we made our move. Our beds had to be stuffed to look as if we were still in them. Then we carefully slipped downstairs. With the exams being so close a lot of boys were sneaking back down at this time to do extra study. That was to be our cover story if we were intercepted at this early stage.

We all reached the back door safely and escaped into the darkness beyond. We now knew that if we got caught our actions would be more difficult to explain. We could not be studying in the dark. We quickly distanced ourselves from the school buildings, crossing the grounds, tree by tree, until we reached the perimeter wall.

The initial objective had now been achieved. The main escape from the school building itself had been successful. I now just wanted to get to see Linda and the band. If we were to get caught, I wished it was to happen after the dance.

The next part of the operation was to identify our route to Shinrone. We decided not to use the road. If we were missed now we could easily be picked up by car. That meant we had to take to the fields. We needed to stay in the ones that were adjoining the road so that we knew the way.

Three of the lads were from Dublin and had hardly ever been in a field before. They certainly had never been in one after dark. Our journey therefore, through four miles of boggy, rutted, pitch black fields, soon became hilarious. The Dublin lads convinced themselves that each new field we entered was filled with imaginary killer bulls. The rest of us were country lads and much more at ease with such surroundings. How we began to enjoy discovering that our super cool metropolitan friends had an Achilles heel after all.

After an hour the lights of Shinrone began to appear in the distance. Our assault course of ditches and drains, nettles and briars and curious but unrecognisable animals was now in its final stages. We made our way through the village towards where the music was coming from.

When we emerged inside the parish hall we were easy to pick out. We were the six lads wearing two tone trousers. The lower shade in each case was a boggy, soggy brown colour. We didn't dare dance. We just stood and watched the band for the night. We were all still fearful that a brown and white clad, red faced, monk could appear at any time and shatter our adventure.

Nobody came. After the show I was only too delighted to introduce the other five to my celebrity friend. Linda and the band were tickled with the story of our escapade. They signed "Chips" postcards for us, some of which we cheekily got them to dedicate to a couple of the monks. The mission had been accomplished.

We were all in high spirits on the return journey and were now much more carefree. Now we were happy to return by the road. Besides we were unlikely to survive the imaginary killer bull gauntlet twice. We were like proper fugitives now. Whenever the night sky was lit up by the headlights of an oncoming car we convinced ourselves the occupants were the monks, the Gestapo, or the K.G.B.

Despite our imaginative paranoia, all cars passed by passively. When we got back to the school all the entry doors would be locked. We had arranged with the student sacristan to give us the key to the sacristy of the church. This was our plan for re-entry. It was about 3.30 in the morning by now. We quietly and successfully slipped in through the church and, from there, through the rest of the school. I negotiated the route to my bed without interception and quietly slipped under the blankets. I started to believe we had pulled off one of the greatest undetected escapes in the history of the school. Then just as my head was dropping on the pillow with a smile of satisfaction across my face the narrow light of a torch was shone directly between my eyes. "My office, first thing in the morning" was the command and the torch was switched off.

As the rest of the school gleefully woke up to the first morning of their summer holidays I was one of the solitary figures trudging along the corridor to Father Peters office. Five familiar and equally sullen faces were waiting in a queue ahead of me. We never discovered how our operation had been rumbled. Chances were that one of us had let it slip to one person too many.

As I had anticipated, our punishment could not prevent us sitting our exams. All that could be imposed was an expulsion from the school for any gaps between exams greater than a day. This was effective immediately so we were returned to the study hall to await our parents arrival.

When my Dad arrived about two hours later, I was summoned. I stood up and packed up the books I needed for the upcoming exams. As I made my way towards the door the entire study hall suddenly burst into a round of applause. To this day this little moment stands out as one of the greatest memories of my school days. I'm not sure where it came from. Spontaneous appreciation of a rebel maybe, or recognition of Chips greatest ever fan. Perhaps it was acknowledgement of a crime that was clever and colourful but importantly non offensive. Nobody got hurt by what we did. At many of our school reunions ever since recollection of our deed has always been on the night's agenda. We have gone on to be famously immortalised as the Shinrone 6.

My dad was straight faced when he came to take me home. He relayed to me how upset my mother was over the incident. She was very concerned about what people would think. As the journey passed however he began to speak for himself. He recognised that different categories of expulsion existed. He told me that if I had been expelled for stealing from somebody or injuring somebody, it would have been a different matter. That was all he said.

As I scrutinised this journey from my sick bed years later I realised that he was subtly giving me a glimpse of the great level of understanding he had. He was discreetly acknowledging the difference between an act that was wrong but inoffensive as opposed to one that was harmful. I have convinced myself ever since that he perhaps admired the courageous ingenuity of what we did. Purely on the basis that it caused no harm to anybody else.

As I looked back I could see this was also the only reason that it became memorable and famous. This was the reason we were all still able to celebrate it 25 years later. Going to a dance was a positive action. We would not be warmly recollecting an incident if it had caused injury or insult to anybody else. I would not wanted to have been part of any act, causing my expulsion, if it was to have had a negative impact on another student or teacher at the school.

My initial reckoning that our escapade would not interfere greatly with my career plans was correct. I went on to complete my exams and did well. I am now probably one of a small group of students who has combined a secondary school expulsion with a university degree. For somebody reading this therefore perhaps I have a second, more unexpected message of inspiration. Even if this time it is a little more light hearted than before. For anybody who has been expelled from school and is worried it may interfere with their dreams of a successful academic career, I can say, once again, "I did it. And if I did it there is no reason why you can't do it too"!

8 – Road to an Architect

I left Roscrea with good leaving certificate exam results. The only problem I now had was I didn't really know what to do with them. As the summer wore on Mam and Dad began to get a little concerned about my career path. The three girls had all gone directly to university after secondary school and performed impeccably well. The bar was set. It was expected that I would follow suit and jump it too. But I just didn't know what I wanted to do.

About a month before I left school a career guidance advisor was the very first person to mention the word architecture to me. It would still take another year however before that seed would take root. Computer science was still a relatively new discipline at that time and late vacancies appeared for a degree course at Trinity College in Dublin. I had always enjoyed maths and on the basis of that alone, I applied. I thought it might appeal to me. What suited me more immediately was that my enrolment on the course automatically relieved the tension that was starting to build up at home. The last child was now going to college just like the first three.

The course began in September 1979. It was great to be at university on Trinity's historic campus in the very heart of Dublin. The scale of the course was good too. Only about 30 people enrolled for the first year. We all bonded together quickly as a result. By the end of October however I realised that computer science was just not for me. We were not compatible. As the year wore on I started to fall further and further behind. The problem I now had was that having just recovered from the impact of my Roscrea expulsion, my Mam was beginning to feel delightfully compensated by the new image of her son, the computer scientist. How could I break her heart again? She was beginning to telephone relatives and neighbours to tell them that Liam would be well able to fix their sewing machine or video player when he had his computer science degree. My chickenheartedness got the better of me. I remained on the course until the following Easter.

My architectural seed had now managed to germinate. I at last knew what I wanted to do. In a furious week of headstrong decision making I left university and got a job on a building site in Bray. I didn't say a word to anyone. This was the very first step of my long career journey. If I wanted to be an architect, I would begin at the very bottom. I swopped the possibility of becoming a computer scientist to start work as a building labourer. I was a week on the job before I plucked up the courage to tell my Mam and Dad.

I will never forget the evening I broke the news. It was a Saturday and Dad came in to watch Match of the Day as usual. There was just the three of us in the room. It was the perfect opportunity to make my announcement. Yet how could I spoil his one hour of uninterrupted pleasure for the week. I waited until after the football had finished. The

33

revelation that followed was probably more difficult for them than the phone call from the school informing them of my expulsion, ten months earlier. They had sacrificed so much to give all of us the benefit of the education they never had. Now it looked as if I was voluntarily stepping off the career path they had worked so hard to construct for me. They were now both fearing the worst. This was the beginning of their son, the park bench tramp.

My father, to his great credit, embraced me at my graduation in Liverpool years later. He told me that he understood then what I had done. He said he admired my conviction. I had not been deterred from following my star. My mother would unfortunately not live to see her adored son bring home her prized degree.

I spent three months on the building site and really enjoyed it. We were building a new church in Bray so perhaps God himself had involved himself directly with my career deliberations. My Dad at the time was friendly with an architect who was also involved with Athlone Town. He asked him if he would take me in to his office to gain some work experience.

I started working in Noel Heavey's practice in Athlone in July 1980. It was to be the start of two very happy years there. The office was located in a quaint little townhouse, just off one of the main streets, with a total staff of ten. I was living at home again by then and working in the pub at night to pay for my keep. Whatever I earned therefore was my own.

I really enjoyed the work. A small town architectural practice is an ideal source of work experience. It will tend to attract a good mix of design projects from one-off houses to small scale commercial and industrial developments. It provided me with a very good grounding in all aspects of the work of an architect. I was an assistant to the four main architectural staff. Paddy Hynes, who would later become a key source of inspiration to me in my cancer battle, was the senior technician. The remainder of the friendly, vibrant staff included two architects from overseas, Michael Williams from Wales and a lovely girl from Australia, Carol Campbell Brown. I fitted in well from the start. After a turbulent twelve months since leaving school I was delighted to have found my career niche at last.

My two years in Athlone were to be a highpoint of contentment and stability in my youth. I was getting paid for a job I loved. My earnings were completely for my own disposal so I was free to pursue Athlone Town and Linda Martin and Chips to my hearts content. I was also really enjoying life back in Horseleap. I was minding the pub in the evenings and orchestrating many memorable nights in Paddy Ryans.

The most important aspect of these two years however was that I got the opportunity to spend quality, mature time with both my Mam and Dad. Mam would die from cancer a few years later and as I reviewed these times from my own cancer bed I realised how lucky I was to have had them. This narrow chink of wonderful association I had with her was bookended by the arrival of my maturity on one side and her death on the other.

As the youngest child and only boy I was always going to be the apple of her eye. My three sisters will justifiably concur that I was spoiled terribly as a child. It didn't take me long to work out that I could get just about anything I wanted through my mother. I made sure this situation was taken full advantage of, as often as possible. I then went straight from spoiled child to terrible teenager. So in the 22 years we shared together, I must have driven my poor mother demented for about 18 of them. However we had an unbelievable relationship for the last four years. Without that I would have carried the guilt of my lack of appreciation for her to my grave.

So here I was, looking back over my own life through my disease and cancer appears where I had practically forgotten it. It took my mother from me when I was only twenty two. Had it taken her a few years earlier I never would have forgiven myself. I would have lived my life without taking the opportunity to show her my gratitude for being the wonderful mother she was. She, in turn, would have been denied the opportunity to meet her real son. Somebody who loved her dearly and will be forever grateful for all she did for me. Somebody who I hope is generally kind and calm, rather than the petulant and demanding child she had been exposed to for years. Somebody, more annoyingly for her, who concealed all of his irritating attributes from every other mother in Horseleap. He was the classic street angel, house devil.

But just as every Irish mother loves her son, every Irish son loves his mother too. It just took me an awful long time to show it. In the end I got there just in time. All of this was much clearer to me now. Cancer doesn't give you time to say things later. You need to say them now.

My dad was heartbroken when she died. We all rallied around him to try and fill the void but his spirit was gone. She was everything to him. He had a number of friends in the soccer club who also died around that time too. Had they still been around we might have had some chance to redirect him, but his heart wasn't in it. He died two years after her.

He was not in good health by then but after initially surviving a big operation for a chest infection we thought he had one last fight in him. He rallied for a short time but then he was gone. This one was hard for the four of us. Now we were truly on our own. We had great parents and now they were both gone.

The more I examined my Dad's death in later years the more I could see that sometimes there is just a time to go. He had no interest in fighting and surviving just for the sake of being alive. When his death approached, he offered no resistance. To live, you must want to live. You must want to fight with everything you have, to stay living.

These sentiments may appear to contradict the very principle of this book. You fight your cancer, or whatever demon, you have in your life to the very last inch. You never give up. To do that however you must have a foundation. Your fight needs a base and that base is an appreciation of life itself. You must love to be alive and will go to any lengths to remain that way. You must recognise that your glass is half full and not half empty. Your fight can only begin at zero. It can not be declared from a position of minus six or seven. We must all realise and appreciate how lucky we are to have got this far and want more and more.

Our fight is not a normal one. It is not a case of fighting back just because you have been attacked. In this fight you will need to out think your opponent before you ever throw your first punch. You will need him to know that you have no fear. You need to be certain that you are going to win before the fight even begins. To do that you must be able to rely on every bit of yourself. Your mind, your body and every part of your life to that point in time. If you show any weakness your cancer will find it.

So our fight is not a case of going into battle spontaneously. We must have the right frame of mind in place first. The entire fight will be founded on that. A positive mindset is that essential foundation. The battle that needs to be fought will then be built on top. Without the former, the latter will not stay up. In my Dads case this foundation was gone. The passing of his life long companion and his close friends had whittled it away. When we tried to rebuild his house for him there was nothing there to hold it up.

9 – Signpost to Liverpool

My job in Athlone was the final confirmation I was looking for that I wanted to become an architect. I began to apply for the only architecture course available to me, in Dublin. There were just two schools of architecture in the Irish Republic then. I was a few points short of the acceptance level for UCD but Bolton Street had a lower entry requirement, coupled with an interview.

I was a little raw for my interview the first year, but didn't mind my refusal. I was more than happy to return to my job. It would just prove to be valuable experience for when I returned the following year. On the second attempt I was turned down again. For the third interview, with two good years of work experience under my belt, I felt I had reached a position where I was going to be difficult to turn away. By now I was doing very well in the office and was obviously very committed to becoming an architect. How could they refuse me this time? But, turn me down they did. I was devastated. I took this rejection as final. If I was to apply for the next ten years I had convinced myself that each trip to Dublin would be in vain before I even set off. I now feared that the job I wanted to do was going to be forever kept beyond my grasp.

The Welsh architect, Michael Williams, was attuned to my impasse. He came to me one day and remarked that I did not appear to be having much success with my quest in Ireland. He asked if I had ever considered the possibility of applying to the U.K. The system over there, he told me, was generally more accessible. There were a lot more colleges to apply to. They also tended to have a bigger intake in the first year. This was counter balanced with a higher failure rate between the first and second year.

At that time Irish students didn't really go to England the way they do now. His proposition was well beyond what anybody had been thinking up to then. However I was so relieved to see my dream was still alive that I rushed home that evening with the news that possibilities still existed for me. Mam and Dad, as progressive as they have always been, were delighted for me. They graciously gave their consent for me to investigate this opportunity further. They wouldn't have wanted to stand in the way of what I wanted to do but perhaps they never really expected that their only son would be leaving the country so soon.

That summer the Royal Institute of British Architects sent me details of all the U.K. universities that were available to me. I applied to every one of them. My inquiries were generally being well received. I was offered interviews in Portsmouth, London, Leeds,

Glasgow and Dundee. Two years after walking onto a building site in Bray my dream to become an architect was beginning to take shape. I started to plan a whistle stop tour of England and Scotland. A British university tour with my portfolio under my arm. I needed to work out the best route so that I could avail of as many of these interviews as I could.

Then, I arrived home one evening, to find a letter waiting for me. It was from Huddersfield Polytechnic Department of Architecture. I opened it and it contained the immortal words "we wish to offer you a place as a first year on the architecture course for the 1982-83 academic year". Wow! The holy grail! I had got a place. A school of architecture had just written to me inviting me to be one of their students.

It didn't take long for my initial jubilation to be supplanted by suspicion. What kind of a college can this be? They have never met me or seen any of my work? I could be anyone. It was a further year before I would realise that the "anyones" don't make it to second year. The English system was to give as many people as possible a chance to start the course, knowing natural wastage would self regulate the numbers by the second year. All I would need to do, to follow my chosen career path, was to survive the first year cull.

Two days later another place offer arrived. This one was from Liverpool. This time there was nothing to restrain the jubilation. Of all the cities I had applied to, the place that I really wanted to go to was Liverpool. I had been a huge Liverpool football supporter all through my childhood. That was my initial link. Then, as a young, first time, emigrant Liverpool is about as close to Ireland as you can get. If I was to leave my country I wanted to make the shortest journey possible. Liverpool didn't seem like somewhere far away. I also knew that it was a city that already had a huge Irish connection. It probably would be able to offer me a home from home that the other British cities couldn't match. Liverpool it would be.

Mam and Dad left me to the boat on that fateful night. I was heading off to open a whole new chapter of my life. In a sad way I think we all knew that this was a beginning of an end. On the first journey to Roscrea they knew it was going to be the end of Liam Ryan as their little boy. But this time it was different. This time it was probably going to be the end of Liam Ryan as theirs at all. He would probably return one day, on his own two feet, as somebody else's.

As I looked back on that night years later from my sick bed it was a much bigger parting than any of us had imagined. Within a few months Mam would become ill again, only this time not to recover. The Irish Sea that night was not only a physical divide. It symbolically represented the final separation of these three people as family.

I remained out on deck as the ship pulled away. I stayed until my mother and father had diminished to two tiny specs at the railings of the ferryport. I was trying to keep them in my sights for as long as I possibly could. I waved constantly. When I was sure they were no longer to be seen I turned to look into the dark cold of the Irish Sea air. I was heading to a place that I was yet to see. I was going somewhere that would end up playing a major role in how the rest of my life would unfold. I was on my way to the great city of Liverpool.

10 – The First Strides of a Runner

It was also about this time that I took up running for the first time. Both Liverpool and the mentality I would adopt from running would become essential elements in my cancer fight, 20 years later. Here they both were, simultaneously establishing themselves in my life in good time.

Horseleap was a very quiet place to be based for the years before I went to college. I needed some form of inexpensive and accessible activity to keep me occupied. The marathon craze of the early eighties had by now gripped the nation. I had always been reasonably sporty and after a few drinks one night with Mike McGuinness, we decided we'd give it a go. Running was also the only activity that was flexible enough to slot in around my commitments of work and my shifts in the pub.

This flexibility would always remain as one of the greatest attractions that kept me returning to running in later years.

You can basically run anywhere, anytime and with very little preparation. You just need a good pair of running shoes and off you go. As I got older, too old for contact sports and my life got busier, too busy to organise a game of golf, tennis or squash, running was always there waiting for me. This was to be a huge incentive each time I returned to the roads. I still wanted some form of taxing exercise and running was the only one that ticked all the necessary boxes. It was non contact, immediately accessible, cheap and could be done at any time, day or night.

Whilst a lot of other people my age were paying gym membership fees I secretly delighted in the unfashionable appeal and simplicity of running. Big, expensive human exercise machines were not for me. Man has run from day one, but rowing machines came a lot later.

It started out purely as a form of exercise but soon running began to captivate my senses. The peace and tranquillity it offered and the sheer pleasure of running on Irish country roads, were an unexpected bonus. For a simple, singular activity it covers many bases. It provided me not just with fitness and mental stamina but also directly connected me with the wonderful natural environment all around me.

Mike was great. The benefit of running with somebody else is that they will generally cover your weaknesses. On the days you are inclined to give it a miss they will make sure you don't. If you run alone it can be easy to find an excuse not to go out today. In my case, if I missed a day I could easily end up missing a month. Mike was always there to make sure this didn't happen.

We lived two miles apart so one of us had to jog to the other to begin our run. This made it almost impossible to refuse to go when your partner had already made such an effort. Mike was great at never failing to turn up. Many evenings I would arrive home from work and convince myself I was too tired to run tonight. I would just plonk myself down in the armchair, with a cup of tea on its way and a good television programme about to start. Suddenly this red face would peer around the door at me. The proposition was always the same "Are ye right"? No matter how much I wanted to I could never refuse the offer. I would be up and out in two minutes flat, quietly cursing him initially but eventually thanking him for the sheer exhilaration of another great six or eight mile run. A run that would not have happened without him.

Twenty years later I began to realise how important these early running milestones were. These were my first experiences of tackling activities that I often didn't want to do. I was discovering that I had the mentality to take undesired tasks and doggedly turn them into rewarding achievements. These were the very first shoots of the mindset I would use to take on my cancer treatment.

The runs became longer and more demanding and my determination increased accordingly. The mental focus I was accumulating would eventually be transfered to what was needed to face up to a lumber puncture, or a peg tube insertion and finally a twelve hour operation. I wasn't running on the operating table but the tenacity that it had nurtured in me was exactly what was needed.

These runs with Mike McGuinness were the very beginning. The very beginning of the mental process that would equip me to face much bigger challenges to come.

11 – Early College Years

I will never forget my very first impressions of Liverpool. During the sailing I became friendly with a London based Irish businessman. He was driving home after seeing his relatives in Sligo. We chatted in the bar and he warmly received my account of the reason I came to be on board. He listened as I explained how I was about to take the very first steps on my delayed career path. I'm sure he saw a bit of himself in me that night. He had probably been in my position 10 or 15 years earlier. He was compassionate towards my situation as a result. He insisted he pay for my dinner and looked out for me the next morning, insisting it was no trouble to drive me to wherever I needed to go. So the first vistas I saw of my new city were the windscreen framed images of Liverpool's north docks that continuously reeled in front of me as I sat in John McColgan's car. Eventually the road began to ascend. We were emerging from the endless warehouse tunnels of the dockland basin. The city that I was so eagerly anticipating was just about to reveal itself.

Then, as if by magic, the Royal Liver Building, just appeared in front of me! It was gigantic. I had never seen anything like it before. A huge, granite, Christmas tree of a building. But crowned by two elegant liver birds rather than a Christmas fairy. It was simply majestic. To this day I will never forget the sensation of seeing it for the first time. Ever since it has always been the first and last building I look for when arriving in, or departing from Liverpool.

The Royal Liver Building has never been credited for outstanding architectural merit. But buildings have different reasons for personal appeal. Some capture the human spirit no matter what the critics say. The Liver Building is an emotional building rather than an architectural one. It is a building that is uniquely synonymous with the city that has created it. As the Empire State Building is to New York, the Royal Liver Building is to Liverpool. The first landmark of my very first view of my new city left a permanent impression.

Architecture is a very sociable course. The students tend to rely on each other from the start. You need your cohorts for their opinion, their advice and the loan of their equipment. As a result everybody gets to know everyone else fairly quickly. The numbers were good for close harmony too. The first year intake was limited to about 40 due to the limitations of having to provide studio space for each student. In Liverpool this natural intimacy of the course was further enhanced by the fact that our department had its own building on Victoria Street. We were dislocated from the huge epicentre of the main polytechnic campus. Out of the 40, a group of about eight of us soon whittled down into our own little social group. We were a mixture of English, Northern Irish and Welsh, with John Carton and myself being the only two from the Irish republic. We all got on well from the start, enjoying a healthy and entertaining banter between the nationalities.

Architecture is a long course. It takes a minimum of seven years to fully qualify. This also helps to foster long term friendships. Over the following years we would all harvest our initial plantation as first year students by becoming life long friends. I am delighted to say that just about everybody from this early group of friends was at my bedside at some stage, twenty years later after my surgery.

Our course had a very human face to it. Rather than exams the method of assessment was for the students to display their work and have their drawings and designs critically examined by the tutors. These sessions, known as crits, were generally extremely tough. The tutors regularly chose to be negative rather than positive to test each students ability to defend their work. A kind of macabre spectator sport often ensued with many students being subjected to twenty minutes of incessant public humiliation. Some of the female students in particular were often reduced to tears by this. They would eventually submerge under the constant waves of criticism.

Each one of us questioned our ability to get through this course when the inevitable bad crit came along. The thinking, I assume, was that this negative approach would toughen you up for the real world when your design decisions might be questioned. Such a theory has remained unproven to me ever since however. I have yet to meet a real life client whose behaviour remotely matched the ranting we had to endure from some of those tutors.

The good thing was that nobody was spared. We all suffered at the hands of certain tutors at some stage. This became the final ingredient that ensured we were a tightly knit bunch of students. It was us against them. We needed to stick together.

Of our entire class one individual shone head and shoulders above the rest. When it came to popularity Peter Morgan from Belfast was just one of those outstanding characters that comes along all too seldom. He had a natural ability to make everybody laugh, almost all of the time. Everybody loved Pete. He was a major catalyst to us all gelling together right from the start. His infectious likeability became the social blood that ran through the veins of our entire year group. Friendships and acquaintances were accelerated between us all as a result of his presence. Pete was the conductor and we were all only too happy to be part of the orchestra. His pranks became famous and were generally ingenious and hilarious. When it was your turn you to be on the end of one you just ended up laughing along with everyone else.

We had all just settled in when one of his earliest tricks emerged. Between books and studio equipment we all needed a heavy bag, usually a rucksack, which was brought from home to college and back every day. We also had many building sample products on display in the studio. One day, Pete, without saying a word to anybody, sought out the heaviest brick he could find. He famously christened it "the Wally Brick". He then inscribed it accordingly in big yellow letters. Further smaller inscriptions read "Do not take this brick home" and "Any person who takes this brick home is a complete and utter wally".

In the afternoon studio session, when we were all preoccupied at our drawing boards, he would make his move. His unfortunate victim would leave their bag unobserved for a sufficient amount of time for him to bury the brick deep inside. Our bags were so heavy and bulky it generally had little chance of being detected.

The next morning the details of the wally bricks journey would unfold to everyone's amusement. Often it would be carried for miles, sometimes at high speed as you dashed to catch a bus or a train. It could end up being brought to the cinema, or on a date and, on one occasion, was lucky enough to get to hear The Smiths live in concert.

It would only be late in the evening, when you were unpacking the very bowels of your rucksack, before you would discover that the "wally" to be revealed tomorrow would be you. It would then dawn on you how your bag appeared to be considerably heavier than normal as you walked home. You also knew that it was now impossible to escape the consequences. Pete would have everybody primed for your arrival next morning.

Liverpool was a fantastic city to be a student in. It has always been well renowned as a friendly city, full of character, humour and warmth. For me the key ingredient that made all these three work so well was scale. Liverpool had a very small, easily walkable, city centre. Every night, when any one of us headed in to town, we knew that any of our friends, who were also out, would be in any one of a small handful of pubs in the university area. This was a great advantage to new students to the city. Socialising was easy and consequently Liverpool became a very sociable city.

Our particular hunting ground was a collection of some of Liverpool's finest traditional pubs, just off the city centre. They were all within a stone's throw of each other. This ease in finding your friends was particularly useful to the likes of me as, for the first three years, I lived in the unfashionable northern suburb of Bootle. I was removed from the established student residential hub in the city and I needed to know my journey for company and entertainment would be successful before I set off.

I was renting the attic room of a large terraced house. The reason I remained there for so long was that my very nice landlord and landlady retained it for me every summer for free. This allowed me to leave all my stuff behind when I went back to Ireland at the end of the academic year. The convenience of this factor alone, coupled with not having the hassle of finding new accommodation on returning, far outweighed the lure of the bright lights of a more stylish location in the city.

Apart from student drinking gatherings my other main leisure activities at this time were music and football. My academic pilgrimage to Liverpool seemed to be, in sporting terms, the equivalent of an Arab reaching Mecca. I had been a devoted fan of Liverpool football club since I was a small boy. Ironically on reaching the promised land I was now discovering that my singular passion for Liverpool was becoming diluted. I began with a few memorable trips to Anfield but before long I had good friends who were Evertonians and Manchester United supporters. I was by then also making regular trips to Goodison Park and Old Trafford.

Ironically, as soon as my thirst for the big football occasions was satisfied, my Athlone Town roots began to re-emerge. I began to miss the scale of the football matches that I had been born and raised with. In the end I found the only football ground on Merseyside that could satisfy this need was across the river in Birkenhead. As a Merseyside football supporter I was happiest of all when I went to see Tranmere Rovers. My football pilgrimage had arrived at the cathedral of Anfield only to find that it was in the little church of Prenton Park where I wanted to worship. Just as I had become accustomed to in Athlone. I needed a place where if I roared, my heroes would hear me!

Musically at that time Liverpool did not have a venue that could cater for the really big concerts. The two universities provided an excellent menu of college gigs for bands that were either on the way up or the way down. The decrepit but wonderfully atmospheric Royal Court attracted the bands in between. Bands that were too big for the college circuit and still too small for the arenas. I saw, soon to be huge, bands like U2, REM and Echo and the Bunnymen there, while they were all still brilliantly young, raw and energetic. Those were also the last years of the new wave era so the universities hosted a succession of dark, edgy punk bands that came, thrillingly scared the life out of us and then just disappeared again.

For bigger concerts it was off, by coach, to the National Exhibition Centre in Birmingham. If Liverpool was the city for intimacy and character then Birmingham was the metropolis for big. A maze of vast roads brought you all the way to the NEC. It, in turn, was an enormous aircraft carrier of a building, floating on an ocean of car parking. It was as if you had suddenly found a part of the world where somebody had adjusted the scale from normal sized to gigantic. As we left the coaches we trooped towards the mothership like endless lines of dedicated little rock ants. We had come from all corners of Great Britain to pay homage. Many times I can remember the elation of the final encore quickly congealing into the dread of missing your bus home. You had delayed just a little too long inside at the end, still hypnotized by the amazing concert you had just witnessed. Now you were running to desperately search for your coach. 300 buses, all seemingly identical, were staring at you and now, one by one, beginning to pull away.

It became the stuff of nightmares for each little individual ant, no matter how memorable the night had been up to then. I saw Bruce Springsteen, The Who, Genesis and Rush at the NEC and loved every second of the gargantuan experience. I also never missed the bus home.

12 – John O'Groats or Bust!

One Friday Pete arrived in to an afternoon lecture and excitedly cornered three of us at the back of the room. He had a brilliant plan for the weekend. "We'll all go to John O'Groats" We just laughed. Yeah sure, another of his infamous jokes. But he was serious. He had discovered that we could hire a car from three o'clock on Friday until first thing Monday morning for fifteen pounds each. This mission was already in countdown. It was John O'Groats or bust! Before we could muster any serious objections Brendan Kilpatrick, Paul Crothers and myself suddenly found ourselves charging up the M6 in a new Vauxhall Cavalier. We were heading for Scotland. Pete had cast his spell over us again. About an hour earlier the extent of our forward planning for the weekend was which laundrette we would go to.

We reached Glasgow at nine o'clock that night. It was time to give the car a rest and find a pub. Pete had all the necessary details worked out in advance. He had contacted a friend who would put us up for the night. After a heavy night in Glasgow the task the next morning was to get four groggy heads into the car as early as we could. That didn't turn out to be possible until the afternoon but at least now we were on the final leg of the outward trip. 200 miles to the very tip of Scotland.

We stopped off to see Aviemore, Scotland's only ski resort and also spent an hour in Inverness. Then it was back to the road for it to take us as far north as the British mainland would allow.

It was the last day of November. The air was beautifully crisp. It was cold but still too early for snow. About an hour the far side of Inverness, just as dusk was falling, our desire to make haste unfortunately coincided with a deceptively sharp turn. Beyond the turn lay a narrow stone bridge. We were going too fast to make it. The inevitable happened. We swerved and shunted sideways into the wall of the bridge before coming to a shuddering stop.

As crashes go for four young impressionable lads, it was perfect. No head-on impact occurred so we were not in any real danger of injury but the car was still a decent looking write off. Paul, Brendan and myself emerged from the car, still high on the adrenalin of being in our first crash but now sad that this was the end of our trip. The end of the road on the road to the end. We just assumed that we now telephoned the car company, apologised and made our way back to Liverpool. Pete, however, once again was a step ahead. All possible eventualities for this trip had been covered. "Don't worry lads. I'll just phone the hire people and get them to send us out a new car." The three of us were dumbfounded. We were blissfully unaware that this could be the case. "What! We've just crashed their car and they'll just come out and bring us a new one? Just like that?" "Yep, that's the beauty of car hire!" he beamed back.

By now a nearby Scottish family, who lived on the other side of the bridge, had heard the commotion. They came out to see what was happening. They were lovely and invited us in for tea whilst we worked out what to do next. They had two teenage daughters who were enthralled to have such rare adventure on their doorstep. It was as if a movie scene had just descended and now the four main characters, four friendly Irish lads, were in their kitchen. The feeling was mutual. We were equally enthralled to be invited into a lovely Scottish homestead with two beautiful girls in it.

We sorted out the details with the hire company over the phone and Pete went back to Inverness to pick up our new car. He returned two hours later and we all bade our delightful hosts farewell. It was time to get back on the road. We were still driving a new Vauxhall Cavalier, only now it was red rather than white. We would all delight on how our car magically changed colour when showing off our photos when we got back.

Our already tight schedule had now suffered a severe setback. We stopped in Wick for chips and eventually reached John O'Groats at eleven o'clock that night. In the darkness there was little to suggest that this was a place of settlement. John O'Groats was merely a single pub with a few houses nearby scattered across the headland.

We just caught last orders in the pub. Our late arrival generated puzzled expressions on the faces of the handful of locals within. We were now in deep Scotland. We thought it best therefore to order whiskys. They would help to both insulate and tranquilise us for the cold night's camping that lay ahead. The pub was only a short distance from the sea so we pitched our tent right outside. We were in the perfect position to take the last few remaining steps of our epic, Peter Morgan inspired, escapade, the following morning.

In spite of the cold we all slept well. The next morning we made the short walk to the very northern tip of Scotland, John O'Groats. By now, having probably slept as close to him as any visitor ever did we felt we knew him well enough to just call him John. When we reached the top of the cliffs the windswept, rugged beauty of this barren place was revealed to us, and to us alone. We had "John" all to ourselves. The ferocious North Sea pounded relentlessly below as we all just stood there, both collectively and individually, savouring the awesome display of nature. It was as if we had now become part of that bleak landscape. It was a powerful antidote to the pace and restraints of the city life that we had briefly escaped from.

The sense of a long journey to an awesome, expansive end destination was very strong. I'm sure we all used those few hours to reflect on our own personal journey in life, to that point in time. Although it was Scotland, it also contained a great sense of Irishness for the four us. It was a patriotic moment. The landscape, isolation and climate returned all four of us, momentarily, to places we knew in Ireland that Liverpool could never reawaken in us. We were brothers for a few hours, thinking of the family and friends that we had all left behind us at home.

We toured along the north coast until late afternoon on the Sunday and then we needed to start heading south. We had to get the car back in time on Monday morning. With two drivers we drove through the night, without stopping, and reached Liverpool just in time for breakfast. The staff at the car hire company were bemused to see us return in the same car but in a different colour. Then we all reported in to college for a nine o'clock lecture. We were desperate all morning for the first person to ask us what we had done since they last saw us on Friday evening.

I thought about that crash on the Scottish bridge many times after I was diagnosed with cancer. I thought of how frivolous it all was at the time. It was almost like an accessory to our weekend away. Almost as if we had planned it as part of our itinerary. We were young and looking for our adventure to be as exciting as possible. We were delighted it happened. It was a right of passage crash. It became the main highlight every time the story was re-told. We were indestructible then and it was an incident that could never have had an unfortunate ending. It was never going to be anything other than a positive, colourful anecdote to our trip.

Now I was lying on my cancer bed staring down the barrel of an early demise. I considered myself a young man. I was just 40 years of age. I was now fighting for my life. It was no ordinary fight. I was prepared to take it all the way to the very last breath, the very last drop of blood, the very last hair on my head. My cancer was not going to get an easy ride. It had picked the wrong guy for that.

But now, with the benefit of maturity, I looked back at this other guy. He was half my age and he was happy to smack into a stone bridge in Scotland, with his three friends, for the sake of telling a good story when he got back to Liverpool. I couldn't equate these two personalities. I couldn't believe they were the same person. I appreciate youth played a role but death didn't exist for me then. Yet, for an instant on that weekend I was just as close to it as I was now.

I now knew how lucky I was in that incident and a few more like it. I also realised that if I had died then, how foolish I would now feel. Foolish because it didn't have to be then. It would have been completely preventable. As four carefree adolescents not one of us could see the tragic consequences our actions that day. We were totally blind to the ripples of sadness, for both ourselves and our families, that could have emanated forever from that incident. I now had a sense of delayed foolishness, twenty years too late. Only now could I picture the devastating scene of four families preparing for the premature funerals of four fine young men.

Now with the grim reaper knocking on my door I was whacking him on the head and poking his eyes out. Then I was practically inviting him in for tea. As you move through your life you get a chance to view it again from different angles. The beautiful but wild innocence of youth. Indestructible close up but extremely fortunate when seen from a distance.

13 – Marathons and Foreign Study Trips

For my first three years in Liverpool, culminating in my first degree, I managed to strike a good blend between the academic work required and a lively social life. We were a good, cohesive bunch of students that got on very well. Pete generally was at the centre of much of what we got up to in the evenings. Thanks to him our nights out tended to be numerous, well crafted and very memorable. Yet we were all still sensible enough to keep our studies in check. We all came through with solid, middle ground, degrees as a result. I got the balance between entertainment and study about right for those three years. The "good horse" was still running well.

I didn't really have a girlfriend for any of this time. This was partly due to being too wet behind the ears to do the right things about looking for one. The main reason however, at least in my own mind, was that I didn't want anything to offset my response to the call when it came. When the boys were getting up and going down I didn't want anything to get in my way.

For these years I was a man's man or perhaps more accurately, a lad's lad. One lovely girl did come along and was interested, but it never really got a chance. I was far too distracted at that stage to commit to anything serious. The opportunity passed before it ever materialised. All of the other lads were single and available. I was having far too much fun to suddenly want to leave the herd.

I ran my very first marathon at this time too. I had been home in Horseleap for the summer of 1984. The first Dublin marathon had taken place a couple of years earlier so running fever had its grip on Ireland. Mike McGuinness and myself decided we'd target our running that summer to completing a marathon. We ran the Dublin marathon at the end of October. Although my training got a little disrupted when I returned to college in Liverpool I was still in good enough shape to record my best ever time, 3 hours 22 minutes.

It was a great day. The first marathon is your best one of all. The sense of achievement as you cross the finish line is just sensational. For an amateur sportsperson this is probably as close as you will ever come to matching the professional who wins a cup final or an olympic medal. You have just achieved something very few people will do. You have entered your own personal history books. It is an achievement that can never be taken away from you. You have run a marathon.

This was the initial phase of my two part running career. This was the youthful stage. After a ten year gap I would eventually return to running. I would be wiser then and more appreciative of my ability to run but the speed would be gone. However the later stage of my running would fall each side of getting cancer. It would end up offering me a lot more than a medal or a T-shirt. It would be there to be part of the jigsaw that saved my life. It was as if it had reintroduced itself into my life when it knew I would need it most.

I went on to run two more marathons in my initial running period. The first was in Liverpool itself and the other, rather than running in a loop, was from one town to another, Hull to Grimsby. It was named after the great landmark that lies between them, the Humber Bridge marathon. I didn't have Mike McGuinness to badger me to train properly for either of these runs. I was back in college and surrounded again by all of Liverpool's social distractions. My times suffered as a result. These are the only two marathons that I stopped to walk in.

In those early running years I tended to disregarded these two runs compared to my first marathon. But now having acquired the wisdom that comes with middle age I can see that every marathon completed is good one. To be able to run a marathon is not just an achievement, it is a gift. If you are disappointed on reaching the finish line just remind yourself of the many people who cannot do what you have just done. Your achievement is magnificent. You are privileged to be able to say you did it. It took my second running stage to help me appreciate some of the achievements of my first.

One of the great things about studying architecture is that you get to travel. You will undertake at least two foreign study trips as part of your course. These were some of the most memorable trips anyone could be lucky enough to make. They took you to some of the finest architectural locations in the world. In my case I upped the number to four. I added in two extra trips. One when I was working in London and the other when I returned to the finish the course as a part-time student. The opportunities they presented, visiting amazing buildings as part of a group of young, lively students, would not be presented to you again for the remainder of your life.

Each trip was momentous in itself. We had a packed itinerary of magnificent sights and incredible buildings to see. We were granted access to a series of wondrous spaces, both internal and external, that were often not available to the normal tourist. However it was the social element of these trips that made them truly memorable. The infectious mix of being part of a group of carefree students and a tourist in a foreign country produced a legendary outcome. It could only be availed of in this narrow window of our lives. We were old enough and young enough. Our days were spent transfixed by the amazing sights we were seeing. But in the evenings our exuberance for fun and entertainment knew no bounds. We had the energy to party all night and get up and do it all again the next day.

I feel very lucky to have been part of four of these foreign study trips. Had I not studied architecture I may well have missed out on the chance to see two of world's most iconic structures of our time. Two sights that are no longer to be seen today, the Berlin Wall and the World Trade Centre in New York. Both of these structures made very brief appearances in the history of the world. They would not be around to be seen by generations like the pyramids or the Taj Mahal. But in their brief lifespan I saw them both. I saw them thanks to my architecture course.

I was also profoundly captivated by the experience of seeing Andrea Palladio's Villa Rotunda in Vicenza and the graceful modernity of Frank Lloyd Wrights Guggenheim Museum in New York. Still, no matter how memorable all of the buildings were, it was invariably the antics we got up on each trip that left us with the greatest memories.

Venice came first. That was the trip when eight of us decided to reverse a trend by defecting into a communist country, even if only for a couple of hours. On that same evening I was to receive the news of my mother's death.

Berlin was next. This was an extra study trip I added whilst I was working in London. The highlight of that trip was the separate journey I had to make to get there. I missed the flight from London with the tour party and had to travel to Berlin on my own by train. I arrived two days later. The transformation of the landscapes I observed from the windows of the train as I passed from the wealth of West Germany to the starkness of the East will stay with me forever.

Berlin itself was a microcosm of those two diverse lifestyles. One city, but with an austere concrete structure drawn across it to break it in two. A city of two halves, separated physically by a wall and ideologically by everything else. This was the touching point of world history at that time and every visitor knew it. If America and Russia were arm wrestlers, their hands were clasped in Berlin.

It was an incredible place to visit. You were in the only place in the world where the east and west met in a single, concentrated flashpoint. Two sides of a wall pitted against each other with hatred and distrust that was underpinned by suspicion, contempt and fear. The two sides of Berlin were like the Punch and Judy show of world politics. Only here would the communism of the east and the capitalism in the west share such a small stage.

West Berlin was simply wild. It was completely untamed. I had never seen a European city like it. It was as if it had to demonstrate western culture to an excess just to irk its neighbour. It wanted to show the eastern half of the city what it was missing, multiplied by ten.

In the East I met nice people who were polite and subdued. They were warm but their faces rarely smiled. They appeared to reflect inner spirits that had been downtrodden and broken.

After Berlin it was Paris. Peter Morgan took this one over. He was the one-man highlight all on his own. It was a stage that was set for him and he did not disappoint. Right from boarding the bus in Liverpool he took up his baton as the conductor once again. We all gladly took our seats in the orchestra. Every evening we roamed across the city to a selected Parisienne bistro for coffee, wine and music. These were filled with extremely cool French people. Then it was back to one of our rooms where the drinking and madness continued. It generally lasted until the sun began to interrupt through the curtains. That was our cue to get a few hours sleep before breakfast.

Our last evening, when the money had finally run out, was the most memorable. We could no longer afford the chic little bars and restaurants so a plan B was required. We decided to make our own entertainment in one of the subway stations. Pete had brought his fiddle and it didn't take long for a small crowd to gather around our lively Irish music session. This was the first time that he also introduced us to the art of using your nose to inflate a condom over your head. Before long we became a troupe of singing and dancing condom heads. In any other city the police would probably have been called but this was Paris. High spirited exuberance in one city is art in Paris!

The French public loved us. They shook off their commuter inhibitions to start joining in. They warmly appreciated our bout of free, colourful entertainment. We had illuminated their normally unexciting journey home. It was our last tango in Paris, literally. Perhaps the king had no clothes on. He certainly had no money. But at least he had an inflated condom on his head.

My first foreign study trip to Venice was to become unforgettable for much more than just a lively student tour. It was where I was to be when my mother died. This was the biggest event of my life in my first three years in Liverpool. If boarding school had been the beginning of my transition from boy to man, this was the closing chapter. The death of a parent is a poignant landmark in all of our lives. It is a uniquely personal tragedy for everybody. My grief on the death of my mother was extended by not being beside her when she died. I was in Venice.

Our trip was scheduled for March in 1984. By then my mother's cancer had returned to ravage her. She was now in palliative care in St. Lukes hospital in Dublin. Her remaining time was now being quantified in months rather than years.

I came over from Liverpool to see her as often as possible and the week before the trip I asked my Dad and sisters if they thought I should go. She was weak at that time but was as bright and brave as she had always been through her ordeal. They felt it would be another couple of weeks before her final decline would begin. Nobody could be sure but it appeared as if she would still be there for me after the week long study trip. My dad advised me to go. I returned to Liverpool and arranged to come straight back to see her as soon as I got back.

Our college trips were always run on a tight budget. This was to keep the costs down for the students. Rather than fly to Venice we were travelling by coach. The journey itself therefore was always destined to become an essential element of the overall experience. We were an excited bunch of students, about to be unleashed on mainland Europe. We were determined that our adventure would begin as soon as we crossed the threshold of the bus waiting for us outside the university.

I have always loved to travel by both coach and train. They offer a social quality to your journey that the airplane cannot match. We had two drivers so that the coach could be on the move at all times. While one was driving the other was asleep in a special compartment under the seats.

We left Liverpool before dawn and having crossed the English Channel at Dover, spent most of that day driving down through France. My most vivid memory of the entire outward journey was crossing the Alps that night. It was now 3 a.m. and those of us that were still awake were treated to a magical cinematic presentation of these magnificent mountains through the windows of the bus. We got to see the Alps close up in all their reflective, snow-covered glory contrasted against the jet black sky. The power and serenity of these wondrous two tone images seemed like the perfect tranquilizer to our mad cap, alcohol fuelled, coach confined, day.

The next morning we stopped for breakfast at a roadside café somewhere near Milan. The memory of my first gulp of clean Italian mountain air as I stepped down from the coach will always remain with me. As fresh air goes, I must have been inhaling some of the very best that morning. Not far behind it, sensation wise, was my first taste of great Italian coffee and pastry that followed soon afterwards.

The Alps stood imposingly in the distance. They had been conquered. Now we were in Italy. Only a few hours later it was almost as if we were leaving again. The road on the mainland ended at the Ponte della Liberta. This time the barrier was not the mountains but the sea. We were crossing the bridge that would take us to the unique aquatic phenomenon that is Venice.

We were all exemplary architectural students for the first two days, at least by day. We dutifully visited every building on our daily itinerary and soaked up the historic and sombre ambiance of this wondrous city. Venice must have a thousand truly beautiful churches. After a couple of days of intense scrutiny however, it became almost impossible for us to see the wood from the trees. If any one of these churches was taken away and placed in the middle of Tipperary all of Ireland would come to see it. Their abundance in Venice however was such that one beautiful church was cancelled out by the next. The magnificence was endless and consequently lost its power to captivate. The ability to appreciate each one of these churches, purely on their own merits, became difficult. Quality became blunted by quantity.

For every Italian church we saw by day we drank at least one bottle of Italian wine by night. On our third night eight of us found a great little bar on the Venitian holiday island of The Lido. The Lido is to Venice what Venice is to Italy. A little treasure beyond the main attraction itself. Half way through the evening Pete suggested we all needed a break from all this renaissance architectural overload. He declared his tiny little brain could not cope with eight more churches to appraise in minute detail. He could not cope with another tortuous assessment on whether it was correct to use Doric rather than Ionic detailing on the church of St. what's his name again. We needed to be rescued by the John O'Groats of Italy. Giovanni O'Groats! Who was in? We all were! Another bottle of wine was ordered. This one was to induce our breakaway plan. With full glasses in hand we tightened the circle. Where would we go?

It took a second bottle before we decided that the goal of our mission should be to reach another country. That boiled everything down to Yugoslavia. Every other country was just too far away. We knew that Venice had a regular train connection to Trieste and Trieste was only a short hop from the Yugoslavian border. Our objective was to get to Yugoslavia. The Shinrone 6 were dead. Long live the Venetian Magnificent 8!

The next morning we had time for breakfast at our hotel as usual. This would help to delay any knowledge of our disappearance until sometime later in the day. We then all feigned joining one of the days architectural tours before making a break for the train station. We boarded the train to Trieste and three hours later we were as east as the Italian rail company could take us. We emerged from the station and immediately began to negotiate with the first two taxi drivers that approached us. They would take us across the border to Yugoslavia. I had seen this scenario in a hundred films. The two taxi drivers fitted the bill perfectly. They were both shady looking, wore cheap sunglasses, had no English and sported thick moustaches! The nearest town we could see on the map was called Koper so that became our coveted destination.

Just before the border, which was to the then east European communist state of Yugoslavia, now Slovenia, the two taxi drivers mysteriously stopped to change their metres with replacements they took from the boot. Our driver tried to explain to us in his own language, why he had done this. Maybe it was to show a smaller amount of money on the meter to reduce his necessary bribe to the border guards. We all suspected some kind of scam was going on. A few moments later we reached the border crossing. The border guard peered in menacingly at all of us. We had our passports inspected and stamped and then our taxi driver passed him a paper envelope. At this he nonchalantly waved us on. Mission accomplished - we had reached a non-Italian country.

Koper was an industrial coastal town. It appeared to have little to attract the tourist but yet radiated a sense of appeal as a friendly, down to earth little town. We assumed we had now enrolled in a very select group of tourists to visit this place. Consequently we convinced ourselves the extra friendly welcome we seemed to be receiving was because we were a rare sight. Koper was happy to see us and we were happy to be there too.

Our escapade now had credibility. We had crossed the border between eastern and western Europe to a town few other visitors would ever see. We had calculated that allowing for a repeat of our curious border crossing manoeuver, Koper would only have the pleasure of our company for two hours. By then we would need to be making our way back. We had to make sure we caught the last train from Triest.

The only sensible thing to do therefore was to go for a meal. We found a nice little local restaurant, overlooking the small working harbour. As we took our seats the cross border jokes began to flow. We didn't like Italian food so had come all the way to Yugoslavia for dinner!

Of the eight who sat down to dinner that evening, three were English, one Welsh, two Northern Irish and two from the Irish Republic. It was as if we were some kind of discover Koper, United Nations expedition. This meal was the planting of the flag on the summit. The staff were extremely friendly and delighted to have such rare guests. The food was incredibly cheap. We had a lovely time. Our visit to Koper comprised only one simple action but it is the little things that provide the best memories. Years later we could not remember one magnificent Venetian church from another, but we all remembered the little restaurant in Koper.

We arrived back in Venice at ten o'clock that night. I had no idea then that this day was still to take a momentous twist. As we approached the hotel, another good friend of mine, Dave Rudkin, approached. He had an anxious look on his face. I assumed he was about to tell me that we were in trouble with our lecturers. They had obviously discovered by now that we had been missing for the day. But this wasn't Roscrea. There was no question of being expelled this time. To my shame now, I was almost dismissing Dave as he reached me. "Its okay Dave, don't worry. There is nothing to worry about, I'll be fine." I wasn't hearing what he was trying to say to me. "There has been a call from Ireland. The staff need to see you." In that instant I knew what he meant. I ran to the hotel, guilt now creeping all over me. I had not thought about my mother all day.

Our three staff members were waiting for me. They confirmed to me that they had received word that Mam had died. They were very good to me. I felt drawn to the only woman, Pat Birtles, as the best qualified to comfort me. Pat had lost her husband suddenly two years earlier. It was as if we had common ground. She appeared to be the best equipped to appreciate how I now felt.

All of a sudden my jack the lad antics in Yugoslavia, a few hours earlier, seemed very insignificant, both to them and to me. My mother was gone and as a neighbour in Horseleap reminded me three days later at the funeral – you only have one mother. Venice and death. Of all the cities in Europe I could have been in, how surreal that it was this one. I was in Venice and my beautiful mother was dead.

My family had made all the arrangements for me to get home the next day. Two of the Yugoslavian eight, Pete and Simon Cushing accompanied me to the airport by vaporetto. I was scheduled for an early morning flight to Frankfurt, with a connection from there to Dublin. I had two hours to wait at the airport in Frankfurt. Now I was all alone. My life was in a vacuum. Two hours that almost didn't exist. I was somewhere that could have been anywhere. Reality had ceased momentarily and I was in a transit zone. Frankfurt had been selected to freeze frame my life between my study trip to Venice and seeing my mother's corpse in Dublin. Now I just wanted to get to see her. See her for the last time. There are pinnacle moments in your life when you are truly alone. This was one of them.

I watched all the passengers as they passed by. They flowed by in endless streams busily searching for the planes they needed. I wondered where they were going and wondered if they knew where I was going. I wondered if they could see the heavy heart I concealed inside me. In the end I sought out the airport chapel. It was not easy to find. I was alone in my heart but now wanted to be alone in reality too. This was the only place where I could find that refuge. I waited there until my flight was called.

14 – Cancer 1; Ryan Family 0

When I arrived at the hospital morgue they were ready to close the coffin. They had been waiting for me. I just had time to kiss my mother for the last time. One last cold kiss. The lid was then put in place and she was gone. I would never see her in this life again. In later years I realised she must have been in great pain at that final stage. The relief she would have received made her death easier to take. She had taken on her cancer with dignity for over ten years. She had come out on top for all that time, in an era when treatments were not what they are today. But now her time had come.

I couldn't see any of that then. I was just a boy and that boy's mother was gone. The sorrow I was feeling was amplified by the pain etched on my Dads face. He was visibly ailing at the graveside as he buried his beloved friend. If I was feeling all alone, he was truly abandoned.

Cancer had now left its mark on our family. Now we all had a history of the disease for any future reference. We had watched it slowly take our mother away. I don't give much credence to previous medical family history when it comes to cancer. The fact that my mother died from it had little significance on my reaction to getting the disease. Cancer is such a slippery customer that it cannot be accurately projected or traced by history, statistics or previous experience. Not having had it in the family is no assurance that it will not come to you. A cancer history in your family is equally no certainty that you will get it too.

My greatest regret with my mother's case was that I had so little awareness of this disease then. I had hardly any knowledge of her condition or what she was going through. I have tended, over the years, to put this lack of understanding down to my age. As the youngest I was screened from much of the detail of her initial diagnosis and mastectomy. But I was 22 when she died. I was at an age where I should have had a better awareness of her pain and suffering.

This is also a man thing. Men, especially young men, are generally useless when it comes to disease. They rarely focus on their own health let alone understand somebody else's.

My complete lack of understanding of what cancer really is, was more profoundly demonstrated years later, when I met Paddy Hynes again. Paddy is a true gentleman. He was the senior staff member in Heavey's when I started there as a young, raw, trainee in 1980. He would still be there over 30 years later. Everybody who dealt with Paddy, builders, clients, consultants and fellow staff, took an instant liking to his sincere and easy going manner. He was always on hand for any patient help and advice I needed from the outset. This was often not an easy thing to do when you have a new, inexperienced novice in a busy office. Paddy was always patient and kind.

He also had an excellent sporting career behind him. He played rugby and gaelic football at the highest level in the locality and he continues to be an outstanding horse rider.

During the summer of 2001, about nine months before my own diagnosis, I met Paddy and another colleague from Heaveys, Philip Brady. We were all attending an architectural conference in Galway. It was lovely to see both of them again after about a fifteen year gap. The three of us had lunch together and during the meal Paddy informed Philip and I that he had recently beaten very serious bowel cancer, not just once, but twice. To my great shame now, this statement made very little impact on me then. I barely knew what a cancer diagnosis really entailed. If he told me he had just recovered from a heavy head cold my level of sympathy and appreciation would not have been much less.

I really had no idea what the phrase "I've just beaten bowel cancer" actually meant. Perhaps it was similar to a minor skin cancer. Almost a "very little to worry about" cancer. He didn't appear to look any different or have any obvious side effects. I was completely unable to credit the information he had just given me with the value it deserved. I now know that the words "cancer" and "very little to worry about" just do not go in the same sentence.

I told this story apologetically to Paddy many times after. He reassured me that my reaction was nothing to be disappointed about. We both agreed that it was the typical reaction of a man, especially a younger man. It was down to a complete lack of awareness rather than a lack of appreciation. The difference was Paddy was in the club then and I was yet to join. He had passed on architectural experience to me before I really understood what it meant and now he was doing the same with cancer.

I only began to take solace from this interlude years later when the tables turned. I had then become a member of the cancer club and was encouraging men who were fearful of following the path I had trodden. Some of them told me later that they hadn't fully appreciated what I had gone through until they had had a scare or a diagnosis themselves. I was now Paddy Hynes and they were me at that conference in Galway. What goes around will come around.

The cancer survivor has a role. That role is not necessarily to repay or even understand the inspiration that you have received. The role is to pass it on to others when your turn comes. Paddy Hynes knew that. He knew he was one of the few people who could provide that role for me, nine months later when I was diagnosed. He knew that my job then was just to go and beat my cancer. There would be plenty of time later to understand what he was telling me. Then when my turn came I would just do as he did. I would use my survival and recovery to encourage others just as he had done for me.

15 – Back Home to Paddy Ryan's

After our three year degree we were all required to take a practical year out as part of our course. We had to get a job in an architect's office to gain work experience. I was lucky enough to already have an established link with a practice so I returned to my old office in Athlone. My Dad's health had by now been in continual decline since my Mam had died. His will to live on without her appeared to be reducing day by day. My middle sister, Dolores, had graciously re-settled in Horseleap before my mother died to run both the house and the business. By returning home I would also be able to help her look after the pub in the evenings.

So now I was a trainee architect by day and a young publican by night. I became a popular figure behind the bar. I suppose, with the fact that it wasn't my own business to worry about, I was a little more carefree when it came to closing time. I also made sure I generated as much entertainment as I could, with all of my customers, every night I was behind the counter. We had some great characters in the village and I usually managed to orchestrate a good night's hilarity around them. They were the players but now I was the conductor!

One day I was filling petrol for a man who was travelling back to Dublin from Galway. When I had finished and replaced his petrol cap he reached into the back of his car and gave me a bag of mussels. I thanked him and watched him drive away without fully realising what they actually were. Being an inland, seldom visited, village, Horseleap had probably never seen a mussel before. He told me to boil them and when they open they were ready for eating.

That night whilst I was looking after the pub I disappeared into the kitchen for ten minutes and boiled up the mussels. We had one of our finest characters, Tom Nally, in that evening and I knew he was the perfect foil for some revelry with my bag of strange creatures.

Just as all of my customers were beginning to get desperate for their next drink and wondering would I ever return, I reappeared with a large plate. I placed it on the counter in front of them. They all gazed astonishedly at the pile of small black alien creatures that was set before them. They had never seen anything like them before. Everybody, including me, was afraid to touch, let alone eat one of these unearthly objects. We all circled the plate, observing them from different angles, peering right into their gaping shells. A hard black shiny surface on the outside and yet something that looked like human entrails within.

The entire bar was now fixed on the plate on the counter. There was a complete hush. Five minutes passed. Nobody had the courage to do anything more than just look at these bizarre creatures. Nobody was fully sure if they were dead or alive.

Tom Nally stepped forward. "Begod lads, I don't know about you, . . . But I'm starvin'"! He was about to go where nobody else would. He was going to eat a mussel. In that moment he rose out of our midst and became Spartacus.

He carefully selected one of the black shelled creatures. He picked it up and prised out the little alien inside. We then all watched in sheer disbelief as he placed it in his mouth, chewed it briefly and swallowed. Time stood still as we looked on. We wondered what would happen next. Would he simply keel over and die. More alarmingly would he now turn into one of these things himself and take over our village.

He didn't say anything. Suddenly he moved towards the plate again. We all remained spellbound. "Jeez lads, . . . they're lovely" and he quickly devoured another one. That was the signal we all needed. Our great leader had shown us the way. He was our village chief. Now the rest of us, the ordinary indians, could follow suit. The entire plate of mussels disappeared in less than a minute. They were divine of course, and I have loved mussels ever since. Without the courageousness of Tom Nally however it could have taken me another ten years to have tried my first one. That was just one of our many memorable nights with Tom "mussels" Nally.

Most of the eventful nights would involve some kind of "lock-in" drinking session. I became a master in the practice of subtle segregation when it came to closing time. I was able to clear the bar without unknown customers realising that the night was only just beginning. A chosen selection would then re-emerge for a much later session.

On warm summer nights I began to vary the venue for these late night gatherings. At closing time I would often slip in to the kitchen and begin to make sandwiches. These would be ham, cheese and tomato sandwiches in "wedding reception" quantities. A large group of us would then make our way down to the old station. If the village just happened to fall off the planet at that particular moment we would have enough food, drink and entertainment to survive for a week.

Everybody would sit along the two platforms where the trains used to run. A huge fire would be ablaze in the middle that I would have tipped off Johnny and Jimmy Gaynor to prepare earlier. Pat Ennis would have his guitar and for four hours we would fill the night air with music, story telling and warm conversation. Just us, the crumbling walls of the old station and the star studded black sky. These nights were very special.

Horseleap was a village that never really had a great sense of community. It had very little to offer its young people. The only place for social interaction was the pub and this divided the village in itself. Half of the population never went anywhere else. The other half considered it to be a house of damnation.

On these nights therefore we all knew, that for these few hours, we were escaping the mainstream. We were creating our own little haven. A place where we could all come together, both young and old, and just enjoy the moment. There were no agendas or objectives. There was no negativity. We would amuse and entertain each other. We would make each other laugh. No facilities existed for us all to get together so we were making our own.

Those nights were just friendly gatherings. They were full of friendship, entertainment and solidarity. We were not there to gossip, backbite or complain.

As the sun rose, we would all begin to drift back to our real lives again. These get-togethers were just a brief escape. They were just a happy snapshot in otherwise ordinary lives. They would become cherished memoires for all of us. We had brought the village together in our own way. We had generated a collective harmony between people who live in the same place. Those nights remain some of my fondest memories of all my time in Horseleap.

16 – London Calling

Although I thoroughly enjoyed my year back in Horseleap I began to get itchy feet during the summer of 1996. Many of my friends had used their year out to travel to much more exciting locations for their work experience. They used it as an opportunity to also sample an entire new life experience in a new city, country or continent. Wild and wonderful stories were starting to get back to me about the activities colleagues were getting up to in New York, Sydney and Paris. I decided I had missed out on a chance to broaden my horizons. I decided I wasn't ready to return to college just yet.

A long time friend of mine from Horseleap, Sam Carton, was the only person I knew living outside of Ireland who could offer me somewhere to stay. It wasn't very far away or very exotic but I decided I was going to go to London.

Sam lived in a squat in Elephant and Castle. This was part of the appeal. I wanted a complete change of scene. I was swopping my fully serviced home comforts for what I imagined could be a scene from Mad Max. From a hot meal being set in front of me to eating my dinner directly out of a tin.

To be honest living in a squat is generally nothing like as squalid as you can be led to believe. Sam had a small two bedroom ground floor unit with a small living room and tiny kitchen. The two essentials that ensured we had a modicum of normal living standards were in place, water and electricity. The four storey block was owned by the local council. I assume it had slipped off the radar somewhere between "not in a fit state to meet current standards" and "we must get around to doing it up". While they were waiting to make up their minds someone had merely slipped in and connected both the water and electricity. Now it was a squat.

Two other lads from around home had arrived just ahead of me. Poor old Sam had seen his occupancy level quadruple in one fell swoop. In an attempt to minimise our intrusion, the three of us squeezed into the second bedroom.

For a first time Londoner "The Elephant" was a great location. It was close enough to the city centre that if you needed to, you could walk home. The last tube consequently didn't become a life and death scenario. If we were out on a good night at a pub, a gig or a party we were never the ones who had to cut out early to get home. Where we lived was nicely within striking distance of nearly everything London had to offer.

I also really liked Elephant and Castle as an area. It had an honest, earthy feel to it that appealed to me. It was friendly and colourful on one hand, but gritty and almost unloved on the other. This splash of characteristics gave it a blend of charm and edge in the same mix. This was the big city and I was an Irish midnight cowboy. By day and by night it ignited the senses of a fresh faced country lad, every time I walked its streets.

My architectural development at this stage was generally in line with most of my fellow students. We were young impressionable trainee architects with serious notions of changing the entire world. My leanings at this early stage of my career had a distinctive socialist flavour.

London was doing well at this time. I had plenty of opportunities to become an assistant with a number of impressive practices. My preference however was to bypass the palatial office of the mighty architect and get my hands dirty with the artisan who realises his dream, the builder. How could I design when I didn't know how to build. I took a job as a building labourer in Kensington. For the second time in my young life I was back on a building site but this time through youthful idealism rather than a rejected computer course.

The work involved the refurbishment of a period, four storey town house on Kensington Square, with the addition of a new rooftop penthouse. My change of scene was now complete. I was living in a squat and working on a construction site. I felt I was a man amongst men. The architect can only draw but I was one of the people who actually made his buildings come to life.

My early, idealistic vision of a collective bonhomie between all construction workers was to be naive. It didn't take long for me to realise that what appeared like solidarity on the surface was only a shallow veneer. It could easily be cracked to expose the time honoured principle of every man for himself, underneath.

We all arrived to work one morning to discover that all of the tools belonging to the carpenters were gone. These were hidden on the top floor every evening so it had to be an inside job. A few months later I met one of my fellow labourers in a pub. We had both left the site by then and he boasted to me that he was the one who had "done the job". I was shocked. How could he have done this to the people he worked with every day. People he was friendly with, or at least appeared to be friendly with. Were there no rules at all. How are you to know if your brother is a comrade or an assassin.

Apart from concealed individualism I was also enlightened to the elemental pecking order that exists on every building site. The lowest rung on the ladder is reserved for the boot of the labourer. When the shit hits the fan, or in my case continually clogs up the manhole, the only person you cannot refuse the call to sort it out is the labourer.

These details were only minor drawbacks. I was still thoroughly enjoying life on a London building site. As an experience it had way more good points than bad. I liked the physicality of the work. I loved being in and out of the elements, both rain and shine. Best of all was the entertainment of the day long banter that prevailed from the majority of the workers. This tends to be a hallmark of all building sites.

What got me in the end was not the nature of the work itself but the restraints it was imposing on my social life. I was to be in London for a year so I had a stopwatch on how much I could pack in. I wanted to experience absolutely everything this great city had to offer. From ballet and markets to cricket and punk gigs, I was here to see it all but I was now finding that any mid-week socialising was seriously curtailed by my line of work.

I would leave the site at 5.30, having arranged to meet the others at a distant venue like the Tramshed in Woolwich. We became dedicated followers of a madcap Irish band called Lick the Tins and went everywhere to see them. On route to the tube station I would catch a glimpse of my reflection in a shop window. The realisation of what my actual appearance looked like would then dawn on me. Building boots caked in a variety of substances, the least offensive of which would be mud. Clothes that looked as if they were bomb damaged. Hair sprinkled with sand and sawdust and a face that looked as if it hadn't seen a decent wash for three days. No pub, club or theatre in London, in their right mind, would consider letting such a creature through its doors.

Suddenly my already finely tuned schedule needed to be completely recalculated. It now needed to incorporate a return to the Elephant for a shower and change of clothes. An entire new route would then need to be identified to get to the others at the film, match or gig in question. At best this generally resulted in disconnecting me from the group by arriving late. At worst I missed the night completely. Something had to go. It wasn't going to be my social life so I decided it was time to start being an architect again.

Within three days I got a job, through an agency, with a lovely architectural firm in Bermondsey. They were called the John Brunton Partnership. Bermondsey was an earthy little backwater, like Elephant and Castle, but even more appealing because it was beside the river. Bruntons were a Yorkshire firm and, as a result, the office enticed you instantly with its appealing fusion of a friendly northern English approach and a young dynamic London practice. I was immediately slotted into a team of five working solely on a big residential development across the river near St. Catherines Dock.

I was being paid what I considered to be a huge salary and with no rent to pay at the squat I was rich for the first time in my life. I couldn't seem to get rid of my money no matter how hard I tried. The capitalist cells in my brain now emerged to scold their socialist counterparts. They began to castigate them for keeping me on a building site for so long.

I loved my new office. I got on instantly with the people I was working with. The work itself was both challenging and exciting. Our project, Quay 430, was the jewel in the crown of the entire practice. It was a massive, multi-storey apartment development in four separate blocks. Our team, consequently, were dedicated solely to it and worked independently from the rest of the office. We had a charismatic leader in our project architect, Steve Harrison. Steve was a tall, gangly Birkenhead lad full of unconventional scouse spirit and warmth. He was also a great architect.

As a team we were all hugely committed to both the project and each other. Every day, on Steve's insistence, we relocated as a team to a lovely little local pub for lunch. In England, more than any other country I have ever been to, lunch in a pub does not exist without at least one pint of beer. Here we would continue to discuss many of the unresolved design issues or constructional details that had preoccupied our morning. Our lunchtimes, as a result, not only tended to run well past an hour but also ran well past just one pint. But we were the elite Quay 430 squadron. The normal office parameters did not apply to us.

We would return sometimes as late as four o'clock, having often solved many of the problems we had brought with us. Then we often all worked until nine or ten that night to ensure that all of the items we had resolved were incorporated on to the drawings for issue the following morning. It was an unusual but great way to work. These bespoke working arrangements only enhanced our dislocation from the rest of the office on one hand and increased the bond between us on the other. It was a working relationship that was not only built on commitment and good cohesion but also on great friendships. I was delighted to be part of this great team.

When you live in a squat the one thing you can be sure of is that your future is uncertain. You are waiting for the knock on the door when somebody in authority arrives to tell you it's time to go. Consequently you are always on the lookout for somewhere new to live. This worked to our advantage when Sam heard about a house that had become available not too far from where we were.

We moved into Monkton Street, about half way between Kennington and Lambeth, in the spring of 1987. We had a house now and that meant we had room for more people. Squatting, or at least good squatting, is very sociable. If you can, you try and put people up. We always had an open door policy. Everyone who turned up and fitted in could stay. We all knew what it was like to be Irish and looking for accommodation away from home.

Two little girls with rucksacks would knock on the door and say "Our cousin Eileen stayed here three months ago and told us we could come here if we needed a place to stay." Their anxious expressions would then turn to smiles when a warm chorus would invite them to "come on in". They would intend to stay just a couple of nights but in three months time they would be leading the reception committee for the two new little girls with rucksacks.

It was also great fun. I was meeting new people all the time, most just staying a night or two. Everybody was carefree and friendly. There were no rows. I had never experienced anything like it before. On return trips to Ireland I would describe it to curious friends by saying "It's a three bedroom house and on a bad night there could be 12 people sleeping there. On a good night it would be sleeping 23!"

We spent our time on an endless quest for entertainment. Being able to travel in a large group was a great facilitator of this. No event was beyond our reach. We were like a swarm of socialising locusts, eager to maximise every second we had in London. With my John Brunton salary I was able to finance anybody who couldn't keep up. The food, drink and entertainment was often on me but I just didn't care. This was probably the only year of my life that I truly had nothing to worry about. I loved my job and was getting very well paid for it. I had a great bunch of friends at work. I had a completely separate group of wonderful friends that I lived with in Monkton Street.

In the end I managed to cover every corner of London, just as I had set out to do. I had been to all the venues of note from Ronnie Scott's to the Royal Festival Hall. I had gone to the ballet at Covent Garden, a test match at the Oval, the Pogues in Brixton, Arsenal at Highbury, England at Wembley, the Royal Philharmonic at Regent's Park, Ted Nugent at the Hammersmith Odeon and seen the inside of 10,000 wonderful English pubs of all shapes and sizes.

Our greatest night of all was at the Royal Albert Hall. We went to see Christy Moore. I had seen Christy in concert many times all over Ireland but they were generally in tiny folk clubs or at festivals held in G.A.A. Fields. This was the Royal Albert Hall. He was holding court in the greatest London venue of them all. This was one man with nothing more than his voice, his acoustic guitar and his talent before a captivated audience. He was Irish and so were we. He was, in his own words, an ordinary man and so were we. We were all fiercely proud that night.

The Albert Hall is absolutely magnificent. We had plenty of time to admire it as our giddy anticipation got us there well before the start time. Eventually a cheer went up, the lights dimmed and Christy's trademark single spotlight was switched on. It was like a spear through the darkness, illuminating the solitary stool waiting for him in the middle of the stage. Between anticipation and pride we were all on the point of human explosion with excitement. We waited with bated breath as he moved into position. Which song would he launch into first. Would it be Lisdoonvarna or Nancy Spain or Ride On.

When Christy reached his stool he just stood and stared. He began to look around and around. As the seconds passed a complete hush filled the entire arena. His devoted followers now puzzled with his delay to the proceedings. He moved towards the microphone, still admiring the spectacular interior of this wonderful building. "Jaysus" he said . . . "Isn't it amazing what Paddy can do when he puts his mind down to it". Brilliant!

We all knew that London was a short run. A narrow window of youthful, exuberant opportunity for all of us. A chance to live almost entirely in the pleasure zone before the shackles of maturity and later life were thrust upon us. A chance to burn it up!

We took that chance. We had an amazing year. A once in a lifetime year.

By the summer of 1987 I knew it was time to go. It was time to say goodbye to London and thank it for being a wonderful sojourn in my life. It was time to get my career back on track. It was time to go back to Liverpool.

17 – Return to Liverpool

Ireturned to college in September that year. I was happy now that I had sowed what I considered to be a lifetime's worth of wild oats. That was me done. The rest of my life could be as dull as it wanted. I wasn't expecting much out of the ordinary to happen for the next few years. I would apply myself to my studies, work hard and get my final diploma. That was my plan. I unfortunately hadn't made an allowance however for moving in to live with Peter Morgan.

It wouldn't take long for the extent of my miscalculation to emerge.

Pete had also taken an extra year out between his degree and diploma. As great friends it appeared to make good sense to share a flat together on our return to Liverpool. Good sense for everything apart from the only thing that really mattered, successfully completing the next year of our course.

We made an impressive start. We managed to secure one of the best student flats in all of England. Falkner Street, set in the heart of the city, is one of Liverpool's most picturesque streets. Its cobbled roadway is framed on both sides by a splendid array of imposing, three storey Georgian houses. The finishing touches of traditional Victorian lamp standards, polished stone pavements and cast iron balconies completed its Dickensian film-set charm.

Originally the finest of Liverpool's merchant class would have lived here but now the gentry were long gone. They had been replaced by current day investors who had acquired it to avail of the city's lucrative rental market. Every night when I walked along this street, especially when the Liverpool Bay fog had come in, it was just like as if you had been transported 100 years in time. It was a magnificent slice of Victorian England that was still perfectly intact.

Falkner Street had now become an upmarket rental area but Pete had somehow managed to get the first floor flat at number 20 at a reasonable rate. We were now the envy of all our fellow students. Instead of a hall of residence or a basement flat, Pete and I had a huge Victorian living room and a balcony to each of our bedrooms that overlooked the cobbled street below.

I didn't know it then but No. 20 Falkner Street was to be the backdrop for one of the most momentous years of my life. Momentous for very different reasons. On one hand I was just about to fail my fifth year in architecture, a huge disappointment to every student. On the other I was about to meet the woman I would later marry. Falkner Street was to be a major junction on road map of my life.

For young students, who can begin to believe that the world is only there to be revolved around them, failing an academic year is tough. In hindsight it probably only inconveniently delays your career journey by a year or two. At the time however, this is impossible to see. Your entire vision of life is limited to academia and your world, as a result, has just come to an end. The ramifications can be so vast that you begin to question everything you have done to that point. You begin to doubt your ability to now ever complete this course. It has been everything to you and now it has been whipped from under you. Your raison d'etre is gone. If you can't complete the course you won't be able to get a job. If you can't get a job you won't be able to eat. If you can't eat you will die.

The more immediate impact of academic failure is that your entire social structure, which you have so carefully nurtured up to now, appears to be on the verge of total collapse. If you are brave enough to socialise with your friends after the results have been announced two imaginary hats can be seen on every head around the table. One says "Ecstatically smug, I passed" and the other "Highly embarrassed, I failed".

Between Pete and Pam Teese the distractions of this year were always going to outweigh the academic resolve. Thankfully my career would get back on track a couple of years later. No harm was done in the end. When I eventually left Liverpool I left as the architect I went there to become. I was also leaving with a great wife and a wonderful collection of friends and memories. I had managed to have my cake and eat it. It just took a little longer to digest!

At least if I did fail my fifth year it was to be a glorious failure! It was the kind of failure that you would almost be proud of. Pete and I, (well mainly Pete!) developed a reputation for hosting some of the best parties in Liverpool. From the very beginning we embarked on a whirlwind year of constant socialising and memorable nights. These took place all over the city and especially back at our wonderful flat. Our parties became unmissable. We had live bands, all night dancing, fancy dress and great traditional Irish music sessions. The ever-present magical ingredient was just the lovely selection of friends we had. They made every night special and all we had to do was bring them together. .

Liverpool was a great party town. As a city it had a warmth and a buoyancy that promoted this. It didn't take itself too seriously. Its natural bonhomie was underpinned by the lovely sense of ease and friendliness of its inhabitants.

In the end my return just became a seamless continuation of the social lifestyle I had been leading in London. The transition from entertainment to dedicated studies that I had promised myself, just never materialised.

All of the many social events were also set against the hilarious backdrop of just living with Pete. I became accustomed to arriving back from Ireland only to find my wardrobe out on the balcony with a big "Welcome Home Liam" sign on it, for all of the street to see. I got used to being unexpectedly photographed whilst sitting on the toilet. I could then do nothing but smile the next day when I would discover the photograph pinned up on the college notice board. The sitting on the toilet photo became the new wally brick! There was just no pre-empting where his next opportunity to make you laugh would come from. The only certainty was that it was always going to be at your expense!

The other big detractor from any hope of passing the year was our location. I began to realise how good it had been for my studies to have stayed in an unfashionable suburb for my three year degree. Falkner Street was in the middle of the social hub of the city. Most of our friends had to pass under our balconies on route to their night's entertainment. The temptation to knock us up on passing was generally too strong to resist. In return the temptation for us to either accompany them or just invite them in was usually too strong for us to resist too.

We thought we would catch up on our college work as the year wore on but of course we never did. The very final nail in both our coffins was each other. We were too alike. One of us needed to be the ying for the others yang. On the rare occasions when one of us stayed in to get some work done a false logic would prevail. "Well Pete isn't working tonight so its probably okay if I take the night off too." We were like two snails at a grand prix track. If I am going as fast as him then I must be doing okay. The only problem was the rest of our class were driving Ferrari's.

Pete recognised what was coming to both of us and jumped ship before it arrived. He left at Easter, saving himself the ignominy of the end of year results. I hung on grimly to the bitter end, somehow praying that the avalanche might just start going back up the mountain. My final destiny duly arrived on the last day when I made my way to the fifth year studio. Our final results were put display on the notice board. I knew, deep down, what that result could only be. A miracle of some kind did cross my mind but perhaps it was better to save that until I would have a better use for it, fourteen years later.

Afterwards at least I did have the courage to go to the pub with the others. On entering I had no option but to don the "Highly embarrassed, I failed" imaginary hat. I was hoping my brave face would conceal my hollow core inside. My career had stalled and my heavy heart, shrouded in uncertainty, was a sombre contrast to the wild celebrations ringing out all around me.

18 – Settling Down

In my first three years in college the issue of a girlfriend simply never arose. There were two reasons for this. The first was that I had become a dedicated foot soldier of the Irish lads drinking brigade. I didn't want anything to get in the way of the call of duty. The second was that even if I was on the lookout for a potential partner I didn't seem to have the credentials to land the prize. I was a country lad, unfamiliar with dating techniques at the best of times, and this was the big city. All of the boys who were monopolising the female interest were suave and cool and, to be honest, generally pretentious. The girls seemed to only be attracted to this type of character profile. They queued up to swoon over the smooth talkers whilst the rest of us just looked on like farmhands who had taken a wrong turn.

When I returned to Liverpool to do my fifth year I found things had changed. Attention from girls unexpectedly started to come my way. It was as if all the flash Harrys of yesteryear had played all their cards and performed all their tricks. The girls were bored with them now. Suddenly it was hip to be yourself! Leather jackets were out and the big wooly jumper that you had been wearing for ten years was in.

I was still fairly oblivious to any attention coming my way so when this one particular girl kept persisting with an invite to the cinema one of the lads needed to put me straight. "She fancies you Liam" he enlightened me. "Bloody Hell! Are you serious?"

And so off to the cinema we went.

Pam Teese was a lovely girl. I was smitten instantly. She had grown up in the Liverpool suburb of Maghull and now lived with her mother in Mossley Hill. We got on very well from the very start. We got on so well that pretty soon afterwards we both knew that this was the one. This was the person that we wanted to spend the rest of our lives with. We had reached the point in life where both the time and the person was right. We had lived it up in our twenties. Now we were both ready to settle down.

With my college course now on hold and Pam and I beginning to plan for a life together the sensible thing to do was to get a job. Opportunities weren't as good as when I had been in London but still good enough for somebody in Liverpool to have a slot for a half-baked trainee architect. It was also difficult to make an immediate return to the course after failing a year because your confidence was low. An extra year out at this point to acquire some good work experience and stabilize my career path, seemed like the right thing to do.

I got an interview, before too long, with one of the smaller practices in the city, the Franklin Stafford Partnership. They were one of the pioneer architects in the restoration and conversion of the Albert Dock, one of the finest collections of Victorian dock buildings in all of England, just off the city centre. They had a lovely little office down in the dock itself. For location alone this was the job I wanted. The Albert Dock had become the jewel in the crown of the new renaissance of Liverpool. The city was at last beginning to emerge from its forty years of bleak decline since the war. The refurbishment of the dock was the epitome of this revival. The quaysides, once thronged by busy dockers, were alive again. Now the dock workers had been replaced by a mix of shoppers, office staff, well heeled residents, tourists and the strolling Liverpool public. These were the new twentieth century dockers. The cargo now was art galleries, cappuccinos, knick-knacks and cocktails rather than crates of grain, coffee-beans and Scandinavian timber.

This wonderful collection of waterside buildings had found a whole new lease of life. It was easy now to forget that the Albert Dock was incredibly due to be demolished only ten years earlier. In the seventies a brutal and unsympathetic modernist building policy had swept across England. The Albert was lucky to survive.

Now these magnificent six story Victorian warehouses had been saved and regenerated to house a vibrant ensemble of shops, museums, pubs, restaurants and deluxe apartments. Their reincarnation had in turn brought life back to the dock basin itself. It now housed an eclectic collection of boats of all shapes and sizes, old and new. Albert's reinstatement as one of the finest docks you could find, anywhere in the world, was complete.

The Franklin Stafford Partnership turned out to be a lot more than just a good location. Their brick vaulted, mezzanine office, overlooking the dock basin was instantly appealing. The staff of eight exuded a pleasant mix of vibrant personalities with a good working relationship. I had found the John Brunton Partnership of Liverpool!

The partner in charge, Steve Quicke, ensured I settled in immediately with his wonderful qualities of strong but caring leadership. Steve's approach was the mainstay of the happy staff that worked around him. Just like Bruntons it was an office that appeared to have captured the right balance between a friendly, easy going approach and a steadfast desire to produce good work.

F.S.P. was a London practice that opened a Liverpool office after they were appointed to restore, refurbish and re-design the Albert Dock. The Liverpool director, Mike Franklin, would visit from London about once a week. From his visits it was evident that the personable and committed work ethic, that ran through the veins of the practice, had come from the very top. Mike would spend a busy day at meetings and assisting all of us but had an unwritten rule that all staff join him for a drink in the pub below the office just before his train returned to London. This was his way of making sure that the hectic working day always ended on a personable note. Good relations between all of his staff, both socially and in the office, were important to him. Hard work should not come without any loss of personal acquaintance. In fact I found that the combination of the two created one of the best working environments of all. A good architectural practice is a great place to work.

So I had managed to find another excellent practice. Some new staff members were often uncomfortable with Mike's end of day ritual, only seeing it as a delay to their journey home. This generally was the first indication that this was not the practice for them. For those of us who were more than happy with this "work hard but leave time for a drink and chat" approach, it generally paved the way for a long term relationship with this great little firm.

When I joined, most of the staff in both the Liverpool and London offices had been there a long time. They had all honed into a harmonious, hard-working group of friends. I was only too happy take my place on the team.

Steve became a great friend and mentor to me over the following years. He would become a good influence on my eventual successful return to college. Mike was equally great to work under. He ran the practice with minimal interference, allowing each staff member as much responsibility as they could handle. Yet he was always there in a supportive role. He would never expose or abandon any member of his staff when trouble came.

The work at the dock was now in full swing. I became site architect for four floors of luxury apartments and penthouses in Block E. This was the line of warehouses on the west side of the dock, sandwiched between the river Mersey and the dock basin itself. It was my first real experience of running a major building contract on site. The work was complex and diverse. It ranged from the painstaking restoration and repair of the original warehouse buildings to the new, state of the art fit-out, that ensured the interiors were now updated to meet the requirements of the 21st century. We had elderly experienced brickies working alongside young dynamic space heating engineers. It was my job to co-ordinate them all.

My rural Irish family business personality equipped me well for this task. A completed building requires not just the direction of the architect and the work of the builder, but also inputs from the engineer, plumber, surveyor, joiner, electrician, roofer, etc. All of these elements are woven together to create the desired result. They all depend on each other. The ability to keep all of these work elements cohesive and on schedule is the essence of the role of the site architect. His or her performance can be the difference between the job going well or going badly.

With this development requiring specialist conservation work and new construction in tandem the necessity for good co-operation between all the various activities was even more critical. I was about to discover that a strong and popular personality was going to be a more useful asset to me than any text book. I didn't pretend to know more about bricks than the sixty year old brick layer standing beside me. He had been laying bricks all of his life. I had seen more bricks in books than I had in the flesh. I was more than happy to let him take the lead as we worked out how best to repair the 150 year old brick vault over our heads. I explained to him what was needed and gave him the latitude to work out the best way to achieve it.

The detail of the work was so specialist that the best solution was always going to be found in the expertise that was all around me. What I needed to do was keep everybody in unison and focused on the overall objective. As long as I could maintain the right spirit between all of the diverse activities, they would all come together to make it happen. As a result, the entire process became a collective assignment. We all had a hand in it. Everybody had contributed, in some way, to the final completed building. This generated great working relations between all involved. I was merely the referee. Whilst the game was flowing I was still essential, but hardly noticed.

After the apartments were completed my next job at the dock was a bit special. I was to be the site architect for a new museum to the Beatles in the basement of Block B. The Albert Dock had by now become one of the main tourist attractions in Liverpool. The old brick vaults in the basement of the warehouses made it the perfect location for a new visitor centre for the many people coming to Liverpool purely because they loved the Beatles. They needed a focal attraction to satisfy their devotion to the fab four. The vaults were ideal for making a perfect recreation of the original Cavern Club. This became the centrepiece for a life story exhibition of the band.

F.S.P. had come up with an inspirational design that chronologically re-created the various events and places in the history of the Beatles. As the paying customer you would journey from A to Z, through a sequence of magical displays and experiences that brought the history of the band to life. It began with the early days in Hamburg, through the Cavern and Beatlemania and ended with the eventual demise of the band and the solo careers of all four. It was to be called The Beatles Story.

This was quite simply a wonderful job to be part of. It became an even greater collective effort than the earlier restoration work I had worked on. This time we were putting a little piece of the history of Liverpool back in place. Now we had people who stood in the very spaces we were now trying to replicate. As the exhibition was under construction a delivery truck driver could step forward and say "I met my wife in the Cavern in 1962 and the counter to the tea bar was actually higher than that. It was more like three foot six."

When we were finished we had re-created not just the Cavern but also Matthew Street outside it and the Abbey Road studio. We also had the interior of an airplane from which you disembarked to thousands of screaming fans awaiting your arrival in the U.S.A. and a walk-through Yellow Submarine.

The most thought provoking experience of all however was stepping in to the White Room just before the end of the tour. It was a single room, painted completely white with large windows and fine net curtains billowing in the breeze. It just contained a single exhibit, a white grand piano in the middle of the room. The only other item in the entire room was a pair of steel rimmed round glasses that were placed on top of the piano. The powerful poignancy of the display however came not from the visual display but the uninterrupted playing of John Lennon's song "Imagine" all day long.

Everybody who worked on this job knew that we had all been privileged to have been involved in something unique. When it was completed each one of us was able to stand back and identify the little part of the exhibition that we had personally shaped. The sense of job satisfaction for all of us, as a result, was immense. It was as if in a little way, we had all given something back to Liverpool. We had given the city a place to honour its four most famous sons. We had played our role in allowing the city to re-tell a story that it was very proud to tell, The Beatles Story.

On this project there were no divisions. Design staff and construction workers were on an equal footing. We were all working together. There were no disputes between architect and builder. No one-upmanship between contractor and sub-contractor. I had never been part of a job before where everybody was on the same side. We all knew this one was special. Something very special for the city of Liverpool itself. I was honoured to have been in the right place at the right time to have been part of the team that made this story come true.

19 – International Wedding

The year after I started working with F.S.P. Pam and I got married. We had a great old selection box of a wedding. A few months earlier I received a small inheritance after my Dads death and it was enough to fund a good wedding and honeymoon. Coming from a large extended family I had a big crowd to consider on my side. I was under the impression that many of my older relatives in Ireland would not make a trip to Liverpool. We also felt that many of our college friends might not be able to afford a trip to Ireland. To solve the dilemma we decided on a two-centre celebration. The main ceremony would be in Liverpool on the Friday with a second night in Ireland on the Sunday also arranged. This plan would suit everybody. Outside of the main families and close friends, the rest of the guests would opt for one venue or the other.

What actually happened was that just about all of my relatives came to Liverpool and all of our friends came back to Ireland. We ended up with a 3-day wedding!

Apart from my career the other area of my life to benefit from my move to Liverpool was my religion. When I left Ireland I was a lapsed Catholic. I was still going to Mass on Sunday's out of respect for Mam and Dad but my religion was little more than a badge. Sunday mass in Horseleap for most young people then was a social rather than a religious affair. We had no Facebook or Twitter in those days. It was your one big opportunity to catch up on the week's news. "Did you go to see Joe Dolan last night?" "Was he any good?" "How did you get home?" "Did you get to shift anyone?"

There was absolutely no problem in getting any of us to go to Mass. To get us to go to Mass and pay attention to a single word the priest was saying was an entirely different matter. He simply couldn't compete with the information that was being exchanged down at the back of the church.

When I arrived in Liverpool I had gone from a country where just everybody went to Mass, paying attention or not, to a land where very few did. This was a big change for me. Suddenly nobody cared whether I went to mass or not. My only reason for going was also now defunct. There would be nobody there to fill me in on the local gossip for the week.

The predictable outcome should have been that I stopped going completely but, the opposite happened. This is obviously how reverse psychology works. As a lost soul in a strange land my Irish Catholicism emerged to declare itself as an undeniable part of my identity. It had been content to lie dormant as long as I remained within the sanctity of a good Catholic country. Now that I had emerged out from under that umbrella it sprang to life like the guard dog of my soul. I went from disinterestedly attending Mass on a Sunday to devotedly going to as many as I could. I had gone from the complacent majority to the determined minority. My nationality and religion had forged into one. I was now proud to go to Mass. For the first time in my life I was going by choice rather than by instruction or to be part of the herd. Everything was different now. Each Mass was attended by a handful of dedicated worshippers rather than a hoard of distracted ones. Everybody was there for the right reason. I began to find peace and solitude in churches that I never knew they contained before.

By the end of my first year I knew just about every Catholic church in Liverpool. The greatest of all of these was the Metropolitan Cathedral of Christ the King. Its iconic structure stood proudly on a hill overlooking the city centre, right beside the university. The Metropolitan was one half of the twin set of Liverpool's two great contrasting cathedrals. The breath taking, traditionally styled, sandstone Anglican at one end of Hope Street and the modern, but equally striking, concrete Metro at the other.

For Pam and I, as both architects and Catholics, the selection of the cathedral for our wedding ticked two major boxes. It was a design masterpiece and the most famous Catholic church in Liverpool. The actual deciding factor however, was a little less obvious. Neither of us wanted a ceremony in the main cathedral with our wedding party lost in its vast interior. The Metropolitan however also contained a beautiful little, much older, vaulted church in the basement called the Crypt chapel. It was ideal for the intimacy we were seeking. We had the best of both worlds. The invitation would direct everybody to the cathedral itself only for each guest to discover the wonderful little church it concealed below.

Most of our Irish guests arrived over on the day before the wedding. The first gathering of the wedding party was in one of the pubs at the Albert Dock that night. This was where I worked and it was nice to be able to show them the Dock. The benefit of this pre-wedding session was that it allowed both family groups to get to know each other casually before meeting formally the next day.

The wedding day itself spanned three different venues, all within walking distance. It began with the ceremony at the Crypt. Then everybody walked down the hill to the Adelphi hotel.

Every city has an hotel that is the equivalent of the Adelphi. A hotel that is more like an old friend to that city rather than just another building where you can stay the night. A hotel that has become synonymous with that city. They can often lack the sophistication and modernity of their more glitzy competitors but this is more than made up for with an elegance and a grandeur that can only be inherited from a bygone era.

The Adelphi is right beside the main train station at Lime street and was the original railway hotel in Liverpool. Its magnificent interiors still radiate the great sense of old style character and relaxed ambiance that would have greeted the disembarking gentry from the very first train carriages over 100 years earlier. Just as Dublin has the Shelbourne, New York the Waldorf and London the Savoy, Liverpool has the Adelphi.

We had 100 guests for dinner. The Adelphi was the ideal setting. This was to be the poshest part of our day. There were about four pubs between the cathedral and the hotel and most of our guests got waylaid on route. They knew they all had plenty of time for a drink before the first course was due to be served. Many years later I discovered that many new acquaintances had already been formed by this stage. Pam's uncle, a bus inspector, and my Dad's cousin, a farmer, managed to visit half of the best pubs in Liverpool in the gaps to the ceremony without missing any of the formalities.

When the meal and speeches in the Adelphi were concluded we all trooped back up the hill again. It was time for the final event, the hooley. We were almost back where we started as the nearest building to the cathedral was the Liverpool Irish Centre. The night's entertainment was going to be a wedding céili.

In my time in Liverpool I always had a love hate relationship with the Irish Centre. On the outside it was a foreboding, unwelcoming building. Inside it transformed into either a delightful cornucopia or an embarrassing mishmash, depending on the event and your mood. A night in the Irish Centre immersed you in some of the finest attributes of being Irish or the worst of Oirishness. I had wonderful nights there at some of the greatest traditional Irish music sessions I have ever witnessed. The music itself was magnificent but when heard beyond the homeland it stirs the heart to an even greater degree. On other nights I saw the parts of Ireland I was only too glad to have left behind. The dreadful showbands whose lack of ability was blind to an audience desperate to recreate a night "back home". The bar filled with downcast elderly men trying to pretend they were still living in the Ireland they had left 30 years ago. If the Adelphi was the stately and suave part of the day, the Irish centre was there to bring the evening back down to earth.

Our Scouse/Irish gaggle of revellers were now in full flow. The Irish centre had a huge function room to the rear. I had been there many times. Every Saturday night you could transport yourself to a dance hall you knew back in Ireland. Joe Dolan, Margo or Big Tom would perform the same set they had done the night before in Roscommon, Tyrone or Tipperary. The Irish Centre was also one of the few pubs in Liverpool to contain those two great Irish drinking institutions, the bar and the lounge. Every night it subconsciously promoted a sort of sexist drinking apartheid, only men in the bar and only women in the lounge.

My favourite part of the Irish centre however was the shop. Pilgrimages were made to the shop for those most seriously blighted with homesickness. It was the only location in all of the northwest of England where you could find a possible cure for your ills. Galtee rashers, Tayto crisps, Calvita cheese and Marietta biscuits were all on the shelves to give you a little bit of home via your tastebuds. The shop also had a full range of leprechauns, shillelaghs, aran jumpers and shamrock ornaments of all shapes and sizes. If this was Ireland it was only a very small part of it. It was only the Ireland you would find in tourist shops in Killarney, Galway or Shannon Airport. A part of Ireland that is a lot more familiar to the besieged American tourist rather than the Irish themselves.

Every room in the Irish centre had a fifteen foot high ceiling. This ensured it was void of any real atmosphere unless it was packed. To counteract this we made this part of our celebration an open invite. We wanted a full house for the céili, or as close to a full house as we could get. The outcome of this was that for years later I would bump into complete strangers on the street. They would then delight in telling me that they had been at my wedding.

One of these was an Australian who beautifully recounted his impression of my brother-in-law Rory Robbins. He told me how amazed he was by this one particular guest at the wedding. This guy, he told me, was very drunk by the end of the evening but amazingly still managed to keep a perfectly still baby, alseep on his shoulder. "As long as that baby remained there it was not going to move an inch" he enthused. He then verbally painted a wonderful image of Rory. He was motionless from the shoulder up and would remain so as long as Orna was asleep on his shoulder. Below the shoulder however it was as if the rest of his body was made of jelly. From the neck down he was in constant motion as his body wobbled and shimmied and tottered. But the baby remained motionless. "If that baby was taken off him that man would just have poured onto the floor" he concluded.

The Liverpool céili band entertained us for the evening. They did a great job. One of the band members called out the necessary instructions required for each dance type and we all followed, as best we could. They were also receptive to participation by the audience so by the end of the night the guests had taken over the stage. Pete played the fiddle with the band behind him and a procession of singers, of mixed ability, came up to take their turn. It had descended into a typical night at the Irish centre. It was relaxed and friendly and in the end, a bit of a free for all.

As the night was drawing to a close I made my first major error of judgement as a married man. I was told that some of our friends had gone across the road to the Casablanca, one of our favourite student nightclubs, to prolong their evening. The Adelphi was providing us with a late night bar for our guests and I wanted to try and keep everyone together for as long as I could. I decided to dash over quickly let them know this and redirect them down the hill. It would just take a minute so there was no need to delegate or tell anybody where I was going.

My calculation however was to go badly wrong. When I got in the door of the Casablanca somebody said "Ah, here's the groom". Before I could utter a word a drink was placed in my hand. Unfortunately, at this precise moment, the céili across the road decided to wind up. English entertainment venues tend to end proceedings much more abruptly than those in Ireland. Whilst I was finishing my drink, which wasn't long, the Irish centre was closing and evicting its occupants rapidly. This scenario was completed with a concluding scene of Pam, complete in her big white dress, and her mum being the last two to leave. As the doors were closing behind them her mother queried the whereabouts of her new husband. Unfortunately another guest was within earshot and declared "Oh I've just seen him with friends over in the Casablanca"!

In all I was in the Casablanca for about ten minutes but it was to be the worst timed ten minutes of my life.

I got down to the Adelphi a few minutes after they arrived. By then the story was beginning to get grow legs. Pam's mother was now convinced her daughter had unwittingly married some sort of party animal. No matter how hard I tried to explain that I was foolishly but innocently trying to re-direct a few guests to the hotel she was not to be convinced. She was now certain that her daughter's new marriage would not last the week!

The next day, Saturday, Liverpool became like Dunkirk. We had up to a hundred people trying to scramble to Ireland for the final part of the wedding at the Grand hotel in Moate.

Pam and I flew over in the afternoon with my sister Dolores and her husband Seamus. They were now running the pub and in between the two wedding nights a great highlight of the three days was arriving back in Horseleap that night. Paddy Ryan's was full when we got there. The locals and many of our college friends were celebrating side by side. Pam and I were carried in, shoulder high, like a scene from a Latin American wedding. This was a special homecoming. This time I wasn't coming home alone.

The following night the pub organised two buses to bring everybody to Moate for the final event. Many of our guests had by now spent these days in constant companionship. New lifelong friendships were being formed as a result.

In Moate we met new guests that we hadn't seen on the previous two days. They brought a fresh enthusiasm to the festivities. The Grand Hotel had been a popular destination for us all in my time in Horseleap. It was the right place to be that night. This hotel had known me all my life so this was a celebration to mark the end of that era and to toast the start of a new one. It was a new beginning. The carefree, single, live for today days were over. I now had a job, a house and a lovely wife called Pam. It was time for me to settle down.

20 – The Patient Journey

All through my life the analogy of "a journey" has been very strong. There is nothing original about this. Everybody's life is a journey to a large degree. You start off with a definite time and place when you are born. You then progress through childhood, adolescence and adulthood. Sometimes you can pass the way of marriage and perhaps separation or divorce. The journey only ends when you die. The essence of any journey is that it is ever changing. On the journey of life these changes will not just be limited to your surroundings but also your attitudes and perceptions which will change as you progress along the way.

For cancer sufferers our disease will become one of the major milestones on our journey of life. To try and wrestle control of my disease I tried to isolate it as a journey all of its own. This helped me to keep its entirety in view whilst allowing me to focus on each specific stage I needed to tackle. Your cancer has a definite birth in diagnosis. If you had the mind of an adult as a baby you would never forget the day you were born. You will similarly never forget the day you are told you have cancer. All of the initial assessments and early treatments are like your childhood years. You can do very little for yourself and are almost entirely dependent on others. Very few expectations are being placed on you. In the later stages of treatment, chemotherapy and radiotherapy, more is expected of you. You are now more like an adolescent. You are still under the care and instruction of others but you are now relied upon to take a more active role to help them complete their work. It is only at the recovery and remission stage that you have fully matured. You are now an oncological graduate! You are ready to be released out into the world to make your way again.

Cancer is a little microcosm of life itself. By narrowing down my vision of it into its own mini-cycle I could keep a better mental stranglehold over it. I could manage it. Then, when necessary, I was able to isolate a particular stage and sharpen my focus specifically for that section. I knew I had a three hour exam to do but for the next twenty minutes all I needed to concentrate on was this question on the Shakespearian sonnet. It allowed me to identify where I was at any given point in my treatment and just concentrate on that stage. It was a mini life cycle. If I was only 6 months old and all I was required to do was crawl, there was no point in worrying about riding a bike. That only needed to be addressed when I would reach four or five.

I could also now see how easy it was to compare my cancer to my running. Each run was another tiny little mini-cycle that had established itself within the vastness of my entire life. My cancer was now just one tough, long run. It had a start and it was going to have a finish. But the finish would not come without all of the individual strides in between. All I had to do was focus on each one of those. If I did, the finish line would come to me all by itself.

I was getting the upper hand now. I had a fix on my cancer within the context of my life. I had it pigeonholed. I had it reduced down to studying for a difficult exam or going for a challenging run. All I had to do was concentrate completely on each subject I needed to study or each section I needed to run. By breaking it down and regarding it as a journey it could no longer daunt me. I suspect Lance Armstrong used his Tour de France experience in the same way. Once you begin to categorise your cancer with other challenges in your life it starts to lose its mysterious grip on you.

One of the greatest advantages of all, in equating your cancer struggle to a journey, is that it identifies one of the essential ingredients of your fight – patience. Patience is an inherent part of every journey. All you really want to do is get to the match in Dublin, or complete the marathon in Lisbon or start your holiday in Florida. In each case however you must first endure the long traffic jamb at Naas, feel the pain when the mile marker reads 17 rather than 18 or queue endlessly at a busy airport. With patience you can overcome all of the unwanted elements of your journey because you know they are a necessary means to an end.

Cancer treatment also demands a similar level of patient composure. You must apply yourself to take each step as it appears in front of you. You must crawl before you can ride a bike. All of the steps will eventually piece together to form the completed journey. Your final destination is full recovery, but your journey is the treatment it will take to get there. Impatience is futile. You need to be where you are now in order to be able to reach where you want to be at the end. Cancer may have struck your body in an instant but it will not leave with similar haste. You need to accept it is here for the long haul. You need to know it will require patience to remove it.

When Pete Morgan, Brendan Kilpatrick, Paul Crothers and myself went to John O'Groats we all knew, deep down, that it was only half a journey. You can't have Adam without Eve, Tom without Jerry or Laurel without Hardy. You can't go to John O'Groats without going to Land's End. A few years later the opportunity eventually presented itself for us to complete the mission. The circumstances were different by then. At least two of us were married and all four of us were working. It was never going to be the cheap student hike that our Scottish trip was. This time instead of almost freezing to death in a tent we stayed with friends in a lovely cottage in Devon. Instead of rambling around in the rain because that was the only activity we could afford, we went jet skiing at St. Ives. Instead of fish and chips in Wick we dined in some of Cornwall's best gastro pubs.

It was as if Land's End was aware of our upgrade in circumstances. Rather than rugged and bleak it was commercial and spoiled. Instead of windy and wet it was sunny and calm. Instead of free we had to pay to use the car park. We had been to both extremities of this great country and found two different extremes. And yet for all of its glamour and amenity, the magic was missing. It was as if nature had moved out and commercialisation had moved in.

As we drove home the next day I was comparing both journeys. For all our privilege and advancement sometimes less is more. Give me a windswept Scottish headland any day before a sanitised tourist resort. Give me the memory of four indestructible young men peering out at the sunrise from a wet tent rather than another comfortable but indistinguishable hotel room. Give me back that all too short period of your life when you have the freedom, the spirit and the nerve to do just about anything!

21 – The Finished Architect

I was well established at F.S.P. by now. Apart from my work at the dock I became site architect at a large urban regeneration project at Trafford Park in Manchester and I was running a large council housing landscape regeneration project near Glossop. I was also making regular trips to help out in the London office. One of architectures major appeals for me had always been the variety of the workload. No two days are the same. Now I was thriving not just on the range of work I was involved with, but also on being able to perform that work in four very different locations.

I knew however that I still had some unfinished business to attend to at Liverpool John Moore's University. I was thoroughly enjoying my job but my mission to become an architect had stalled two years short of its target. I needed to get my architectural education back on track. But how could I give up the adrenalin, satisfaction and prestige of working with a great little practice and running major building contracts on site. More importantly, I now had a wife and a mortgage to support. How could I give up my monthly pay cheque.

John Moore's University itself came up with the solution. In 1988, having now achieved university status, the college had extended its range of courses. One of these was a new part-time course for the final diploma in architecture. This would span three years rather than the normal two. The uptake for the initial year of this course was low. Only three students opted to go for it. They became the pioneers. The rest of us watched on to see if both they and the course would survive. They all successfully got through their first year and the part-time course was established. This was now a viable option to complete my studies.

I assessed the two choices now available to me. This new course would only take an extra year to complete. It required that I attend college for one full day a week and F.S.P. had already agreed to allow me to do this. The biggest bonus of all was that I could keep my job and complete my course at the same time. I could have my cake and eat it. Decision made. The remaining choice to give up my job and go back to college full-time did not even get to the starting blocks.

I enrolled for this new course. It was the second year of intake. After the brief distraction of a hectic social life, followed by a wife, a job and a house, my career was back on track. The course numbers had doubled to six for its second year.

I had a lot in common with my five new fellow part-timers. We were all male, all about the same age and had all taken the scenic route to becoming an architect. Most of us had got married recently and we were all working in either Liverpool or Manchester. Our allegiance was to our practice first and foremost but we were all grateful of this opportunity to complete our studies.

The part-time course was very different to the full-time. We were a minority group within the department and due to the similarity of our circumstances we all formed a very close bond from the start. There was great solidarity between us. We used this to our advantage. On the full-time course, with its greater numbers, a handful of high flying students could generally dictate the pace and agenda for the rest. They usually had all of their work completed well in advance of any scheduled deadline. This left no room for the rest, who sometimes had a genuine reason for not quite getting everything complete, to negotiate some required leeway.

Our design projects would span two or three months from start to finish. As the final submission date loomed we were all under intense pressure to get everything drawn up and presented. This invariably resulted in many of us not getting to bed on the night before the final pin up. Anything could then go wrong at this critical stage. One time my electricity went at three in the morning and I didn't have any change to put in the meter. Those were the critical hours when you were frantically and exhaustedly putting your final display together after three months work. On arriving at college, knowing your work was incomplete, you could then be unfortunate enough to be pinning up beside one of the top students in your year. As you desperately tried to arrange your presentation to best conceal your unfinished elements, he or she would be casually sipping a cappuccino after a full nights sleep.

But now we were six. Six comrades and all we wanted to do was get out of here with a degree under our arm. We each understood and appreciated the others difficulties. The pressure of work, family commitments and now the additional juggling act of a three year architectural course was the leveller for all six. There were no high fliers or low fliers. We all just wanted to come through this together.

We began to use the unity between us to our advantage. If the tutor said "now the hand-in for this project is next Thursday, isn't that right?" to a man we sometimes replied "Oh no Geoff, you definitely said Thursday week." Geoff Hackman was one of the most knowledgeable men I have ever met but a busy schedule meant he would occasionally confuse agreed dates. He would look down over his bi-focal glasses at us with a puzzled expression. He may have suspected he was being duped but with the vote at six to one there was little he could do. We all knew that as long as we stuck together we could swing some things our way. There was no genius now to pipe up "Oh yes Geoff it is this Thursday and in fact I have mine already complete."

When I returned to complete my studies on the part-time course the foreign study trip broke new ground. For the first time it took us beyond Europe. We were all going to New York City. The travelling party included all the full-time fifth years, the six part-timers and a few additional guests so Pam came too. New York in a week is a tough ask so we began meeting up in the weeks beforehand to plan our trip. By the time we reached the airport we had a military style itinerary worked out so that every minute we were there would be accounted for. We were going to squeeze every possible pip out of the big apple.

All of the major sights were on our list, Central Park, the Empire State, the World Trade

Centre and the Statue of Liberty. We also had a selection of additional delights to cover all tastes, the Museum of Modern Art, the Empire Diner and the Harlem Gospel tour. We had a different restaurant selected for each night. By the end of the week, we would have sampled cuisine from all over the world. From our extensive guide book collection we had selected restaurants located all over Manhattan that would serve us Caribbean, Japanese, Lebanese, American, South African, Chinese and Italian food for the seven nights.

Everything was slotted into a precise daily schedule. Once again we were able to exploit the fact the we were travelling in a large group to maximise the length of our day. Using the subway after dark held no fears for us. Apart from a few hours for sleep we had as much of the 24 hours as we needed to complete our extensive daily agenda. Besides we also had Gary Bate from Salford. No New York hood in his right mind would dare take Gary on!

Every day began with a late breakfast at our nearby diner. It was run by a friendly bunch of Greeks who seemed only too delighted to have some fellow Europeans walk through their door every morning. Football is a great currency at times like this. Our new Greek friends loved football and so did we. They had perfect English and were itching to talk soccer to somebody who shared their passion for the game. We had fervent Manchester United, Liverpool and Everton supporters in our ranks so we were trading our opinions of their chances of making the Champions league for those of A.E.K. Athens, Olympiakos and Panathinaikos. This was the great melting pot that the best New York diners are. Ten people, two thousand miles from home warmly discussing Greek and English football over steak, eggs and coffee.

As the week wore on we had ticked off the Guggenheim museum, the Circle Line ferry, the Statue of Liberty, Central Park and Chinatown. We still had the tall buildings to do, the World Trade Centre and the Empire State. We went up the World Trade Centre first. As luck would have it we got there at 5 o'clock in the evening due to how that day's itinerary had panned out. It was still daylight but only for another hour. As both architects and tourists we remained a little longer on the viewing platform than most other sightseers. We were just about to leave when the New York we had been scrutinising slowly began to redefine itself. Endless arrays of twinkling lights were slowly beginning to illuminate the panorama that stretched out in front of us. Each one of the views we had just examined so intensely began to transform right before our very eyes. Mesmerized by this visual transmogrification we stayed for a further two hours. The first hour was to see all of the lights finally emerge from the receding daylight. We watched, spellbound, as each set of lights sketched their particular segment of the magical web of illumination that was forming right in front of us.

The second hour was just to absorb the breath taking sight of New York after dark from 110 floors up. Had we not arrived at the towers at the time we did we would have missed this incredible transfiguration. I had seen how New York changes from day to night and how Germany changes from west to east due to studying architecture. Neither of those views are there to be seen today.

Those contrasting vistas of New York on that warm evening, were a lifelong memory in their own right. I wasn't to know then that this memory would generate an entirely different sensation a little over ten years later. The World Trade Centre would be gone and many innocent people would die as it came down. The Berlin wall would fall too but in contrast, the world would rejoice at its downfall. I had been fortunate enough to see both of these structures. Two structures that are now no longer with us. Two structures that shook the world in completely different ways when they came tumbling down.

By the end of our New York week we had just about managed to complete everything on our own itinerary. We had also adhered to the schedule our tutors had set for us and seen many of the city's most inspirational buildings. As we boarded our flight at J.F.K. the unanimous sensation was one of exhausted satisfaction. We had successfully completed our mission. In one week we had left very few stones in New York unturned. But we were all older now. Our bodies weren't able for this the way they used to be. We were all looking forward to getting home for some sleep. As I took a last look at New York from the window of the plane my own private reflections were also tinged with sadness. This was to be the last of four amazing foreign study trips. I would never get the chance to experience travel like this again.

22 – Back to America

Our trip to New York may well have been the end of my group travel adventures but Pam and I did manage two return trips to the U.S. before the kids came along. America has always fascinated me. I was always under the impression that it was going to be pretty much all the same. Each city would have a similar splattering of high rise buildings with a MacDonalds on every corner. Every street would be choked with a carpet of traffic bespeckled with yellow taxis. The diversity I saw in New York put an end to these notions. And New York is like nowhere else in America. The realisation now was that I had just seen the tip of the iceberg. The huge volume hiding below the waterline contained 50 states, from Alaska to Mississippi to Utah to Texas. Each one more like a little country all of its own, rather than a carbon copy of the other forty nine.

The people you meet in New York are completely different to those you meet in Chicago. The lifestyle in the cities on the east coast is an entire world away from what you find on the west. Los Angeles and San Francisco are in the same state but that is where the similarities end. Visually, climatically and socially they are a world apart. The mid west is very different to the north east which in turn is a light year away from the deep south. In which other country in the world could you find two states as unrelated as Alaska and Hawaii. And Las Vegas is just a completely different planet! How could I have indoctrinated myself for so long that this was just one big country. One big endless mall of high rise buildings with the same shops on different streets and each city centre indistinguishable from the one before.

The one thing that is the same in America is the hospitality of its people. Across a range of locations from a diner in New York to a dusty convenience store in Arizona, we met nothing but nice people. Decent, hard working people who were always friendly and helpful to you in every way they could. Bruce Springsteen kind of people. Ireland is famed for its hospitality but the genuine warmth of the reception Americans give you in everyday interactions makes their country a pleasure to visit.

Our second trip to the U.S. was in 1990. We were invited to Pam's cousins wedding in Costa Mesa, about an hour south of Los Angeles. Pam's uncle, John Dooley had left Liverpool at a young age to make a new life for himself in America. He had been over to our wedding and we were friendly with all of the family, his wife Candy, their children Robert and Susan and her husband to be, Barry Wong.

When we were invited to their wedding we decided it was an invitation too good to miss. It was another chance to see America. This time a completely different side of America, to what we had experienced in New York.

We took a month off. We planned an extensive trip based around being in Costa Mesa for the wedding. We began in Chicago. I really like Chicago and felt at home there instantly. It is a city that appears to be very comfortable with itself. A smaller, more relaxed version of New York. It is the only city I have ever been to with a beach in the very heart of it. Generally a waterside city has a commercial centre, with an industrial dockland zone beyond and eventually a beach area on the very periphery. The nearest beach is usually any hour away from the city centre. In Chicago you can walk down and swim in your lunch break. What a wonderful amenity it has by having Lake Michigan at its very core.

The people we met in Chicago seemed to consider their city as a better version of New York. They felt Chicago matched the drive and focus of New York, only in a much more composed and intimate manner. It had the businesslike approach of an east coast city, something they doubted we'd find in the west. Having now discovered Chicago they couldn't believe we would want to go anywhere near California or the west coast!

We flew directly to Los Angeles from Chicago. John met us at the airport and drove us down to Costa Mesa. It was three days before the wedding so we took the chance to visit both Disneyland and Universal Studios. In both cases we were blown away at how good America does theme parks. When it comes to making sure you have a great time, the Americans know how to keep you smiling and laughing all day long. Disneyland was just incredible. No matter who you are, you can leave your real self at the gates on entering. You put all of your troubles, worries and real life concerns in a neat little bundle and leave them outside. You are not going to know they even exist for the next seven or eight hours. Having stepped outside of yourself you then become the version of you that normally is only found in your dreams. As long as you remain within the boundaries of the theme park you will not wake up.

This is fantasy at its best and the Americans are the worlds best at turning fantasy into reality and reality into fantasy. Every possible measure is taken to ensure everybody in Disneyland has one of the most memorable day's of their lives. You are under a spell. A carefree, happy spell. This must be a little sneak preview of what heaven can be like. Pam and I knocked 20 years off our lives that day. In the end we were the last two to leave. They practically had to drag us out. We were desperately trying not to return to reality and pick up our baggage at the gate.

So now I had seen New York, Chicago, Disneyland and a little bit of Los Angeles. I was beginning to think I knew something about the American way of life. All of that was before I attended a Californian wedding. In Ireland your wedding is the one day in your life when the world is allowed to revolve around you. In America a wedding is just business as usual. Susan and Barry got married in the local mall complex in Costa Mesa. The ceremony was lovely. We had glorious sunshine, a cascading waterfall and an eloquent wedding service. Afterwards we all moved back inside the building to a large function room. It was two o'clock in the afternoon and the wedding reception was about to begin. Great, I thought, now we all have at least twelve hours of eating, drinking, singing, dancing and celebrating ahead of us. We were all seated for the meal, followed by the speeches and then the floor was cleared for an evening of music and dancing. Everything was going to plan. It was just as if we were back in Ireland.

At 4.45p.m. I left the room to go to the toilet. The music and dancing were in full swing. The first sign that the rest of the evening might not materialize as I was expecting, then became apparent. Outside the door I found another bride, in her full regalia, with a nervous looking groom beside her. They were encircled by an entourage of well dressed people. How strange I thought. Our wedding is already well underway so they must have been given either the wrong room or the wrong day. What an unfortunate mix-up on what should be a perfect day for them.

When I returned the music in our room had stopped. As I re-entered I could see six smartly dressed burley but polite gentlemen that I knew were not part of the wedding party. They began to usher the guests towards the exits. I couldn't believe my eyes. Our wedding was over just as it was beginning to get going. As we made our way out to the lobby I could see the new bride and her guests were filing in quickly to take our place. It was five o'clock in the afternoon. I then discovered that three weddings had been booked in for that room that day. We had the first slot from two until five, the next group had their wedding from five until eight and the last wedding would run from eight o'clock until eleven. I had just been on a wedding conveyor belt. I believe the complex had up to a dozen similar rooms in use that day so that's over thirty weddings in all. They don't do things by halves in America.

The following day we were strolling down the streets beside Huntington Beach. We were beginning to wonder what we would do next. The answer soon presented itself right before our eyes. Most of the shops we were passing were Mexican owned. There were little cafes and delis, furniture shops, souvenir shops and grocery stores all displaying offers to entice the customer in Spanish rather than English. The most common shop types of all were travel agents. Having walked by the first few we then noticed all of their windows were advertising tempting offers of cheap flights to Mexico. There were only so many we could pass before the temptation took effect. We decided this was a great opportunity to go to Mexico. We went in and booked return flights to Mexico City, two weeks apart, with an extra flight on the outward leg to Oaxaca.

Our American cousins could not believe what we had done. Here we were in the entertainment capital of the world with Disneyland just down the road and Hollywood only an hour away. Why would we want to give all that up for Mexico? The answer to that question I suppose is that we were Europeans rather than Americans. We were still backpackers at heart. We liked our travels to include a variety of experiences. The sumptuous attention we had received in California had been wonderful but the opportunity to contrast it with life across the border in Mexico was too good to miss.

Two days later we flew from Los Angeles to Mexico City and caught a connecting flight directly to Oaxaca. Oaxaca was a charming little city. Everything seemed to radiate from its central hub, the zocalo. The zocalo was not just the heart of the city but the heartbeat too. It seemed to be invaded by the entire population every day and transformed into an endless busy market. The stylish department stores we had seen in L.A. had been replaced by simple but vibrant market stalls trying to sell you everything from clothes and trinkets to fruit and live chickens. We had travelled 1,000 miles in distance but what seemed like a hundred years in time.

We stayed just one night and then went south by bus to San Christobal de las Casas. San Christobal is the main town of the southern state of Chiapas. This is where most of the Mexican Mayan indian population live. These were the original indigenous people of Mexico who, in many ways, have got left behind by the more sophisticated Spanish descendent population. Chiapas, as a result has become somewhat of a backwater in the political identity of Mexico. It is to Mexico what Kurdistan is to Turkey, or the Basque region is to Spain. The black sheep of the sovereign family. The Mayan Indians are a shy, simple people. They were here first but now they are viewed unfashionable and backward by a Mexico determined to be a big player on the world stage. Chiapas is their last enclave.

In all my travels my favourite destinations have always been developing nations or so called third world countries. If you visit Paris tomorrow for the first time, you will already know most of what you are about to see. The Eiffel tower, Champs Elysee, Notre Dame, Pompidou centre and Sacre Coeur have all been so well documented and illustrated that there is often little surprise left for the visitor on seeing them for real. If however you travel to Botswana or Guyana, Mongolia or Macedonia, you will know very little of what to expect beforehand without undertaking extensive research. The sense of wonder in discovering sights you were not prepared for, as a result, can lead to a much more rewarding travel experience. An experience that often the more luxurious, but predicable, locations are not able to recreate.

Third world travel does this for me. You literally do not know where you will be tomorrow or what you are going to see. It will often depend on who you meet and what recommendations they pass on to you. Travel within these countries is more spontaneous and tends to have much more reliance on your associations with fellow travellers and with the local population. Because of your dependence on these interactions you also tend to meet more people and make more friends than you would on standard packaged travel trips. A complete stranger can become a perfect travel companion within hours.

This is exactly what happened in San Christobal de las Casas. We met and instantly liked four fellow travellers who had just formed their own little group. They comprised a couple who were the reverse of ourselves, an Irish girl with an English boyfriend, a lawyer from New York and a Dutch based college lecturer making his way home to Peru. They were spending a few days there and then heading south to Guatemala. Now we were too.

San Christobal was a beautiful place. Its friendly people evoked much of the gentile Mayan spirit and this contrasted nicely with the simple but majestic architecture that echoed the elegance and grandeur of its one-time Spanish rulers. Initially we all just relaxed and made short trips out into the surrounding countryside. We visited many of the nearby Mayan villages, each of which revolved around the only building of substance, the church. No matter where we went during the day we would all meet up in the evening for a meal. Over dinner and wine we would exchange the accounts of what everybody had seen that day. From the information and recommendations that were provided we would then work out the various agendas and groupings to be arranged for the following day.

Three days later the six of us boarded a bus heading south towards Guatemala. After two hours, before any sign of the border became apparent, it was as if the dramatic and immediate transformation of the landscape, from flat arid plains to hilly lush vegetation, was already informing us we were about to enter a new country. We had just passed through the last town in Mexico, Comitan, and before long the passport stamps from the expressionless border guards told us we were now in Guatemala.

Suddenly it wasn't just the landscape that had changed. If the Mayan Indians of Chiapas are calm and serene, the Guatemalan Mayan Indians were wild and excited. This was the kind of country that hits you right in the face as soon as you cross its border. It was chaotic. Hoards of people were milling around in every direction. And yet, through the chaos, we could sense that this was an extremely friendly place. Guatemala is one of those countries that a few minutes after your arrival, you are already glad you are there.

As soon as we cleared border control we had our first experience of a Guatemalan bus. These were generally outmoded American school buses. They still had their distinctive yellow paint finish that they had left the factory with. They must have been at least twenty years old. As you boarded you could just make out the faded notification that, in its prime, this bus seated 44 American school kids. But that was in America. In Guatemala 44 seats meant a bus could carry about 120 people! A hundred would be squeezed within the bus itself, the rest would cling on externally to rails and ladders and anything that could be used as a handgrip. The roof rack was reserved for what often resembled a multi-coloured, miniature representation of the Andes. It was crammed with an amazing, gravity defying, structure constructed from the various items the passengers below had in transit. It had boxes of fruit of all shapes, sizes and colour on route to being sold at the market. It had rugs and baskets with live animals and birds in them. The mini mountain range was completed with clothes, household items and a vast array of all kinds of wonderful gifts and trinkets.

If you were fortunate enough to get a seat on one of these magical buses it was normally beside an old Mayan woman. They seemed to do most of the fetching and carrying to the markets. They were all distinctively wrapped in their delightful traditional Guatemalan shawls that seemed to be weaved from every colour under the sun. Apart from whatever goods they had on the roof additional space was always availed of on their laps. As you sat down the basket right beside you could contain live creatures like chickens or small dogs, or dead ones, like fish or rabbits.

You would always be greeted with a broad, often gap-toothed, smile and an indecipherable greeting. A delightful one-way conversation would then ensue that often lasted the entire duration of the journey. These women didn't speak any English and I had no Spanish but that never seemed to deter them from talking to you non stop. Irrespective of our inability to communicate there was always a lovely sense of warmth in these encounters. These women always made you feel completely welcome to sit beside them and share their journey. At some point their offering would be extended to more than just conversation. A small bag of simple food would be produced. It would contain some bread, fruit and a bottle of water. They would then insist that half of whatever provisions they had brought for themselves now belonged to you. These incredible women would literally give you half of everything they had. Guatemala is one of the friendliest countries I have ever been to.

The bus would twist and turn its way along the frighteningly narrow mountain roads. No matter how full it seemed to get, nobody was refused entry. And no matter how cramped it got everybody remained in good spirits. Of all the journeys I have ever made this was the most amazing experience I have had in getting from A to B.

Our eventual destination was a wonderfully named little hillside market town of Chichicastanengo. Chichi is a sleepy little place for six of the seven days in the week but Thursday is market day. On Thursday's its population swells twenty fold. Thousands of people, both native and tourists, pour into its narrow little streets to create a remarkable spectacle, Chichicastanengo on market day. The entire town is simply awash with colour in every direction. Endless stalls selling just about everything you would ever need or want as a human being and a lot more besides. We arrived the night before and such is the popularity of the market, all of the overnight accommodation was already gone. Some local families will then greet you off the bus and offer you a night's sleep in whatever spare space they have. With all of the conventional accommodation taken they are glad of the opportunity to make a small bit of money for themselves. Realising the scarcity of available lodgings, after we stepped off the bus, we too were equally delighted with their offer of somewhere to spend the night. Pam, myself and Greg, the New Yorker, ended up with a young family couple who directed us, through the streets, to their home. The extent of the welcome we received was again undiluted by the fact that we had no common language between us. The accommodation we were shown to was extremely basic. I was led to a wooden bench in a windowless shack behind their small house. This was all they had but it was fine by us. These were the genuine local people of Chichicastanengo and they were offering us whatever they had. We were all glad to be giving our money, and it wasn't much money, to people who needed it rather than to a commercial hotel.

As it turned out, after the long day on the bus, I slept as well that night as I ever did in a proper bed. Any lack of comfort was more than compensated by the sincerity of the welcome these people had for us after inviting us into their home.

It took the entire day to see all of the market. It had swept into this amazing little place like a multi-coloured tidal wave. It took so long to cover it all that we needed to stay a second night. Our hosts were delighted to be able to offer their hospitality to us all over again.

The other couple wanted to head north at that stage to see the Mayan temple and ruins at Tikal. So now the six became four. With Greg and Umberto we moved on to Lake Atitlan to spend a few days relaxing by the water after the pleasant chaos of Chichicastanengo. Palenque, the main town in this area, was well equipped with hotels, bars and restaurants. It was just like any normal tourist resort town that we had seen before. It was beautifully located at the foot of a mountain, right on the shore of the lake.

We just all degenerated into beach bums for a couple of days to recharge our now weary batteries. Once that was achieved we began to explore the selection of small Mayan villages, around the lake. These villages were very remote due to the fact that they were all inaccessible by road. They could only be reached by boat across the lake. It was a short trip but just like the contrast of our journey from L.A. to Chiapas, the shore on one side of the lake was a world away from the shore on the other. We had left the Latin American glitz and glamour of Palenque to discover very simple fishing villages that looked as if they had been untouched by time. The people in these villages were leading very simple lives. There were no shops or bars or restaurants. They looked as if they had never been to Palenque let alone London, New York or Sydney. We found both sides of the lake fascinating and equally rewarding to visit. Once again we were amazed at the diversity of civilisation that this planet can display over very short distances.

Our time was up now and we needed to start making our way back to Mexico. We bade farewell to Greg and Umberto. We were sad to leave them as we boarded the bus to take us back up north. They had become good friends over a ten day period. We reached the border by nightfall but were too late for an onward connection to San Christobal. Our only option was to stay in the very basic accommodation that was offered to us at the checkpoint in Comitan. If our accommodation in Chichicastenango was basic but sincere, this was just overpriced squalor. Should a movie ever be made of our night there it will be called "The night of the Cockroach"!

The next morning we bade the cockroaches farewell and caught a bus that would take us all the way to Mexico City. Pam and I were unable to get adjoining seats on this bus. I ended up sitting beside a young lad, probably in his late teens. Once again we had no language to communicate with but we both exchanged the kind of body language that let each other know we were happy to sit together. In the middle of the night the bus stopped and I woke up to discover we were being boarded by the police. Two stern looking uniformed policemen came on board. A junior assistant, who looked to be no more than sixteen years old, waited outside. The entire bus tensed up. Up to then it had been filled with lively conversations, laughter and smiling faces.

One of the policemen came down the central aisle and checked everybody's passport or identity card. He handed them back to each passenger without saying a word. I had my passport ready as he approached. As a tourist I was relaxed but acutely aware of the silent tension of everyone around me. I wasn't sure if this was a moment when I should be just as concerned as everybody else. To my surprise he just passed over me, ignoring my outstretched offer of a passport to be inspected. I assume he recognised that I was a western tourist. He continued on down the bus in this fashion to the very last seat. He turned then and began to make his way back towards the driver. As he passed back along he tapped three people on the top of the head and said "You! Come!" The boy next to me was one of the three. My final sight of him was when the young assistant gleefully grabbed him as disembarked. He was then hurled into what I perceived to be a small, single storey, holding cell immediately beside the bus.

This episode haunted me for the remainder of the journey. Who was this young lad and what had he done? Was he Mexican or was he from further south trying to get to America? Was he a genuine criminal or just the victim of a callous policeman exercising his authority? Would he simply be released in the morning or would his life now be changed forever? Would his family ever see him again? And should I have taken a role in what I had seen? Even though we never spoke I had become attached to him, as my silent travel companion, in the course of our journey. We didn't know each other but our life lines had intersected for a couple of hours. Should I have protested against his arrest? Would I have had some influence as a European tourist or would the police have only been too glad to have me accompany him to the cell? The fear on the faces of the other passengers probably extinguished any thoughts I had of intervention. I didn't do anything. Perhaps any action would have been futile and the only option was to remain silent. I didn't take the chance to find out.

This incident put a face on a story for me. It gave me a personal connection to a story I could read about in any newspaper, any day, in any part of the world. Without an experience like this, these stories barely register with me. They only happen to strangers. But the next time I read about a son or a daughter missing in an oppressive country I thought about that boy. He was my travelling friend and then he was gone. Where to and what was to happen to him I will never know.

When we got back to Costa Mesa we had five days of our holiday left. For our final excursion we hired a car and decided we would go to see Las Vegas and the Grand Canyon. Hollywood to Chichicastanengo and now Chichicastanengo to Las Vegas. Our cultural experience dial was turning full circle.

Chichi and Las Vegas had similarities. Both were unbelievably alive. Each was a unique visual extravaganza. In both cases there were hoards of people milling around in all directions looking to do business. But that was where the similarities ended. The type of business being done in the decadent playground that is Las Vegas was just another universe from the busy market stalls of Chichicastenango.

There can surely only be one Las Vegas. As soon as we arrived I just signed up for the full hit. I joined the vast ranks of the gambling pleasure seekers, albeit on a very modest budget. I went from one dazzling casino to the next, each trying to outdo the one before for spectacle and enticement. The hoards of patrons were like a swarm of hypnotised moths, irresistibly drawn to the lights, or, more precisely, the millions and millions of lights. I loved every second of it.

By the end of day two I began to feel the need to come up for air. All of my senses were now beginning to go into the red zone. There was just no cessation to the gambling and entertainment on offer. As you walked along the strip one incredible visual sideshow after another was carefully orchestrated to ensure each casino kept command of your attention. To complete your absolute disorientation there was now no real distinction between night and day. Acres of tiny light bulbs were switched on every evening just as the daylight was fading. It was endless. My initial fascinations satisfied, I began to question the purpose of humanity. Surely life can not exist on the pleasure principle alone?

On the third day we sought the refuge of the big calm that is the Grand Canyon. We needed to reinvest in our sanity. Our time was running short now, so we booked a cheap package by air to see the canyon in a day. California to Guatemala, now Las Vegas to the Grand Canyon, we were shuffling our cultural experience deck of cards once again.

America does 'big' better than any other country in the world so it seemed only fitting that when God was looking for somewhere to locate this magnificent natural wonder he picked Arizona. The Grand Canyon is simply an awesome sight. Its huge silent presence was the perfect antidote to all the madness that we had just left behind.

By now we needed to start making our way back towards California. Our return flight to England was now only two days away. We headed south initially, to swim in Lake Mead and see the majestic Hoover Dam, before aiming the car in the direction of Costa Mesa.

About an hour into the journey we passed a very busy looking petrol station. I noted from the illuminated displays that the prices were exorbitant. Checking that we still had a quarter tank full I remarked how foolish the queuing drivers were for paying over the odds.

An hour later there was only one foolish car in all of eastern California. No sooner had we passed that petrol station when all evidence of life as we knew it on this planet seemed to evaporate. We were now just driving through mile and mile of endless, lifeless Californian desert. It was only then the penny dropped. That was the last petrol station for 200 miles, hence its high prices. The needle on our petrol gauge began to get alarmingly close to its little empty petrol pump symbol. We consulted our map to discover we had as much desert to come as what we had just driven through. We were still miles and miles from civilisation. If I had a time machine I would gladly have gone back an hour, eaten humble pie and paid $100 a gallon at that petrol station. It was the drivers in all of the cars around us who had the smug grins on their faces now.

John had given us some very detailed AAA maps for our journey. One of them showed a small town on the stretch of road just up ahead. It was called Rice. In Ireland or England any village worth its salt has a pub, a shop, a church and often a petrol station. This is America. Surely Rice will have a gas station, no matter how small it was beginning to appear on the map. The petrol gauge needle was now gone well beyond the little empty petrol pump symbol. It was just about to reach for its hat and coat. Then, the first building we had seen in two hours appeared on the horizon. We were coming in to Rice.

The closer we got the more we began to realise that the building we were seeing was not just the beginning of Rice. It was the end of Rice too. This was a one building town. We pulled up and began to scrutinize what appeared to be an old, dilapidated general store. It obviously hadn't seen a paying customer for many years. There was evidence that petrol had been sold here but the two skeletal pumps looked like museum pieces. They were strewn with cobwebs and the ineligible sign above them creaked eerily. It was like a classic scene from an American road movie. Only this was no movie. We were in a car, in the middle of a desert, without anybody knowing where we were. We had no petrol to get us home and now we had arrived at the town that time forgot. This Rice had only one grain.

We got out of the car, not knowing if we would find any inhabitants or not. A man in his fifties came out. He had been perfectly cast for the part with bare shoulders protruding from a pair of blue dungaree jeans. The road movie scene we were both now visualising in our minds was getting more realistic by the second. His wife soon followed him. Then came their eighteen year old son. We told them we needed petrol to get us to the other side of the desert. They then began to tell us their tale of woe. They had made several attempts to run a petrol station here but the big oil companies wouldn't listen. Now they were left all on their own. Just the three of them left to eek out a basic living on welfare.

These people were literally forty miles from anywhere. They were forty miles from a loaf of bread, forty miles from a pint of milk, forty miles from the sound of another human voice. We could not believe the isolation of their existence. Even the remotest village in Ireland could not compare to this. But this is America! The capital of the world for motion pictures and celebrity was just two hours down the road in one direction and the capital of the world for gambling and entertainment two hours in the other. We listened patiently to their entire hard luck story of big business crushing the little man. They were gentle, if aggrieved, folk. We were grateful for that, given the vulnerability of our situation. The husband eventually offered to siphon petrol from his pick-up so that we could reach the next gas station. I paid him handsomely but the money by then was of little value. They literally held our future in their hands. We thanked them and started the car.

As we drove away little Rice got smaller and smaller in our rear view mirror. We both knew we had been incredibly lucky. Nobody knew where we were. We were completely at the mercy of those three people. So many times, all over the world, that exact scenario can have a very different ending. Our other reflection, as the lights of the twenty first century began to appear on the horizon again was that we had just met the remotest family we had ever seen in our lives. Las Vegas to Hollywood with Rice in the middle. And this is the man who once thought that America was all the same!

23 - Florida

The final part of our American trilogy came the following spring. We went to Florida for two weeks. Pam was now visibly pregnant with Christy. This was to be our very last adventure as just a couple. Our final trip BC – before children. I was still not able to drive at this stage. I was due to take my fourth driving test just before we left. Having failed three times I was far from confident. I was beginning to develop a phobia that I was just one of those people destined never to drive a car. For this test I was under even greater pressure. Pam's mother would never have forgiven me if her pregnant daughter was expected to chauffer me around Florida for two weeks.

I will always reserve my greatest empathy for cancer patients. Not far behind however are those who are about to take their driving test! I now had developed a mental block about this one, relatively straightforward, hurdle on my life path. With every failure the desperation to pass the next test grew in direct proportion to my shrinking confidence of my ability to succeed. It was like insomnia. The more I tried to sleep the more awake I was going to stay.

My first failure was acceptable. I deserved it. For the next two I considered myself a little unlucky. In one of them I turned into a long, quiet residential road. It was near the end of the test and everything had gone well until then. A parked truck restricted the width of the road at my end and I could see an approaching car in the distance. I indicated to pass the truck on the assumption that I would be well clear of it before reaching the other car. The only problem was that I was toddling along at nervous driving test speed whilst the oncoming car was travelling like a bullet. The outcome was that both cars met at each end of the truck and had to crawl past each other with only inches between us. As the other car drew alongside the driver lowered his window. Only then could I see that it was occupied by four, bare chested, delinquents, commonly known in Liverpool as "scallies". The driver leaned out of his window to leer at me. We were so close at this point that if my window wasn't up he could have kissed me. He cupped his hand against his forehead to make a gesture that is well understood in Liverpool. Then they all sped off laughing.

When I was clear of the truck I knew I had to say something. If this test had any hope of being salvaged I had to rescue it now. I pointed out that I had remained within the speed limit and my four "driving test friends from hell" had obviously been speeding dangerously. I should not be blamed for what had just happened. My examiner, of course, was always going to retain the higher ground. He agreed but told me that I should have been able to anticipate what was about to happen.

99% of the cars on those suburban roads, at that hour of the morning, are normally occupied by little old ladies going to charity shops. Of all the cars in Liverpool that morning, I was supposed to have the physic ability to identify the one with the four lunatics in it!

By the time test number four came along the likelihood of failure was the only card player at the table. The prospect of Pam's mother waving me off at the airport with a shotgun now looked to be a certainty. By the time I arrived at the test centre I was a nervous wreck. An hour later it was all over. I seemed to have got back to the test centre and brought the car to a halt without a major incident having occurred. Nobody walked out in front of me and the shirtless crazies were all having a day off. However my mental block remained. I was in no frame of mind to expect anything other than the worst. At this juncture the examiners next eight words were always "I'm sorry to have to tell you but . . ."

The examiner turned to me. He said "Congratulations, you've passed". It was as if he was speaking to me in a foreign language. The words I was hearing just did not match the scenario I was in. I was so unprepared for them that my immediate response was almost "Are you sure?" Thankfully my brain kicked in just in time to ensure such an utterance was not sent to the lips. It was not the time to give him the opportunity for a re-think. "Thank you very much" I blurted out instead. I then jumped out of the car as quick as I could to ensure he had no opportunity to change his mind.

Halleluiah! The Holy Grail had been found. Now I could start to get excited about the fact that I was about to go on holiday.

Our trip to Florida was part of the famous Hoover flights fiasco. In 1993 Hoover devised a marketing strategy that offered free flights to America to anybody who bought one of their vacuum cleaners. We already had a perfectly good hoover but Pam always had a great eye for a bargain. The cheapest hoover in the offer was £109 and for that amount we not only got a new, if unnecessary, hoover but also a free trip to the U.S. I was bragging in work for the following weeks that we had now become a one car, two hoover, family.

The deal was that you were offered three dates for your flights. You had to take one of them. The thinking apparently was that the inflexibility of the three dates offered would greatly reduce the uptake. Hoover would gain maximum publicity from the stunt, at minimum cost. The reality however was that the deal attracted massive public interest. People began to arrange holidays, weddings, honeymoons, family reunions and all kinds of personally charged trips on the basis of their hoover purchase. When these events did not coincide with the dates being offered heartbroken stories began to emerge. "Hoover won't let me fly to my own wedding". The company never stood a chance against this ever increasing deluge of human emotion and all of the negative publicity in its wake. The promotion became a complete fiasco. Hoover had no option but to honour every single flight, at a cost of millions, to regain its reputation with its customers.

In our case, we were easily able to comply with the three dates being offered. We were off on a practically free holiday to Florida and were very grateful to Hoover for it. This was to be our last trip before parenthood and we were determined to make the best of it. We flew to Orlando but having already enjoyed the Disney experience we hired a car and headed straight for Miami.

As architects Miami Beach had always been high on our "must see" list. We had long been familiar with images of its amazing array of brightly painted, beautiful art deco buildings that line the promenade. Art deco is a very popular strain of modernist architecture. It introduced a twist of colour and fun to buildings that most architects love. Miami Beach did not disappoint in reality. We both instantly loved it and its unique collection of vivacious art deco designs. It was Disneyland for architects.

But we were tourists as well as architects. We were now discovering that these pretty buildings were merely the backdrop for the incessant and visually stunning social playground that Miami Beach is. The promenade, all day and night long, was a continuous procession of vibrant, glamorous people, stunning cars and gleaming motorbikes. It was an endless parade of the finest human specimens and the greatest machines on the planet. If you were inviting an alien to a universal beauty pageant to demonstrate the greatest examples of man and machine on earth, you would sit them on the roof of one the hotels on the strip. This was what made Miami Beach sensational.

The art deco buildings, beautiful in themselves, knew they were a mere prop to the main stage show. This was a human extravaganza that oozed stylish confidence wherever it flowed. It filled the bars and restaurants on one side of the promenade and the beaches and the sea on the other. If you were searching for the coolest place in the world it would have been hard to say that this was not it.

Like Rice, Miami Beach is a unique American experience. It is an intoxicating mix of offbeat glamour and carefree, friendly people set against a wonderful splash of urban, art deco, colour. All of this makes it one of the most remarkable places I have ever been.

From Miami we toured back through the more gentile parts of southern Florida. We stopped off at the state parks in the everglades, the tranquil resorts at Sanibel Island and St. Petersburg on the Gulf coast and the charmingly placid city of Tampa. For our last few nights we headed up to see the bikers in Daytona and on to visit one of Americas few castles at St. Augustine. America is very proud of St. Augustine and rightly so. It contains one of the oldest buildings in all of North America, the Castillo de San Marcos built by the Spanish in 1695. It came highly recommended to us and although the town was a pleasant little slice of Americana, the castle itself was nothing out of the ordinary. We were a little disappointed.

America may be the most impressive country in the world when it comes to "big" but it will always find it hard to compete with Europe when it comes to "old". We had come from Ireland and England where we have more enormous and wonderful castles than we can find visitors to go and see them. Going to see a castle in St. Augustine seemed to be a little like asking somebody from Disneyland to visit a funfair in Clonakilty! So sorry America, you made a huge impression on me but I still feel we have the upper hand on our side of the water when it comes to all day weddings and historic buildings!

And so that was it. That was the very end of our American adventure. The next day we boarded our free Hoover return flight back to England. Within a couple of months Christy would be born. My life would never be the same again.

24 – A First Child

Christy Ryan was born on the 3rd of April 1994. The birth of any child is an amazing personal and emotional experience for every couple. It is one of life's truly genuine highs. The sense of uniqueness of the occasion is overwhelming. You and your wife or husband or partner have just made this little creature that you now see before you. There will never be another child like it in the world. I cried for one of the few times in my adult life. The birth of a child is one of few events when grown men will genuinely cry.

Christy weighed in at a whopping nine pounds and ten ounces. He was too big to come out the conventional route. Pam gave him every chance. She persevered with a long and frustrating labour, but in the end he insisted on being offered an alternative means of escape. It was all down to "dilation" apparently, or more precisely, a "lack of dilation". This was a new term to me. I had only heard it for the first time an hour earlier after we arrived in the labour ward. Surrounded by all the sophisticated equipment and paraphernalia of medical science I had lost sight of the basics. The peg needs to be able to fit out through the hole.

There was only one thing for it apparently, a Caesarean section. We were off to the theatre. Operating theatre, anesthetic, scalpel, blood, stitches. Up to now all of my anxieties had been focused on the well being of our new born baby. Now they had to be extended to include surgery to my wife as well.

There are two kinds of section they told me, an emergency section and an elective one. Ours would be an elective section, a planned one effectively. This, I was assured, was a much more routine procedure. We were going to theatre by choice rather than being rushed there in an emergency. This allowed me to turn down my concern for Pam going under the knife, but only by a single notch.

We were taken to theatre and gowned up. The good news was that we could both be present and awake for this momentous event. Pam was placed on the operating table and I was positioned at her head. What looked like a non-transparent table tennis net was then placed across her stomach. This was obviously to prevent us, but perhaps especially me, from witnessing the gory details of exactly how Christy would make his entrance into the world. It was to ensure that I wouldn't become an unnecessary distraction by fainting at best, or throwing up at worst.

This tactic however was only partially successful. At one point I looked up at the circular light fitting above the operating table. In the chrome insert between the lamps, I got a perfect reflection of the carnage that was now taking place to Pam's lower abdomen. It was a scene that looked as if it would have graced any half depraved slasher movie. I quickly diverted my eyes back to the safety of the obscure table tennis net.

When everything was set up, the masked surgical team, who were now encircled around the table, nodded in unison. This was obviously the signal between them for the silent declaration of "we're going in". By the arm movement I could identify the medic that had the scalpel in hand. Amazingly, just a few seconds later, they lifted up this blood stained, living creature that belonged to us. It generated one of the most incredible emotions I have ever experienced. Both Pam and I were simply in bits.

They washed him down, very carefully and then wrapped him in a clean white towel. Then they gave us our new born baby to hold for the very first time. The power of creation was right there in our hands. Our hearts melted as we held him. We began to realise that we were holding nine pounds and ten ounces of the purest form of responsibility there is. Now that we had made this little fella we were also going to have to ensure that he grows up safely, goes to school, has friends to play with, brushes his teeth, is brought to the circus and is equipped with all the life skills he will need before he is ready to make his own way in the world.

Your life will never be the same after you have a child. It is no longer your own anymore. Just about every decision Pam and I would make from now on would be dictated, to some degree, by this little chap. He was now gazing back up at us as if to remind us of that fact. Perhaps he was just as daunted as we were. "Will they make me eat porridge?" "I hope they have a piano".

Before Christy came along I had always prided myself on being good with children. I had been a popular uncle with my sister's kids and I had always got on well with any of the children I would meet out playing, wherever we lived. I was now finding out that you really know very little about them until you have one of your own. This wasn't just restricted to the whole host of new activities I now discovered were essential to having your own child. Feeding, sterilizing bottles, nappy changing, winding and walking with a pram had become as much a part of my life now as eating my dinner or washing my face.

In the broader context you are also inducted to a whole new section of your everyday world that you previously never knew existed. Most days on my lunch hour, before Christy was born, I would walk from the office up to the city centre in Liverpool. Church Street would be thronged with masses of people. As I strolled from one end to the other my eye line would be fixed at a height of about five feet above the pavement. I would be on the lookout for anybody I might know in the oncoming crowds. My line of vision was aimed entirely at adult faces. Nothing below that level would register. If asked, on returning to the office, if any children were present on Church Street, I would honestly reply "No. Well I didn't see any anyway".

After Christy was born this scenario was completely reversed. I would again walk down the exact same street with the same amount of people on it only now I would not see anything above five feet. Everything apart from babies and toddlers and buggies and prams would be blinded from my vision. I would want to know if they had got their push chair cheaper than we got ours. I'd be looking at little coats and hats and scarves and know exactly which shop they had come from. I would be silently delighted or disappointed that we had got Christy the red one instead of the yellow one. Anybody I may have known on the street would now not be seen. They disappeared into that oblivion that existed five feet above the ground.

Suddenly I began to see the poor woman trying to manoeuver her way through a revolving door with one child in a buggy and two more pulling out of her. Previously she only registered as an inconvenient obstruction to my precisely timed dash back to the office.

She had now gone from hinderance to heroin status. She obviously had unbelievable organisational skills to get three children of different ages ready at the same time for a trip to town. She then had to run the gauntlet of traffic and cyclists, lamp posts and zebra crossings to catch the appropriate bus or train. On the busy streets her desire to reach her intended shop had to withstand the determination of three children who wished to go any direction apart from the one she needed. Church Street was no longer a mere thoroughfare for this woman. It was an assault course. I would then go back to the office and if asked if there were any adults on Church Street I would only give the same response as before. "No, I don't think so. I didn't see any anyway".

Christy's arrival was like a some kind of universal paediatric enlightenment. I would now go in to department stores that I had known for years, only to discover they had entire sections that I had never seen before. Vast hanger like rooms filled with cots and prams and car seats and paddling pools and tricycles and mobiles and every kind of child accessory and toy imaginable. Christy had given me the key to open the door to this world. Babyworld. A secret, parallel world, within everyday life, that you know nothing about until your first child is born.

There was to be no limit to the impact Christy would have. It was not just going to stop at how we lived and all of this new equipment we needed. He would soon move on to having his say on where we lived and what we intended to do with the rest of our lives.

At this time we were living in a nice little red bricked terraced house, in a pleasant suburb of Liverpool. We were a short walk from Sefton Park and still within easy reach of the city centre. This was the area where most of our fellow, ex-student, friends also lived. We had all began in this area as students and after college, had remained on. Our established social network of friends had been woven into this area over many years.

Just beyond Sefton Park was the great little social oasis of Lark Lane. This was a very popular street lined with lively pubs and restaurants that we all loved. With Lark Lane we didn't even need to go in to the city centre to socialise.

Our house just had a small yard but the lack of a garden was compensated for by the small park at the end of our street. Greenbank Park was like a mini version of Sefton Park. It had a lovely grassy hill for summer picnics, majestic trees to admire in the Autumn and a lovely little lake to delight you every day. For all of the houses on our street it was like having our own great big communal front garden. As neighbourhoods go, we really couldn't have wished for nicer. I wasn't capable of seeing anything on the horizon that would require us to change it in the coming years.

By the time Christy was one I was even more convinced that we lived in the ideal place. He was starting to find his feet now and our little yard was perfect. It gave him as much space as he could handle and gave us the reassurance that he was perfectly secure. It was only when he reached two that he began to hint that he may have had other ideas for our future abode. He began to prompt his Dad that he may need to start thinking outside the red brick Victorian backyard box that he was now rapidly outgrowing.

Pam had realised it long before it would ever dawn on me. We needed to get a house with a garden.

I still had a fairly relaxed attitude to most things at this stage. Future planning tended to be calculated in days rather than months or years. When I began to think about changing house I lacked the vision to think TOO far outside the box. I just assumed we needed to buy a semi-detached house somewhere nearby. Any variables that needed to be changed would be kept to a minimum.

Pam, of course, was way ahead of me as usual. She had a much more comprehensive assessment of the situation we were now in. What was the point in tackling each problem with a short term solution as it came up. Why not make a move now that would be good for us all for many years. There may be more Christy's to come and why not go somewhere with better prospects for our future needs. Lets make one move now that would address everything we required for the years to come.

Wow! I never thought of all that. It makes perfect sense.

Pam had never been to Ireland before we met. By now she had been many times and loved the lifestyle she found there. For a girl who had grown up in the city she had a great affiliation for the countryside and country living. She was completely at ease in the pub in Horseleap or on Carol and Rory's farm in Ballycumber. Pam knew that the environment of rural Ireland was going to be a much nicer place to bring up children. It took the English wife to enlighten her Irish husband. "Let's go to Ireland".

25 – Return to Ireland

We brought the car over to Ireland in the summer of 1995. The main intention of the trip was to have a three week holiday but the sub-plot was to see what opportunities existed for two architects. Our timing was perfect. At the time of writing 1995 was the last really great summer Ireland has had. The glorious weather presented the entire country at its very best. The Celtic Tiger was also just beginning to peer around the corner. An economic boom was about to sweep over the country and employment prospects looked very good. We knew from the reception I was getting at the practices I visited, that a job would not be long in materialising.

We also had a wonderful holiday. The casting vote, if we needed one, was that Liverpool was now sliding into recession. We had watched the architectural profession there reach a point where we knew difficult years were on the way. The decision was made. We were going to move to Ireland.

We returned to Liverpool and put our house on the market. I then, with a great deal of regret, gave notice to my colleagues at F.S.P. that I was going to leave. Before long I began to get calls for interviews in Ireland. After attending a few of these it was apparent that any prospective employers would not consider me seriously whilst I was still based in England. In early 1996 therefore I left F.S.P. and the Albert Dock and moved over to stay with my sister, Carol. She was ideally located in the heart of Ireland in Co. Offaly. I was within striking distance of an interview anywhere in the country.

Ideally we didn't want to go to Dublin. Liverpool is the next city to Dublin and, with all our friends there, we didn't see the sense in just swopping cities. The prime motivator in making this move was to change our lifestyle completely. That meant getting out of the city. Our preferred landing target was somewhere in rural Ireland, within range of one of the larger towns.

This restriction of opting not to work in Dublin soon transpired to have a major impact on my job prospects. I was now six weeks with Carol and had five jobs waiting for me there with no offer of a job anywhere else. I began to realise the huge magnet that Dublin is for the working population of Ireland. To choose not to work there is often a decision you are not at liberty to make. I had given myself a month to find work and that was now up. I was just about to reconsider my geographical strategy when the phone rang. There was a job for me in Limerick.

Limerick had not been on our compass at all. Our two favoured destinations were the cities in the main tourist areas, Galway and Cork. Now on a closer inspection, Limerick

began to look good. It started to look very like Liverpool. Limerick is the third
Ireland, located on a long estuary on the west coast. It often gets bad publicity
throughout the rest of the country. All of this seemed to equally apply to Liverpool in
England. From my time there however I knew how misleading some of these assertions
can be. Liverpool was a great city to live and work in. It was a city full of character and
inhabited by some of the nicest people you could ever wish to meet. Of course it had its
troubled areas, just like any city, but they were just the tail of what was a very friendly dog.

Sometimes the bad reputation of a city is due to its portrayal only being painted from a
singular pot of paint. I was beginning to feel Limerick may have been suffering the same
fate. All I had to do was go there. In doing so I would merely pass through this publicity
smokescreen and discover that a great city lay beyond. We were coming home to the
Liverpool of Ireland!

I phoned Pam with the news. She and Christy had stayed behind until I had sorted out a
new base for us. There was another reason too. She was now heavily pregnant. The birth of
our second boy, Lowell, was imminent. She was familiar with the maternity hospital in
Liverpool and it made better sense to wait there rather than transfer to an as yet unknown
hospital in Ireland. Moving house, between two countries would be stressful enough
without superimposing the added complication of a new birth into the middle of it.

So fourteen years after one Ryan had left Horseleap, three Ryans would be returning to
Limerick and bringing a Teese with them. When I arrived in Limerick I knew only one
person. Billy Lane had been a good friend of mine in Liverpool before returning to Ireland
to open a pharmacy in his native city. He was my only connection with this part of Ireland.
I stayed with Billy and his wife Louise for a few nights and also with my cousin Pat
Naughton and his wife Mary in Ennis during the first week. Then I rented a small bungalow
in Croom, just outside the city.

When Lowell was born and Pam came over, we began to fine tune our Irish arrival more
precisely.

Limerick is a small, tightly knit, city. Most of the people we met would not consider living
beyond the city limits. A couple of well established suburbs were the desired choice for
most home seekers. Any thoughts of settling beyond the urban area were generally limited
to Cratloe, Adare and Lisnagry. Everything else was described as "miles away"!

For our first six months we constantly toured the entire area. We were on our own
residential reconnaissance mission. One day we headed out the Dublin road towards Lough
Derg. It only took us one visit to fall in love with the picturesque town of Killaloe on one
side of an old stone bridge and the charming rural village of Ballina on the other. This was
a hidden gem if ever there was one. You stumbled on this little settlement as if you had
magically taken a wrong turn. You suddenly found yourself in a beautiful setting that you
would be delighted to find in the Lake District, Alpine France or Canada.

Ballina and Killaloe is a delightful twin-town on the banks of the Shannon. The Arra
Mountains gaze down protectively from one side and the Slieve Bernagh Mountains from
the other. The majestic Lough Derg is wedged in-between.

We found it a very friendly place too. Driving back after our third night to visit we realised
we now knew more people in Ballina and Killaloe than we did in all of Limerick. The

decision was made. This was where our return to Ireland would rest.

I went in to work the next morning and told them I was going to move out to Ballina. They all looked at me as if I had two heads. It was as if I had just told them I was moving to Donegal. "That's miles away" they all exclaimed. A fourteen mile leisurely commute was not miles away in my book. It was a small price to pay for living in two beautiful towns, surrounded by breathtaking scenery and in a warm and welcoming community. This was where we wanted to live. This was where we wanted to spend the rest of our lives.

26 – Ryan Teese Architects

We rented a house in Ballina for a year and then we bought in one of the new estates in the town. Once again our timing was good. First time private housing estates were now springing up in every town in Ireland but the Celtic Tiger was still just a cub. All of those who bought at that early stage got good value for money.

When we moved in we found Ballina/Killaloe did not disappoint from its first impressions. It became a wonderful place to live. So good, that if I was allowed to turn the clock back to the day I drove onto the ferry in Liverpool, I wouldn't have picked anywhere else. The two towns, the river and the lake were all just a short walk from us. If you went a little further you had the mountains and the forests and a collection of delightful villages and on both sides of the lake. When you drove your car people waved to you. They then greeted you by name on your second meeting.

It also turned out to be a good move for our work. There was no established architect in this area. With the scenic location and the growth in the economy there was now a good demand for one. Work automatically started to come our way and when Lowell started playschool Pam was able to take some of this on. I was helping out by doing as much as I could in the evenings.

We both realised that an opportunity was presenting itself. If we didn't take it someone else would. The office in Limerick was just not what I had been used to in Liverpool and London. Now was the time to make the break. It was a chance to do what most architects dream of, setting up their own practice. All of the lights were green and if we didn't do it now, we may never get the chance again.

Ryan Teese Architects opened its doors on the second week of January 1998. There were just two staff, Liam Ryan and Pam Teese. We were small and rural so we didn't need a big fancy office. We just worked from home and all of our clients seemed to like it that way. What you saw was what you got. After a twenty year working life, during which I had commuted to work every morning by bicycle, bus, train or car, I could now start work in my pyjamas, if I chose to. My start time could be seven o'clock in the morning or half ten in the morning, depending on what was needed. For the first time in my life I appeared to be in control of my work, rather than it in control of me. At the age of 36 I looked at my life to see a great wife, two fine boys, two lovely towns, a great community, two mountains, a lake, a river and plenty of work. And I was still in my pyjamas.

Our practice began to grow. We had a waiting list of very good clients, all looking for interesting design solutions, on scenic sites, in this beautiful part of the country. I seemed to have reached a point in my life where not only did I have all my ducks lined up in a row but they all had big smiles on their faces too.

Over the next few years we were designing a varied array of one-off houses on both sides of the lake. Pam was the main design force. We dovetailed well as a team to provide the completed building as I had considerably more experience of construction work and site supervision. Apart from the one-off house work we also attracted a nice sprinkling of small town commercial projects. This helped keep our workload varied and prevented us from getting residentially typecast. In those early years we looked as nearly every business premises in both Ballina and Killaloe. All of the pubs were looking for an upgrade to accommodate the wave of new settlers now arriving to both towns.

One of our projects was an extension for my own local pub. It was owned by my good friend and namesake Liam O'Riain (O'Riain is Ryan in Irish). I also did a new extension and theatre for Brendan Grace's pub in Killaloe. Brendan is a well known Irish comedian. Pam designed our most prestigious job in these years, a new built restaurant in Ballina for the chef proprietor Harry McKeogh. It was called The Cherry Tree. These jobs had the advantage of knitting us in quickly with the local community. Between houses and our commercial projects we soon got to know just about everybody in both towns.

Apart from our higher profile projects, I was also very aware of what I saw as my role as an architect within a local community. A traditional rural settlement always has definitive pillars of profession and trade to support the community it creates. Every traditional village had a doctor, a blacksmith, a vicar, a grocer, a solicitor, etc., who in turn become part of the very fabric of that village. I felt that I now had skills that were needed and were a benefit to the place where I lived. This community had been very receptive to our arrival and helpful to our settling in amongst them. I now wanted to return that gesture by assisting where I could. I wanted to be able to offer my services to local people who may not normally approach an architect, even though they may have needed one.

These people were often elderly and would have been daunted by the prospects of travelling in to the offices of a big firm in Limerick. They would have imagined that huge fees would have been incurred by simply going in the door. Good community relations have always thrived on everybody contributing what they can. Often what you give will be returned twofold to you later. I was to discover the true meaning of this four years later. All of these people came to our aid, in whatever way they could, after I was diagnosed.

The initial approaches for these community type jobs would often occur as I was coming out of Mass on Sunday. A little old lady, that I wouldn't know, would approach me. She would then begin to tell me that she was worried about a damp patch that had just appeared on the back wall of her kitchen. Other times an elderly farmer would need planning advice about building a small shed on his farmstead. In each case I would always call and assess the situation. I would then try to identify the best possible solutions and advise on what I thought the most appropriate action was. They would always be extremely grateful for my assistance.

No matter how small my involvement often was, they would insist that I had to take something for my time. I had no intention of seeking payment for the small amount of time these little jobs entailed but their persistence would be relentless. I would not be allowed to leave the house or farmyard without an apple tart, or a bag of fuel or a promise. "The next time you go in to Liam O'Riains there'll be a few pints waiting for you behind the bar". This was country living at its best!

This was just a lovely way to work. I found it hugely refreshing and rewarding. We still had plenty of normal, fee paying projects but these community interactions gave a lovely balance to my working day. It was a scenario where people simply worked well together. Once the working relationship was good, everything else just seemed to fall into place. It was a welcome contrast from many of the difficult working pressures, I had to endure for years. Working against the clock for large corporations and developers whose only interest was maximum product at minimum cost. The kind of work where people didn't really matter, only the end result.

I was still in regular contact with the lads from college at this stage. Three of them were now working for big practices in London. They became curious about my job description now that we had gone out on our own in a small rural town. After several unsuccessful attempts to find the words that accurately captured the variety and essence of our work, I eventually settled not on a word but on a name. On Monday I could be meeting Ted Glen to look at building an extension to his village hotel and on Thursday I am due to meet Mrs. Goggins over tea to inspect at her leaking flat roof. I relayed to my friends in England that having previously worked on major projects with big practices, I had now become a kind of Postman Pat architect!

27 – The People of Ballina and Killaloe

Before I arrived in Ballina and Killaloe I had already assembled a good pool of close friends. I had accumulated these from my time in Horseleap, my two secondary schools and my years in Liverpool. I was a family man now and for some odd reason, I believed I would no longer be adding to this pool. I felt that my window in life for making really good friends had now closed. How wrong I was. I was underestimating the strength of a great community. If there are good people around you, you will never stop making friends.

The advantage of living in the countryside is less is more. The less people there are the more you will get to know. Unlike the city, you begin to bump into the same group of people repeatedly. This provided me with an early platform to form new friendships that I was not expecting. Over the next few years not only did I add to my list of good friends, I found four new ones who equalled anything I had before. This was another early piece of my cancer survival jigsaw falling in to place. Four of these new friends would go on to play a significant role in the management of my cancer case. They, without any prompting, would become my minders. They gave themselves the duty of keeping my spirits up and shielding me from anybody who would detract from my fight. A screen from people who just could not handle the news of my cancer. They knew, from the outset, that any such encounters would only dilute my focus to keep fighting. They became my centurions. They would keep me on the road to survival, without me realising it.

In drafting up their job description they also included the role of public relations officers. They became the official source for information on my condition. They were the go-between between me and my family and the general public. This system appeared to appeal to both parties. As a family we had a filter from total exposure. Well wishers also appreciated having a neutral third party update facility before approaching me directly.

The most important role of my minders was to protect me, when necessary, from people who couldn't hide their emotions. Cancer, at this time, especially when it was as severe as mine, was still very much viewed as a death sentence. Many people would be unable to conceal this belief, no matter how much they may have wanted to. They would just have believed that I was now going to die. My four great friends knew I now needed encouragement not sympathisers. I needed everybody I met to get behind my fight to survive. I could just not afford to meet people who would become upset and burst into tears. No matter how strong I was such encounters would only weaken my resolve.

Nobody could be blamed for reacting in this way but it was something that I was better off not to see. My four sentries recognised this immediately. They knew it would only damage my morale. I needed the right kind of visitor. They screened me from people whose body language could only be read as "I am calling to see you because I know I will never see you again".

When you are diagnosed with cancer friends and acquaintances often don't know what to do. They want to help in any way they can but are generally unsure what is appropriate. If they are not aware of the exact prognosis they will not be in any position to know the best action to take. No matter how long they have known you, suddenly a sense of insecurity can arise over how to interact with you. They will not know whether you wish to remain undisturbed within the privacy of their own family or would welcome their contact and support.

My four minders stepped in to fill this void of uncertainty. They became the point of contact for accurate details of my condition and updates of how my treatment was progressing. They could then advise on what assistance was required if anybody wanted to help or if a visit was appropriate. They became like my own personal custom officers. Everything had to funnel through them to get to me.

The broader community were happy that they had adopted this role. People were grateful for a singular source of reliable information rather than relying on hearsay. From my side they had direct contact with the family. They could then judge what news was appropriate to relay back to well wishers. At times they decided to filter the information to be released if the news was bad. This was always only done in my best interests in order to ensure the campaign stayed positive until the very end.

The first of the four was Bernard Kennedy. When we moved to Ballina, the house we rented was in Ashgrove Meadows. Bernard and Martina were our next door neighbours. Bernard and I would probably have found each other eventually but being neighbours speeded up the process. We didn't appear to be immediately compatible. I was eight years older and Pam and I had two kids at that stage, compared to their none. We would naturally have been drawn to different social circles. As new neighbours however it only took a few chats across the fence to discover we had much in common. In spite of our age difference we had similar tastes in both music and sport. Both senses of humour were also alike. We became very good friends within weeks.

Bernard's two big passions when I met him were the Limerick senior hurling team and Neil Young. In later years he added a third, the Munster rugby team. He gave me a personal demonstration of his deep devotion to the first two every summer. Bernard would take me to see Limerick play in the first round of the Munster hurling championship.

Our day would start early. No matter where the venue was he would have me in a pub full of Limerick supporters at least an hour before throw in. Our excursion would then draw to an end, what seemed like a lifetime later, with him granting me a private audience to Neil Young's entire repertoire which he could play on his guitar. This was his best mechanism to console himself after yet another Limerick defeat.

Year after year Bernard would passionately enthuse that this was going to be Limerick's year. The drought was finally going to end. Limerick are one of the best supported teams in the country. The measure of that great support is that for forty years, their legion of fans have devotedly followed the team, through one disappointing campaign after another. Every year they return with undiminished hope. Bernard is one of those fans.

Our day out together always seemed to follow a similar pattern. At the game Limerick would start well. In the later stages of the second half they would look the likely winners. But then it would all begin to slip. At the final whistle it would be yet another year of heartbreak. Bernard's inexhaustible passion would be speared at an early hurdle once again. He would be downcast for a while, verbally replaying several crucial missed scores and cursing mistakes that were made at key moments. By the time we returned to the pub, filled with similarly dejected Limerick supporters, he would be beginning to return to good form. The wisecracks would begin to flow again. He would now be in the transformation stage between forgetting about the match and contemplating the prospects of a good night out. On returning to Ballina the car would be parked up and the serious drinking could now begin.

Ballina is in county Tipperary, one of Limerick's great rivals. He would have to brace himself for smug commiserations no matter which pub we went to. It was only after leaving the pub that I would then be granted a very rare privilege. Bernard would take out his guitar and play any Neil Young song I named, no matter how obscure. He knew every one of them, word for word. Very few other people would get the chance to discover his talent as he has always been very shy about performing in public. I was honoured.

Three hours later we would have come to the end of what had been a great day. By then the result of the match would have been long forgotten. It wouldn't be long now before the sun would rise. It was time to go. Our two wives could probably have written the lyrics of the very final Neil Young song. "We're gonna give you till the morning comes"

This story came to life in 2001. Bernard and I went to see Neil Young and Crazy Horse at the Point Theatre in Dublin. I had never seen Neil Young before and thought I had left it too late to catch him in his prime. I was wrong. He was simply magnificent. I emerged from the auditorium in the knowledge that it is never too late. Talent doesn't fade away. We were close to the front of the stage all night and for the encores we pressed up to the very edge. When the concert was over and the house lights went up we were still there. One of the roadies, who was dismantling the equipment, bent down and picked up the plectrums that Neil Young had used during the show. He turned and moved to fling them to the crowd. Just before he did, a sea of hands appeared in front of him, each one hoping to capture a prize. Every hand was extended in mid air to its maximum surface area in order to provide the greatest target possible. Then, they all descended as secure clenched fists. The owner of each fist hoping they were the lucky one to have captured a treasured memento. Bernard and I put our fists together when we drew them down. Then we opened them. One of Neil Young's plectrums was in the palm of Bernard's hand.

This was a divine moment as far as I am concerned.

"You know every Neil Young song and I am well pleased."

If anybody there that night deserved a plectrum, Bernard did. Unfortunately God seems to be finding it a little more difficult to come up with his other holy grail, an All-Ireland title for the Limerick senior hurling team.

The second member of the quartet was Geno Reynolds. He also lived in Ashgrove Meadows when we first arrived. Geno is a real character. He was to be my Pete Morgan replacement in Ballina and Killaloe. If you ever went to a house party and Geno wasn't there, you were always disappointed. He was always worth his admission. Just like Pete he always had a trick or two up his sleeve to keep us all entertained.

When we arrived in Ballina the new estates were just being built. We were among the very first batch of new arrivals. It was still very much a local town at that time and the small amount of new settlers did not undermine that dynamic. If anything the infusion of new blood was a welcome addition. A lovely balance soon emerged between the locals and the newcomers. The new arrivals were attracted there by the established sense of community in the first place. They wanted to become part of it. The local people in return were very welcoming to this new influx of people who wanted to be part of their town. They could see that with us we brought new skills and energy that would be a benefit to all.

From being on a navigable river, Ballina and Killaloe have always been towns that were accustomed to strangers. The Shannon has been bringing outsiders to this area long before we arrived. The working boats that had supplied the towns for many years had now been replaced by pleasure craft. Regular visitors had never stopped arriving. Only the purpose of their visit had changed.

This was a stopping point for many years for the Guinness barges travelling between Dublin and Limerick. A number of Kildare men in particular, working on those barges, stopped off here in the 30's and 40's. Many of them met local girls, settled down and never went home.

We were now probably the greatest wave of new arrivals since those times. Our mode of transport to get here however was a little less obvious. Rather than float into town on a bulky Guinness barge, we had all straddled in on the back of a mythical Celtic Tiger.

As well as our immediate good relations with the local community we also found we all gelled well together as a group of new settlers. This was greatly facilitated by the fact that we were all pretty much the same. Most of us were working in jobs in Limerick or Shannon. We were all about the same age. Each couple seemed to have between two and four children. Everybody was living close to each other in one of the three new estates in Ballina. For genuine friendships to form however, you still need personal appeal. Remarkably all of us who came in that very first wave seemed to have that between us too. We all just got on really well from the very beginning.

There were about twelve couples in this core group of new friends. Geno and his wife Michelle were one of those. The blood flow to the perpetuation of these early friendships was a regular round of house parties. The only thing that would change would be the house itself. To this day all of that group all still good friends. The only change now, fifteen years later, is that we are all a little older. Those early halcyon days of continuous socialising are now gone.

It was also important to us that when we socialised we did so without the exclusion of the local people. We had no desire to alienate ourselves into a type of ex-pat group. The neighbours and local friends would be essential guests at every house party too.

These nights generally began in Liam O'Riains pub. Liam himself was still behind the counter then. He was the wonderful ingredient that made this great little pub so special during those years. He knew us all, both locals and newcomers, and going in to his pub was like going in to your second home. We all had memorable, impromptu nights there, nights when music sessions would just spring up from nowhere. We had wild raucous nights full of wit and laughter. These usually had Liam himself somewhere in the middle of them. In contrast, we also had wonderful, enchanting nights when you just sat up at the counter captivated by the power of the conversation and story telling going on all around you. On those nights you just sat and listened.

Liam was a real character publican. Unfortunately, for his own sake, he was also easily excitable. He would begin to show signs of agitation when the pub started to get full. The giveaway sign of this was a furious combing of his hands through his grey hair. The more uncomfortable he would get the slower his rate of service would become. This was fine for the regular customers who knew him but often puzzling for complete strangers.

His best moments for all of us were often when he was irritated and cranky rather than calm and relaxed. It took very little to direct him towards the edge and the likes of Geno, Albert Kelly and Liam Floyd knew exactly the right buttons to press. In the nicest possible way they would lead him towards a complete state of exasperation, before eventually letting him in on whatever gag they were up to. The rest of us would just sit back and watch the show.

However we all loved Liam and we all knew that, deep down, he loved all of us too. His very presence behind the counter was what made this little pub unique. It takes a great publican to make a good pub great.

We all felt privileged to have been there for those years. We didn't know it then but the continuing population growth would eventually tip this intimate balance between the locals and newcomers. Liam would also retire from behind the bar. These wonderful years would only last for a short while and we were all lucky to have caught them.

Whenever you went in to Liam O'Riains you always seemed to have a good chance of finding Geno. I am convinced there were two of him at this time. He had a busy work schedule but still always seemed to be out and about. Geno was the ultimate social animal. He was always looking to be where the action was or, perhaps more accurately, wherever he was the action would follow. He could and would chat to anybody and was instantly likeable.

But for all his suave and charm Geno also had a heart of gold. He would do anything for you. Shortly after I was diagnosed, I was flying to Liverpool, still uncertain if any treatment was possible. Only family and friends knew of my condition. I had a mid morning Ryanair flight from Dublin to Liverpool for which I required personal identification. In the rush to get there on time I could not find my passport. My drivers licence was also an acceptable form of identification but it was two weeks out of date. Given the extreme circumstances, and the fact that it was proof of my identity, irrespective of the date, I took a chance that it would suffice. When I got to the airport the Ryanair staff at check-in told me they could not accept it. I pleaded with them that in this case it genuinely could be a case of life and death but they were unmoved. Rules are rules they told me. I missed the flight.

They had a later flight that would still get me over in time and by now my passport had been found but Pam was not in a position to get it up to me. As soon as Geno heard about our dilemma he jumped into his car. He drove to Pam immediately, picked up the passport and made a six hour round trip to Dublin. He handed it to me and told me to get to Liverpool and do my stuff. Then he was gone. I caught that second flight and the rest is history.

That little story in itself was just another wonderful piece of the finer detail of my story. In its own way it was just as important as the work my surgeon would do months later. This was the piece of my jigsaw that was personally put in place by Geno. It was another of the hundreds of pieces I could not have afforded to be missing if I was to complete the complex puzzle that lay before me. This little detail is not just a testament to Geno but also to the quality of all the wonderful people who had now become the community that surrounded me.

The third musketeer was Bob Noonan. Bob was the minder of the minders. He spent most of his time looking after the other three. He was generally the one who would make sure Geno got himself home on time and didn't get into too much trouble. Bob is the type of individual that always seems to know exactly what to do, on every occasion. He knew how much information people asking about my condition needed to know. He knew what support Pam and the boys needed when people offered to help. With Bob there was also Ted O'Connor and Piers Devereux. All of these people and many more did incredible things, big and small, for all of us, right through my ordeal. Most of what they did was done without being asked. It was done on their own initiative, quietly behind the scenes, without any fuss. These were the incredible people that just emerged all around me as soon as they knew I was in trouble.

When you get cancer, or any life threatening illness, you become completely immersed by it. Your vision is immediately restricted to whatever treatment you need to pursue in the coming months. Everything else takes a back seat. Your entire life is redirected to focus on a singular mission. Nothing else really seems to matter. In the background however the world keeps turning. Bills still need to be paid. The electricity and gas companies will know nothing of your illness. They will not be expecting or authorising any interruptions to your normal payment schedule. Your employer or business clients will be sympathetic to your predicament. They will grant you some leniency to deal with your ordeal. But eventually they will need to move on too.

Whilst most of our friends and neighbours rallied around to directly support us, the likes of Bob Noonan, Michael Fenton, Piers Devereux and Ted O'Connor immediately recognised the serious financial implications that we now appeared to be heading towards. At that stage, it appeared that no treatment would be available. If any was to be found it was likely to be in America. If I was to avail of it I would need to be able to come up with substantial funding.

Without any prompting, this sub group set up an account in our local bank in Killaloe. They began raising money, through donations, to offset the cost of a possible treatment, if it materialised. They also knew that if there was to be no treatment, or if it was unsuccessful, these funds would then provide a support package for Pam in the event of my demise. All contributions to this fund were given anonymously. We never knew where the individual donations had come from. When it was complete, the details of the account were just given to Pam. It was to be spent on whatever she deemed necessary. As well as the fund, hundreds of individual donations of food, flowers, cards and assistance came unsolicited to our doorstep. Every single one of these gestures interconnected to make up one of the biggest pieces of my survival jigsaw of all. It was put in place by the hands of the incredible people I had all around me in Ballina and Killaloe.

28 – Ian Connolly

The final member of my personal gang of four was Ian Connolly. I met Ian the very first day we arrived in Ballina. He, with his wife Teresa and family, was moving out of the house we were about to move into. They were moving to a different estate and they had just arrived home from hospital with their new twin girls. It would take me another year to get to know him properly.

I can trace the inauguration of our great friendship to the night we met in Richardson's pub. We were all on a night out and at the end of the evening Ian and I were chatting at the bar. I had not been running for six years at this stage and was looking for an excuse to start again. In the course of our conversation I mentioned that I had been a runner. He responded that he had always wanted to run a marathon. It had been on his "to do" list for many years but he had never gotten around to it. We knew we were going to become good friends by then so this seemed like a start running opportunity, for both of us, that was too good to pass up. We vowed that we would meet the next morning at Ballina school to go for a run.

The next morning when I woke, I scrambled back through a hazy memory of the night before. Had that been a genuine promise I made with Ian Connolly. Or was it a well meaning but hopelessly unrealistic commitment. It had been a drunken evening after all. Surely all men know that promises made after drink has been taken are not as genuine as those that are made when it has not.

When the alarm clock told me it was 8.30 I still had not worked out the answer. Did I dream last night that we would meet for a run this morning? If I did arrange it with him I'm sure he'll know that I meant it last night but I don't mean it now.

Apparently we both struggled out of bed simultaneously, at opposite ends of the town. We were both motivated by stubbornness rather than actual desire. "I know he won't be there but I'm going to go down anyway. Then I can come back to bed and it won't have been me who let the side down."

We ran to the school. It was equidistant from both houses. As we ran the desire that the other wouldn't be there intensified into a craving. Neither of us really wanted to run that morning. We just wanted to turn up, make sure the other had broken his promise and go back to bed.

I arrived first. There was no sign of Ian. "Just as I thought. I'll wait a few seconds and then run home. That will be that".

Suddenly I could see him down the street as he ran towards me. My emotions were ripped in two. Half of me was disappointed, the other half delighted. My head wanted to go back to bed but my heart wanted to run. My new friend had made a great first impression. In spite of hangovers, we had both been sufficiently committed to each other to turn up. We turned up because we told the other we would. A great friendship was born.

We both struggled to run that very first day but it didn't matter. The important thing was that we had made a start. Just as any great journey needs to begin with its first step, our running needed to begin with that laborious run. Over the next few months we ran regularly. The more we ran the more we talked. The more we talked the greater friends we became. Early pieces of my cancer campaign jigsaw were now beginning to emerge. My association and running with Ian Connolly was one of the most crucial pieces of all. One of those pieces that until you find it you can't begin to start filling in the pieces around it.

Ian was to go on and be the first person, apart from my own family, to see me after my surgery. He told me that when the operation was taking place he just couldn't sit around. He felt he had to jump on a plane to Liverpool to get to my bedside. All of this had blossomed from an intoxicated promise in a pub to meet for a run.

We were out running every other day now. We ran through all of the lovely little country roads on both sides of the lake, in Tipperary and in Clare. We already knew we lived in a lovely place but now we got to see that beauty close up. We saw the landscape all around us inch by inch, stride by stride, day by day. When you run you begin to see roads you have driven for years like you have never seen them before. You see everything in minute detail. You develop a complete log of every tree, every house, every vista, every hedgerow. You can monitor how your route changes, from morning to evening, from season to season. Runners become like countryside archivists.

One night I was out running on my own at dusk. I was running up a hill, overlooking Lough Derg when a badger shot out in front of me. He ran ahead of me for about fifty metres and then disappeared again. I'm not sure which of us was the more startled. I had grown up in the countryside but this was my first time to see a live badger in such close quarters. I wouldn't have seen him had I not been running. He was a graceful, gentle creature and the only sound in the cold night air was the clipping of his nails on the tarred road. Runners and nature have a very strong bond.

Eventually Ian and I were clocking up sufficient miles for a dramatic improvement in our performance. We were both at a reasonable standard for two men pushing into their late thirties. We made good running partners. On the days when I would be looking to cancel he would insist we ran. I would do the same for him. He was my new Mike McGuinness and I was his.

We were established runners now. From our tentative beginning we had now progressed to comfortably completing ten and twelve mile runs. We were ready to start getting our target in our sights, Ian Connolly's first ever marathon. It was 1999. I had not run the Dublin marathon since 1984. Now the last one of the millennium was approaching. It was too good to pass up. This wasn't just any old marathon but the last marathon of 1,000 years. It was our own national marathon, in our own capital city. It was going to be a story to tell our grandchildren. "Your grandad ran the last Dublin marathon of the last millennium". The decision was made. We were setting out for Dublin '99.

If my contribution to our new running alliance was experience, Ian's was preparation.

Up to now I had always just run. No stretching, no warm up, I just left the house and ran. I had always prided myself on the fact the running is one of the earliest activities this planet has known. Man has run from day one, either after a boar or away from a bear. If he had to stretch first the bear would have eaten him. It has remained one of simplest and cheapest things you can do since then and, to me, had changed little in 5,000 years.

But now that I had returned to running at the age of 37 everything seemed to have become much more complicated. Running magazines were telling me to check if my feet pronated or supinated. This would then determine which running shoes I could wear. You couldn't seem to run a mile without having a rucksack full of isotonic drinks, gels and high performance snack bars on your back. The most bizarre change of all was that the majority of runners now hardly seemed to know what a road was. Running could only take place on a treadmill machine in a deluxe gym, whilst you watched MTV videos. And all you had to do was to pay a membership of €360 a year for the privilege.

This was all new to me. I was determined that nobody was going to hijack my running on me. I refused to be blinded by the commercialisation of something I regarded as completely natural. Running is just itself. I didn't need high street fashion accessories or an expensive gym. I'm with the cave man on this one. Give me a dusky country road with only a badger for company any day!

But Ian's input was not commercial. There were no gadgets. He just educated me to the fact that at my age, if I was asking my body to run, I needed to start looking after it a bit more than I had been. He had me stretching and warming up before we ran and cooling down afterwards. I might have got away without it up to this but now it was time to change. We made a good team. I brought the encouragement to keep him going. He brought the technique to keep me going.

We had two favourite routes. On the Ballina side the Tountinna loop was a beautiful eight mile circuit. It began with a testing climb of the foothills of the Arra mountains but for this your efforts were rewarded with breathtaking views as you ran the rim of the valley beyond. It then saved the best till last with a magnificent panorama across Lough Derg on the homeward leg.

On the Killaloe side we loved the four mile "round" at Garraunboy. It again began with a stiff climb through the rolling County Clare countryside before turning you for home at the picturesque little church at Garraunboy. On the home run it laid both Killaloe and Ballina spectacularly in front of you as you ran down the hill to the finish. This view was magnificent by day and truly spectacular at night.

As the marathon drew near we needed to do a twenty mile training run. This was to make sure we knew we had the full distance in our legs. It would be the longest run we needed to do as our training neared its end. A marathon distance is 26 miles but the adrenalin of the day is reputed to be worth six miles to each runner. If you can run 20 miles in training it is considered you then have the marathon distance in your legs.

We couldn't find a suitable loop at this distance so we decided to run ten miles out the Scarriff road to McLysaghts nurseries, turn and just run back. The weather was warm. The old me would have just ran but now, thankfully, I had my "look after your thirty-something body" partner. Ian had a much greater awareness of hydration or, more precisely, dehydration. He insisted one of us drive the route initially to drop bottled water in three different locations on route. Any thoughts I had about this being excessive had completely evaporated, literally, after running three miles under the hot sun. I drank at each water station and ran all the way home with unexpected strength and vigour as a result. That day for the first time in all of my training, having stretched beforehand and taken drinks on route, I ran as if I was a professional athlete. That day I knew I was ready for the marathon. That day, most of all, I knew I had a great running partner.

If the McLysaght run was a pinnacle of our training schedule we completed our most memorable run a week later. We had set off on our normal Garraunboy run. Ian was in great form and as we approached Garraunboy church, ready to turn right he said "Come on. Let's keep going. Let's do a long one." Going straight on meant that the road kept going up. Going up to the point where we were just about to run over a small mountain. Impressed by his enthusiasm and feeling good myself I didn't hesitate. "Great stuff. Lets go".

This was new territory for both of us. Not only were we going to run to a higher altitude than we ever had previously, we were about to take on a route and a distance we didn't know. This impromptu decision was a testament to the level we had now reached. We were both strong runners now. The mental strength we would obtain from shifting out of our comfort zone into the great unknown would be immense.

One of my strengths as a runner has always been that I have a good engine. I will never be the fastest athlete in any race but I always seem to be able to find the resolve to keep going, no matter what. When the running gets tough I am able to drop down the gears and always find one that will keep me on the move. I will believe that I have the mentality to run all day if I need to.

When you stop running it is generally not your legs where the fault lies. The problem, more often than not, will be in your head. The brain will send the message to the legs to quit. All through my running I seemed to be able to make sure this message was never sent. The compromise was that my legs were allowed find the slowest speed they needed, but they could not stop running. I didn't know it at the time but this element of my running was to be my greatest asset as a recovering cancer patient. Through my running I had cultivated a sense of resolve that would pay huge dividends years later. It was exactly the kind of mentality I would need to rely on to survive and recover when my body was once again being pushed to its limits.

After we left Garraunboy church behind us we climbed and climbed. We eventually reached the gentle curve at the top of the mountain. I remember how we both rejoiced when the angle of the road below our footfall started to fall away rather than come to meet us. The scenery was magnificent. We had unearthed incredible views over the flat plains of mid Clare that we had never seen before. It was like an endless patchwork quilt of green fields with a sprinkling of small lakes tossed across it. This view had been waiting for us. It was there as a personal reward for our efforts to get that far.

I have always had sympathy for runners who have to run on dull routes. Inspirational vistas can transform running from a chore into a pleasure. They can become your third lung. That was the great advantage of running where I now lived.

Our decent down the other side ended in the little village of Kilbane. Some parts of east

Clare are like the land that time forgot. Kilbane is in that category. It has all the appearances of a place that hasn't seen a visitor since the nineteen twenties. The only business premises we could see was a single pub. There were no signs on it. It was almost as if it was a public house on a need to know basis only. Only the locals needed to know. As we ran down the hill we joked that we were probably the first outsiders Kilbane had seen in decades.

Three men were standing outside the unidentified pub as we turned the corner in the heart of the village. It was only then we realised how we must have looked. Not only were we two strange men. We were two strange men in shorts. Two strange crazy men in shorts who had obviously just run over a mountain. We took turns checking behind us as we left the village to make sure none of them made a move for a shotgun.

We grafted all the way home after that. We ran through Bridgetown and back into Killaloe. It was a twenty two mile circuit in all. The mountain probably added the equivalent of another two. Now we knew that the mental toughness required for a marathon was in both of us. We were ready.

The night before the marathon we stayed with Ian's parents in Dalkey. Dalkey is a delightful little seaside village that has become one of the most desirable addresses in Dublin. This is nicely balanced however by the longer established indigenous population who originate from its time as a fishing village. Ian parents both come from this stock and live in a little, frequently extended, cottage right in the heart of the village. We were starting to get nervous now. It was the eve of the day that had monopolised our aspirations for the previous three months.

As a distraction we tried to act as if we had just come up for a normal weekend. We went to the pub and did everything we normally would apart from drinking alcohol. A lot of Ian's old friends were there and chatting to them helped to while away the hours before it was time to sleep. By eleven o'clock we were in our beds and it was lights out time. We had calculated this would allocate just the right amount of sleep before the 9 a.m. start time. We hadn't however, factored in our ability to fall asleep. This is a common "eve of marathon" frustration for many amateur runners. The excitement of what we were about to do was now beginning to overwhelm us. It was just us and the darkness now. We were only waiting for tomorrow to arrive. There were no distractions anymore.

Try as we might, sleep would not come. We both lay motionless in our beds for hours, afraid to speak to each other in case it encouraged conversation. We were desperate for sleep to unplug our overactive brains. The longer we stayed awake the more worried we became about our performance. The more we worried the less sleep we were going to get. All our training, all our preparations, but how can you run a marathon if you haven't slept in 24 hours. In the end we both drifted off at about 4 a.m.

Your first marathon is the best. You can never be completely sure about your ability to finish the course, no matter what level you are at. If you are in good shape you may push yourself too fast. If you are not in good shape, you can add another dozen things that could go wrong. You have heard about "The wall" but you don't really know what it is. If you don't know what it is how will you know when you hit it. Your mind starts to race before you do. As you approach the start line your fears of the unknown only grow and grow.

I was delighted for Ian that day. I could remember my first marathon. It will always be the one you will definitely never forget. You will never mix it up with any other. When you finish you have an amazing sense of achievement. Relatively few other people will do what you have just done. You have climbed your own Mount Everest. You have come as close as you can to winning an Olympic medal without being an athlete. You now have a medal or a plaque that you will always treasure. You have a day that can not be taken from you for the rest of your life.

As this was my fourth marathon my sensations didn't hit the same heights of uniqueness. My goal was to try and run a good time. My best ever time for a marathon is still my first. Three hours and twenty two minutes. My second and third runs were considerably slower. My optimistic target was to try and break three and a half hours again. I did it, just. Three hours, twenty nine minutes. I was delighted. Fifteen years older but only seven minutes slower!

Once we had the last marathon of the millennium under our belts, the next mission was obvious. We had to run the first one of the new millennium. This we did and in between we also ran the Belfast marathon in 2000. In twelve months we had run three marathons. A good return from a drunken promise in Richardson's pub that neither of us really believed would lead to anything. Ian Connolly turned out to be a lot more than a good running partner. He is a great man and a wonderful friend.

29 – A Child Needs his Dad

Our third boy, Abe, arrived in 2000. We are all big Munster rugby fans in our house but Abe delights in reminding us that he is the only truly authentic one. He was born in the regional maternity hospital in Limerick. He is therefore the only member of the family to be born in the great province. I love my three boys dearly and equally but I was able to use Abe's arrival as a major weapon to fight with eighteen months later when I got sick. Abe was just one when my cancer came. If it was to take me then I would have been denied the opportunity to hear him speak and to get to know his personality. I turned this desire into a need, into a determination. I used it to fuel my fight when my own resolve might be running low. It wasn't just my campaign now, it was Abe's too. He would like to get to know the man who was his dad. He needed to be able to depend on him to take him to the playground, or the crèche or wherever he needed to go. He was one year old and he needed his dad.

At the lowest ebbs of my fight, which thankfully were rare, I would struggle to find resolve. These would be the worst moments at times of sheer exhaustion, intense pain, unexpected setbacks or a temporary abandonment of hope. My tank would be running on empty. But now Abe gave me a fuel injection. I would bully myself with the responsibility that all of this wasn't just about me. It was about him too. He needed me so now he needs me to keep fighting. I could stop for myself but I can't stop for him. Just as Ian Connolly appeared at my door to keep me running, it was as if Abe arrived into this world to keep me fighting. My mindset was now turning everything it possibly could into an ally. If my guard was low it was ensuring that an orderly queue of responsibility formed immediately to make me raise it again. It was always going to be a step ahead now. It would always find a new angle to make sure the fight never stopped.

Of course all of this resolve applied just as equally to Christy and Lowell, but with Abe being only one, it was easier to concentrate my focus on the youngest boy. Just like a running partner, if you spread the burden of your cancer responsibility to those around you it is more difficult to give up.

Abe and I appeared to have a lot in common right from the start. We were both born in November. He was the first Ryan boy in the family to be born in Ireland since me and by the end of 2002 we would both have been in hospital with life threatening bacterial meningitis. Our paths appeared to have been laid out to cross in several locations from the very beginning. I used this to my advantage. I took it as a sign that we were both destined to fight through this period of our lives together. One was not to let the other down.

In the end we both did come through. Abe then became the living yardstick of my second life. I have survived as long as he has been alive. I hugely appreciated the ability to be able to watch him grow up. I enjoyed every second of getting to know him. Selecting a wish list of things you would like to achieve before a premature death is not a pleasant task, but the chance to get to know all three of my children would always have been top of mine.

Abe has now grown up to become a great little character. Our friendship has blossomed and increased with every year that has passed. Every marker of his young life, every tooth, every achievement, every sports medal is an equally significant landmark to the second life of his dad.

Aged 5, on the old Railway Line in Horseleap.

The old Railway Station.

Hugh De Lacy's drawbridge.

Paddy Ryan's pub and the Ferrari Horse.

One of our last family photos at Carol and Rory's Wedding in 1981.

Cistercian College, Roscrea.

Linda Martin and Chips, 1977.

Tom 'Mussels' Nally in Paddy Ryan's, with Pat Grennan behind the counter.

The Royal Liver Building, Liverpool

In York with Brendan Kilpatrick and Peter Morgan.

The 'condom heads' in Paris.

The Albert Dock.

At work in Franklin Stafford.

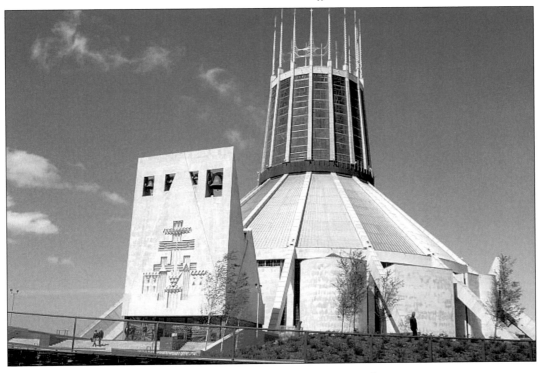

The Metropolitan Cathedral, Liverpool.

Our Wedding Day
July 1989.

The market at
Chichicastenango,
Guatemala.

30 – Family Holidays

After the three boys arrived any travelling Pam and I would do was always going to be completely different to any we had done before. Just as I discovered whole new sections of department stores after Christy was born, we now seemed to be going on entirely different holidays to countries we had already visited. Out went backpacking, youth hostels and Guatemalan buses and in came theme parks, fast food restaurants and hire cars with booster seats. When you have children you might as well just hand the holiday brochures over to them. They will ultimately decide where you go. We had great family holidays in these years in Menorca and Turkey and later returned to America to do California again. This time from a child's perspective.

I loved Menorca. I have always liked islands. They all have their own unique appeal, no matter which part of the world they are in. Menorca had something to suit everybody. It was an ideal location for a family group with a forty four year age difference between the oldest and youngest. It was also a perfect size. It was big enough and small enough. Whenever I hire a car on holiday I unfortunately feel the need to drive it for twenty four hours a day. There are no limitations to where a car can go. This means there are no limitations on where I think I can reach with it. If I was in Italy for instance I would consider the possibility of making a quick dash to see Prague, Paris or Athens. A hired car is asking to be driven and can tempt you into unrealistic ambitions. An island however throws a natural restriction around such lunacy. A surrounding zone where the car can't go - the sea!

Menorca is about the size of one of the smaller Irish counties. No corner of it was beyond the scope of visiting any beach we chose in the morning or any restaurant we chose in the evening. At the end of our two weeks, everyone was happy. I was satisfied I had seen every available square inch of the island. The others were delighted that they hadn't spent 23 hours in the back of a car every day.

It also had the perfect spread of attractions to suit all of us. Scattered randomly amongst the warm and friendly native population we found quiet beaches, fun packed theme parks, romantic restaurants, lively promenades and quaint fishing villages. Pam, Christy and Lowell would invariably go straight to the beach first thing. I have always been a reluctant beach bum and Abe was too young to be subjected to the hot sun so before long we would stroll away, leaving the other three to their sun, sand and sea worship.

Our favourite destination was the lovely old streets of Ciutadella. Traditional Spanish cafes and little toy and souvenir shops would be our main ports of call. Ciutadella is a beautiful little city. It has an enchanting mix of beautiful old buildings that are huddled together to form a maze of narrow, shaded, vibrant streets. Each one was alive with the relaxed and friendly local population that both lived and worked in them. This combination of scale, history and activity ensured Ciutadella captured you in a manner I found few places can. It had an intimacy that bigger cities often lack but without any loss of the buzz and excitement. It also had a laid back characteristic that sometimes only islands can have. In a busy holiday resort, it was simply a delight. As Abe and I strolled through its pretty, narrow little streets we were both glad to be there. If I was ever asked to choose somewhere to walk around for the rest of my life, I would pick Ciutadella.

The best part of a holiday for me is always the people you meet. The sights and facilities are great but generally the stories you will tell, years later, will be about your human interactions. The funny little man you met in a bar, the nice policeman who didn't give you a speeding ticket, the all night sing song on your last night. I now have a tremendous appreciation for all of these trips. I had lived long enough to be able to holiday with my family. In each one we met lovely people. They all played a major role in making these trips great occasions that we were delighted to experience as a family.

We met great people in Menorca. My favourite part of the day was meeting up in the evening with our newly found Irish friends Tony and Marie McManus from Roscommon and Paul and Carmel Norton from Tullamore. I began to look forward to us all having a drink together to exchange stories of how we had all spent the day. Our collective group of children would all be doing the same as they played nearby.

In Turkey a few years later the memorable people we met were not fellow tourists, but the staff themselves. Pam and I had been to Turkey previously when we toured the interior to see the wonderful natural sites at Cappadocia and Pamukkale. That was a great holiday in itself and Turkey didn't disappoint when we returned again as a family. We stayed in a lovely little resort in Bitez, near Bodrum.

Countries like Turkey can often be accused of lacking the luxurious facilities of some of their more illustrious Mediterranean neighbours. That, in many ways, just makes them appeal to me even more. The best people are often found in the less sophisticated places. Whatever Turkey may have lacked in modernity it more than made up for by the warmth of the reception it gave us. All of the staff at Mandarin Gardens were wonderful. We became good friends with just about all of them within days of our arrival.

On these trips Pam and I acknowledged that the days of travelling for ourselves were now gone. I soon realised however that watching Christy shoot down a waterslide, Lowell play on the beach or Abe make us laugh as he helped the waiter was just as rewarding as climbing a mountain in Guatemala or drinking with the locals in Helsinki.

When we left Mandarin Gardens, two weeks later, we were all in tears. The staff were crying, we were crying, all of the other guests were crying too. It had been a fantastic holiday. I felt sorry for the people who worked there. I knew they would befriend our replacements just as much as they had us. And in two weeks time their crying would start all over again.

31 – New Stadium for Athlone Town

I was to undertake one final architectural project before cancer arrived. It was fitting therefore that the last piece of work of my first life was a significant one. It was to be a project that would span the life I had lived up to then. It was a development that would bring together my family history, my architectural training and my love of soccer, all in one fell swoop. If I was allowed to select a final design opportunity before my cancer fight was to begin, I could not have chosen better.

From the time I had been taken to my first game, as a very small boy, Athlone Town had played in their dilapidated, but likeable, old ground at St. Mels Park. Not a single major improvement had taken place in over thirty years. St. Mels merely consisted of a tiny stand that seated about 80 people on wooden planks and loose gravel terraces on the other three sides. Only one of these terraces was covered.

All through the nineties modern new stadia, of all shapes and sizes, were beginning to spring up all over Europe. Football clubs, both big and small, were bringing their facilities up to date for the first time in years. Many of these new developments attracted affectionate nicknames such as the Stadium of Light or the Stadium of Dreams. The faithful followers of Athlone Town, envious of their illustrious counterparts elsewhere, were not to be outdone. Although excluded from the redevelopment trend, they still came up with their own nickname. St. Mels Park became known affectionately as the Stadium of Tin. This was a tribute to the rickety lines of galvanised sheeting that enclosed the ground on all four sides.

In the early years these surroundings were regarded as characterful and nostalgic. They just added a sense of charm to being a fan of the "Town". But now it was 2001. The rest of the world had moved on, exposing the facilities in Athlone as outmoded and substandard. St. Mels Park was easily the worst ground in the league of Ireland by then and a long way behind the second worst. The romantic days when it had hosted some of the finest teams in Europe such as A.C. Milan and Standard Liege were now long gone. Those clubs would not even send their under twelve team to a ground like this now. Athlone Town football club knew they had to modernise or go out of business. But money was tight. Ideally they were looking for somebody who was both a dedicated fan and an architect.

In February 2001 Tom McEnroe approached me to design a new stadium for the club. The site was being provided by the local town council, in a new recreational area that had been zoned specifically for sporting facilities. I was delighted to be asked. I felt honoured to be given the opportunity. This was all my chickens coming home to roost. It was as if the team that I loved and had supported all my life waited for me to go away and become an architect. Only then would they look for somebody to design their new stadium. I immediately thought of my dad. How proud he would now be. Who could have known that his involvement with the club would have led to this. That the little boy he had taken to those first matches would grow up to continue what he had been part of from the very beginning.

A development of this nature would normally be too big for a small residential practice like ours. As luck would have it however, my final thesis in college had been the design for a new racecourse at Bangor on Dee in North Wales. I therefore had a very good knowledge of stadia design and spectator requirements at sporting venues. The Athlone stadium was also to be very modest. On completion it would only require to seat a maximum of 7,000 spectators. I knew I had the capabilities to take it on. My heart would not let my head decide anything else.

I met with the officials of the club and the brief was established. The main stand would run the length of one side of the pitch. This would incorporate a function room that overlooked the pitch, two bars and a fitness centre. The changing rooms and club offices would be located below, at ground level. The viewing areas to the rest of the pitch would then be completed with a stand of similar profile but smaller, on each of the remaining three sides. These three lesser stands were only to be fifteen seats deep.

Only the main stand has been completed to date and due to financial restraints, it has been significantly reduced from the original design. The function room, fitness centre and hospitality areas have been omitted but the facilities are new, comfortable and cosy in a way that St. Mels Park never was.

I was to get sick shortly after the planning permission was granted. The story then took a nice twist when my old practice in Athlone, Heaveys, was appointed to run the job during the construction phase. The official opening ceremony was on March 6th 2007. The very first match took place a week later against Kilkenny City.

Unfortunately the new surroundings have resulted in little improvement on the pitch. Athlone Town, for the last ten years, have been one of the weakest teams in the league of Ireland. Every season we start off with renewed hope. This will be the year when everything will change. But then, not long after the first ball is kicked, that pre season optimism is already dead. The heady days of A.C. Milan in the seventies and two league titles in the eighties are now long gone. Still, I wouldn't have it any other way. This is my team. I will wait, no matter how long it takes. Wait in hope that one day our luck will change. In a strange way, that wait is part of the appeal of following a team like this. The longer the wait the greater the celebration will be when success finally comes.

The three boys and myself attend matches now as part of a small loyal band of supporters. I have abandoned hope of success season by season. Now I do it lifetime by lifetime. I would love to see Athlone Town win the cup before I die. Other teams expect to win it every year. Maybe this is another part of my jigsaw. Maybe God whispered to me that I must keep fighting for my life until Athlone Town win the cup. If so it looks as if he has plans to keep me around for a good few years to come.

Part of the fund raising initiative for the new stadium was to sell nameplates for the seats in the stand. The sponsor could dedicate the seat to any person they chose. Paddy Ryan is there, the three girls and myself saw to that. I'm sure he fills that seat on many occasions, overseeing the progression the club has made since he first became involved when they joined the league in 1969. His name is accompanied in the stand by Christy and Lowell who have seats beside him. Abe Patrick Ryan can take his grandfathers seat, who he has been named after.

Who knows, maybe those seats are just the start of another chapter in the Ryan / Athlone Town connection. Perhaps there is another generational twist still to come. Maybe one day one of these of three boys will pick up where their Dad left off. One of them will become an architect and be asked to design the new 50,000 seat stadium that will be required after Athlone Town win the Champions League. There are no limits to my optimism now.

32 – Mid Life Crisis

The last major social occasion of my first life, before cancer struck, was my fortieth birthday party. With all of our group being around the same age, fortieth parties were now all the rage. The usual format was either yet another great house party or a surprise party in one of the pubs. They had now been taking place over a twelve month period so we were all on a kind of fortieth birthday party conveyor belt. It brought a subtle change to the same party in a different house scenario. It was still the same great party but this time a different person was forty.

As mine approached I began to see it as a last great opportunity for one final big bash. A chance to bid farewell to my youth. I saw 40 as my last big birthday as a "young" man. At 50 it would be time for the chamber orchestra and at 60 all I would be able for would be a string quartet. It therefore had to be a rock band at 40. I floated this notion a few months before my birthday. I wanted to have a rock gig. The suggestion became the key that unlocked a number of frustrated ex-musicians we had in our midst. Friends, with a hidden musical past, who for years had been masquerading as normal people.

Unknownst to me a meeting was called. A series of rehearsals followed and soon a new band was evolving. Charlie McGeever, a professional photographer by day, transformed into a red hot lead guitarist by night. It is rumoured that he once played for Free, but whether this was for the classic rock band of "Alright now" fame or simply without payment, we could never establish. Geno was the lead vocalist and Ian Connolly had always been an excellent drummer. A variety of borrowed bass players were then called upon. Backing singers were needed and quickly found. Pam, Delia O'Leary and Catriona Devereux all passed their auditions and were drafted in. They not only gave the entire ensemble a better vocal range but also a bit of middle-aged sex appeal! Now the band needed a name. Given the way it had all come together and the average age of each band member, the perfect name was eventually found. The band would be called Mid Life Crisis.

So now that I had a band, I needed a venue. You can't put a rock band in a hotel so the obvious choices, our two local hotels, were out. It had to be one of the pubs. At that time however we didn't have a pub in either Ballina or Killaloe that was big enough to take a band and a hoard of middle aged, once a year, rockers.

But I had come too far to fail now. If we didn't have a pub to suit in the town we would just have to look beyond to find the nearest one that did. This was ideal because I also wanted to go somewhere new. All of the parties to date had been in the local pubs. I was hoping to break new ground. As soon as I broadened the horizons of my search the obvious solution became apparent. On the main Dublin road, about three miles from Ballina, but very importantly, "still in the parish", is a pub called the Round Hill. It could cater perfectly for what we were looking for.

The Round Hill is a typical Irish country pub. It has a traditional bar to the front and a big lounge to the rear. The lounge was largely only used at weekends when it attracted large crowds for music and dancing. So when I checked the wish list, it was local, had plenty of room, cosy little bar, atmospheric dancing lounge, somewhere we all hadn't been to before - perfect!

The Round Hill it was!

The headline on the invitation poster was borrowed from Neil Young's classic line. "Better to burn out than fade away" A fine young local band, Chapter 45, would provide the main entertainment, with Mid Life Crisis coming on stage for an hour in the middle. It would be sing-along rock classics all night long.

The only remaining issue now was transport. Everybody would be having a drink so it was unfair to expect the guests to drive three miles out of town. The final missing piece was to hire a couple of mini buses.

The completed invitation was to meet at Liam O'Riains and a bus would depart from there to the Round Hill. Every angle had now been covered. We would meet in our local pub as normal and then bus out to the venue pub. It would be stocked up with plenty of food and drink and the best rock musicians this side of Cappamore! The completed event had grown from a party to a miniature music festival, complete with arrival by mini bus and two hard rocking bands.

It was a great night. Again if I was allowed pick a final celebration before cancer came calling I couldn't have picked any better. Just about everybody that I had in my life was around me that night. We all enjoyed a great time knocking twenty years off our lives. In the middle of their set Mid Life Crisis invited me up on stage to sing the only song I know, Honky Tonk Woman. As I looked out over the dance floor it was like somebody had presented me with a human kaleidoscope of how fortunate I had been for forty years. All these great people were here on my account. With the exception of Liverpool, every stage of my life had representatives present.

I knew that night I was a lucky man. I was lucky to have all those people both in my life and in that room. They were my people.

The entire room was a pulsating mix of happy people dancing to rip roaring music. The last minibus pulled away just before dawn. I was forty years of age and my life could not have been any better. Little did I know what was waiting for me just around the corner.

33 – The Ordeal Begins

And so it all began. The events that have led to this book now being in your hands began in April 2002. My transformation from first life to second, had begun. It all started with headaches. Sporadic headaches. Unusual headaches in hindsight but that is easy to say now. They were not depilating like a migraine. They came and went quite quickly and the pain zone was a little lower than my forehead. They seemed to concentrate on a line that ran across the bridge of my nose. However they were bearable and I was busy. For the first week I was a typical man, I did nothing. Women are just so much better than men when it comes to health issues. For all their wonderful attributes I now know they have one more. Women are also here to prompt us men to look after our health when alarm bells start ringing. As soon as I complained about the headaches more than once Pam was constantly on my case. Go and see a doctor see told me, her tone getting more assertive each time. In the end I relented but only after she had already booked an appointment for me in our local surgery.

In all my time in Ballina I have been a very rare visitor to the surgery. My own doctor Maureen Ryan was not available so I was booked in to see Blathnaid McCurtain. Blathnaid is a lovely person and a wonderful caring doctor. I suspect that from the very start she always had concerns that my complaint might not turn out to be what it appeared. But at that stage nobody could know for sure. She examined me thoroughly and all the signs pointed to a sinus complaint of some kind. She put me on a course of antibiotics that would hopefully eradicate whatever infection I had. She made sure however to re-book me to return by the end of the week to see if my condition had improved.

I left the surgery and effectively thought that was that. I hardly ever take antibiotics and now, when I had to, they would surely tidy up this little irregularity for me.

At the end of the week I returned to Blathnaid. The headaches were still there. They still were not powerful enough to stop me functioning but the antibiotics had made no impact. The next possibility to be eliminated was that I had of some kind of abscess in the roof of my mouth. The next port of call therefore was to be the dentist in Nenagh. He X-rayed me, but concluded that I didn't have an infection in any of my oral cavities.

The sensible conclusion now was that I did have a sinus infection, but one that was too tough for the antibiotics to shift. Blathnaid immediately booked me in to the Regional Hospital in Limerick. I am sure that the longer this process of elimination was extending, the larger her fears were beginning to grow.

It was now mid May and I was admitted to the Regional for a sinus wash. This is a routine procedure where any infection in your sinus is simply flushed out under a general anaesthetic. As soon as I had cleared admissions I was shown to a two bed room in ward 2C.

Ward 2C in the Mid Western Regional Hospital in Limerick is designated for ear, nose and throat cases. It is run by one of the most amazing women I have ever met. I was just about to uncover the first of the many incredible people I would meet on my journey through illness. Ironically I would not have had the opportunity to meet any of them had I not got sick.

As soon as you meet Carmel O'Sullivan, the ward sister on 2C, you immediately know you are in the presence of somebody very special. Her incredible charisma fills the entire ward and the evidence of her amazing influence is apparent everywhere. All of the nurses working under her leadership were a joy to behold, each one reflecting the immense warmth of Carmel's personality. This confirmed that she cared for them just as much as she did for her patients. The ward itself was also a landmark to her thoughtful, personal touch. She made sure it was constantly decorated with flowers, pictures, banners and flags, marking a variety of occasions throughout the year. This ensured it was always homely and inspiring rather than sterile and anonymous. It was like a beacon of distraction and delight in the sea of uniformity that I found all other hospital wards to be.

Carmel emanated a powerful sense of reassurance with her wondrous mix of warm, faultless authority and her sincere, caring, devotion. This was her ward and these were her patients. We became great friends instantly. She doesn't like me saying it but she is the closest person I have ever met to being a living saint.

So here I was, sitting up in my bed without a care in the world. I was having friendly conversations not just with Carmel and her staff, but also with all of the patients around me too. I had brought in a large pile of newspapers and magazines that I didn't get a chance to read in the previous weeks. Now I had two nights of undisturbed catching up to do. I was here for a routine procedure but that was almost an insignificant detail of my two-day visit. I was here primarily for refreshment. I was almost at the point of beginning to enjoy my stay. This was just one notch removed from a two night break in a hotel. I had three days in front of me with nothing expected apart from rest and relaxation. All of that seemed to be just fine to me.

I was introduced to my consultant later that evening and the scenario, if anything, only improved. His name was John Fenton. He was about my own age and had a similar personality and sense of humour to my own. We got on very well from the start. As we chatted it transpired that John had spent three years in Liverpool. This only further enhanced the newly formed friendship that was evolving between us. We both began to swop reminiscences of our times on Merseyside and compare the experiences, sights, pubs and restaurants that we had in common.

When he did get around to discussing my condition he explained to me that the procedure he was going to perform was very straightforward. I had nothing to worry about. It was a very simple operation. He had undertaken it many times before. He reassured me that by the time I would come around I would have very little pain, if any. I could simply then rest for my second night and go home the following day.

Pam had also been in to see me by now. My locker, as a result, was loaded with as many treats as it could hold. This appeared to be the final confirmation that my sojourn, although under the guise of a medical requirement, was actually more for recreational purposes. This was to be two days of forced relaxation. I was away from work, off the phone and had enough fruit and chocolate to last me a month. For the next two days I was completely removed from the hurly burly of my normal daily life.

The trolley arrived for me the next morning and off I went to theatre. I doubt if there was a more carefree patient in the hospital. The operating theatres in the Regional are housed in a new wing of the hospital so the impressive modern surroundings only further enhanced my perception that this operation was a mere formality. John Fenton, barely recognisable now that he was gowned up, came out to greet me. We chatted nonchalantly for a few minutes just before I was pushed through the swinging doors into the theatre itself. He again reassured me that all would be fine. It would just be a simple fifteen minute procedure to wash out the infection in my sinus and that would be that.

After the operation I was returned to the ward. I assume I slept for a further hour or so. Pam came in to see me that evening. On the assumption that my minor ailment had now been resolved all we discussed was what time I was likely to be discharged the following day. We decided that we might as well take advantage of being in Limerick and go out for dinner. She told me she would bring the three boys with her and we could all go for a family meal. All I had to do now was wait for John Fenton in the morning to tell me what time that would be.

34 – This is Serious

I was just down to my final newspaper the following morning when I saw John Fenton on his rounds. I was dressed, sitting on the bed and ready to go. As he approached my room I could see Carmel was beside him. The only remaining issue now was the time of my discharge. I sat upright on the bed with a big smile on my face ready to greet them as they reached my door. Then it was suddenly as if everything began to happen in slow motion. I will never forget those next few moments for as long as I live. For the smiling face I was projecting out to them I was only receiving blank expressions in return. How can this be I thought. I was very friendly with all of these people yesterday. Now they are acting as if they don't know me. All of my senses began to enter a state of bewilderment. They kept coming towards me and it was only then that I could see the entourage of about six house and student doctors trailing behind them. They didn't stop until they got to my bed and without saying a word drew the curtain around me. In a hospital of over two thousand people if was as if, all of a sudden, I was now all alone. John Fenton then leaned down to me, looked me straight in the face and said "Liam, this is very serious." The statement was made with such sombre clarity that nothing else really needed to be said.

It was the news that everybody dreads to hear. I'm sure that if you ask cancer sufferers most will agree that the worst day of all is the very first time you get the news. You have no knowledge of, or preparation for, the world you have just entered into. You literally go from 60 to 0 in seconds. It is cancer with the biggest possible "C". It is cancer and YOU. At that very moment in time it is almost impossible for any cancer patient to see beyond the worst case scenario. You are quite simply, just going to die.

A year or two later I met somebody whose wife was one of the theatre staff from the day before. He was able to enlighten me on the details of my sinus wash from the other side of the anaesthetic. One of the nicest things about surviving cancer is that it gives you an opportunity, often years later, to uncover many of the finer details of your case that you will have missed out on first time around. There were about eight people in the operating theatre that day. The mood in the room was upbeat, just like my own. There was no reason to expect anything other than a very straightforward procedure. When John Fenton initially flushed out my sinus, nothing came out. This is generally a good sign. It usually means that no infection is there at all. The theatre staff were now beginning to think that this minor operation was going even better than planned. John Fenton however knew differently. From my condition he knew that something had to be in there. This was the first sign to him that he was dealing with something more serious than just an infection.

He went back in to my sinus compartment with a syringe and proceeded to extract what he later described to me as a "cheese like" substance. None of the theatre staff had ever seen anything like this before. The entire room was filled with shock and disbelief. They had all assembled to flush out a common infection, a procedure they had all undertaken many times, but now from their reaction to the material being deposited in the discharge bowl, it was as if an alien was being extracted from the middle of my head.

When John Fenton broke the news to me he desisted from using the words "cancer" or "tumour". He could not be 100% sure of the diagnosis until he sent me for a scan the following morning. His visible concern and his body language however could not conceal the fact that he was 99.999999% sure of the predicament I was now in. He also knew that I now knew it too. The only miracle available for the remaining 0.000001% was that my body had invented some new "cheese-like" infection, not previously known to the medical world.

For that single day alone, I was simply in pieces. I cried every time I was alone. Once I knew what I had I was better equipped to take tougher news than this down the line, but for that day I had nothing. Bigger bombshells would later be dropped regarding my survival chances but they would only knock me sideways. This one just blew me to bits. I could not see anything beyond the fact that I was now just going to die.

The first place I was sent was down to the eye department. They wanted to know if my newly discovered facial intruder had caused any damage to my eye movement and sight. One of the nurses brought me down in the lift. I distinctly remember, once I had escaped the busy, crowded ward, just crouching down towards the floor. I began to sob uncontrollably. How could this be happening to me. I was thinking of Pam and my three young boys. They were all entitled to have a provider and father around for a lot longer than this. Something was just not right. Who would earn the money that was going to be needed to run the family. Who was going to take my three sons to football matches. Who would teach them to ride bicycles or climb trees. It was almost as if some mistake must have been made.

But I knew there hadn't. This was all happening for real. There was only one image now. My mind had nothing to fight back with. It was now dominated by a single, sombre vision. All I could see was a young widow and three very small boys in the front seat of Ballina church at a funeral.

I am proud to say that those are the only hours of my entire campaign when I went backwards. That was the only time when I could not accept that I had cancer. I was asking that immortal question that is almost the prerequisite of cancer sufferers. The question that assumes the patient is bigger than the disease. The question that needs to be banished as soon it arises. If it is not, it will begin to devour your fight to survive just like the cancer itself. As the lift was descending down to the eye department I was asking "why me?"

The CT scan the next morning confirmed that I had an enormous tumour in the middle of my head. Pam came in and we both went to see John Fenton in his office. My condition was diagnosed as squamacell carcinoma. This is a broad description for a range of head and neck cancers including many skin cancers. My personal version however was exceptional. Only about two cases of my type of tumour are found in Ireland every year with cases as advanced as mine, almost unheard of.

John waited until he had the scan in his hand to confirm the seriousness of my condition.

He was now able to physically show me the extremely aggressive tumour that I had in the middle of my head. It ran from my sinus pocket, around my eye and was backed right up against my brain stem. It now had total occupation of all of the soft pocket in the middle of my head. Having overcome the easy material it was now attacking my cheek bones to complete its domination.

My knowledge of cancer was so limited at this point that I didn't even know that tumours were graded. When John told me mine was classed as a stage 4 tumour, I had to ask him what this meant. He told me the numbers don't go any higher than 4. Mine was the most advanced possible. One of the consultants in Liverpool later put the severity of my tumour in a better context for me. He told me that rather than stage 4, mine would have been more accurately classed as stage 44.

At this point it looked as if there was little that could be done. John Fenton was an E.N.T consultant rather than an oncologist but he had seen plenty of cancer tumours in his time. From what he had seen of mine he felt that I was beyond treatment. It was now just day two of my ordeal and he knew that what he now had to say to me was devastating for any cancer patient to hear. He also knew I was now strong enough to be able to hear it and that I didn't want to hear anything other than his honest, truthful assessment. In his office that morning John Fenton told me that I was the second worse case he had ever seen and the worst case was dead in a month. He had nothing else to compare me to. He was effectively telling me that he did not expect me to live much longer than a month.

There is a lovely little post script to this encounter. I now meet John Fenton about once a year. We have remained good friends. When we meet I now say to him "Well John when the third patient comes along you can tell them that you now have two patients who went before them. The worst case was dead in a month but the second worse went on to become Taoiseach seven years later!" He laughs but importantly tells me that the essence of my wisecrack is true. When that patient does come along he now has a wonderful success story to dangle in front of them and that is me.

My great association and friendship with John Fenton was crucial to my direction from this point. I was lost with nowhere to go. He was the only connection I had between me and my newly discovered disease. He was the only link I had to whatever was next to come. I was very grateful therefore to have known him well enough by then to be able to say to him "John, as my friend, if this was you what would you do?" I was desperately hoping he would be able to tell me some chance existed somewhere. If such a chance existed we would then pull out every stop we could to take it. Perhaps there was a world renowned surgeon in Tokyo, Toronto or Timbuktu. I was a young man with a very young family and death was knocking at my door. Whatever money I had completely changed its value. If that chance existed, no matter where it was, nothing else now mattered. We also knew we had a great community around us. They would help fundraise in every way they could to ensure that any escape route I had could be availed of.

By a delightful coincidence, the time John Fenton had spent in Liverpool, which we were chatting about only two days earlier, had been in what he regarded to be the best head and neck cancer facility in Europe. From his experience there and knowing the calibre of the surgeons he had worked with, he felt Liverpool was the best place for me to go. It would have the required expertise to evaluate if I had any chance. The two hospitals he had trained in there, he told me, were on a par with the best treatment I could receive anywhere in the world. After all of the bad news I at last had my first lucky break. I didn't have to go to Tokyo or Toronto or Timbuktu. My first move was to go back to city I knew so well, Liverpool.

The key factor with my diagnosis was that if any treatment was to be found, I needed not just one but two very specialist procedures. I had to find one hospital to perform very complex and high risk surgery to remove the tumour in the first place. Then I would also need radical and extensive radiotherapy treatment in a second specialist hospital. This was going to be required to expunge any of the tumour that could not be removed surgically. I might have found one or other of these specialised treatments in some cities throughout the world. In Liverpool I would find them both.

John felt that was where I needed to go if I was to be in best possible hands to establish if any treatment was possible. If it was, it also had the two hospitals I needed for the work to be done. If John Fenton was in my shoes he would go to Liverpool. I had complete trust in him. If that was good enough for him, it was good enough for me.

As we left the hospital in Limerick I was buoyed by the fact that the very first tiny silver linings were beginning to appear on my very black cloud. Had I not been fortunate enough to have met John Fenton I would not have been signposted to Liverpool so quickly. Now, until Liverpool said no, there was still hope. My fight had now begun. It was time to focus on that little flame I had flickering rather than the endless darkness that surrounded it.

On the assumption that mainstream treatment would not be available Pam began to ransack the entire internet to see if any other possibilities existed. At that time the destruction of cancerous cells using photo dynamic therapy was beginning to emerge. It was being billed by some as the great white hope of cancer treatments of the future. When it emerged as the only alternative treatment that could potentially offer me a chance she exhaustedly investigated its progress to that point in time. She made contact with one of the main pioneers of this new treatment, Colin Hopper in London. He was investigating its potential for head and neck cancers and informed her that although some impressive results had been achieved, the establishment of P.D.T. as a recognised cure for the more life threatening cancers was still a long way off. The more disappointing news however was that the only reliable successes that had been achieved up to then were predominately on superficial cancers such as shallow or early-stage skin cancers. To our disappointment he confirmed to her that, as a treatment, it had not yet reached a stage where it could offer any hope to a tumour like mine.

By sheer coincidence a former Californian eye surgeon, William Porter, was also offering photo dynamic treatment to cancer patients at this time in Killaloe. He was promising amazing results as a cure for all types of cancer. I appeared to have little to lose, if his claims were to be believed. I have always been hesitant however, to be convinced by the pronouncements of many alternative medical practices. Besides we had already spoken to Colin Hopper and he had confirmed to us that it would not be appropriate for my case. I decided I would steadfastly remain focused on my signpost to Liverpool as my best possible hope of an unlikely escape. I would remain blindly committed to the possibility that I would get recognised treatment until that door was closed. I had total faith in John Fenton's

With Carol, Dolores and Eleanor.

Ballina and Killaloe.

The new Athlone Town Stadium.

On our way to Croke Park.

After the Belfast Marathon in 2000 with Ian Connolly.

Christy's First Communion, five days after I was told I had cancer.

Reading out my poem in Liam O'Riains.

Veronica Molloy, Una Kennedy, Roisin McGeever and Ted O'Connor laughing along as I read.

With Pam and Geno that night.

Hugging John Clifford before I slipped away.

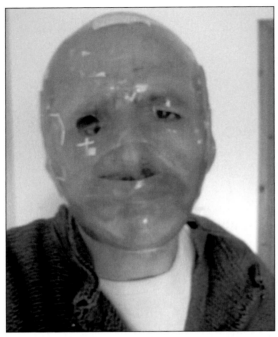

The man in the plastic mask.

With a fellow pirate in San Diego.

Family picture in 2006.

The Eco Village, Cloughjordan.

The face behind the eye-patch.

Keep on running

recommendation and I didn't want anything to distract me from that for now.

Keen to investigate all potential options, Pam made an appointment to see William Porter. Meanwhile stories were now beginning to emerge that these treatments were costing vast sums of money and that the results may not have been as successful as were being broadcast. She still felt that every possible option available to us should be examined so, on my behalf, she booked an appointment to meet him to investigate further.

On meeting her, Porter asked Pam to outline the details of my condition to him. He then spent the next ten minutes vigorously trying to convince her that we were pursuing the wrong option. He told her that if I lived I would regret my decision to seek treatment in Liverpool. If she could only persuade me to transfer to his clinic he guaranteed her he would cure my cancer. Pam, fully aware of what Colin Hopper had told her, began to probe. She was surprised when Porter told her he didn't need any details from my medical team.

After his offer to cure me, her reluctance to dash home and return with me immediately seemed to surprise him. His wife, Maggie, was then introduced to Pam. She was heralded as the living proof of the success of this miraculous treatment. She declared to Pam that yes, in her opinion, she had been cured from her cancer by William Porter's P.D.T. He again tried to pressure her to postpone our appointment in Liverpool and sign up now for treatment in his clinic. He would definitely cure me. She had been so lucky to have come to him just before we may have opted to go down the wrong path.

Pam then asked for documentary evidence of the successes Porter was claiming for his P.D.T. treatments. His assistant, Mr. Barton, then left the room and returned with a hand written note, declaring that the success rate was 95%.

Porter's next tactic was to concentrate on our three young boys. How will they feel when their dad is heavily disfigured from extensive surgery to his face. Won't they be ashamed, in front of their friends who will consider their father to be some kind of freak. With his proportedly non-invasive P.D.T. treatment there will be no surgery or scars. Not only will I be cured but I will look the same as I ever did. He kept using the word 'mutilation' with reference to the visual impact of the conventional treatment I was opting for. We needed to think of the children.

His final move was to try and secure a down payment in the hope that he had now convinced her that his treatment was the answer to our prayers. Each treatment would cost €7,000 and I would need two or three to be cured completely. Surely this was a very small price to pay to save my life. Places were however booking up very fast. There was a big demand for this treatment due to its amazing results. If she could now just provide him with a deposit he would be able to book me in. I would be guaranteed a place and he again repeated his promise to cure me.

Pam said very little during his hard sell. Then, armed with the information she had received from Colin Hopper she began to counter many of the claims he had made. She wanted to see the appropriate proof of the claims he was making and evidence of his authority to make those claims.

Visibly surprised by her knowledge of the subject William Porter suddenly became very uneasy. He made one final attempt to secure a deposit from her and book me in for treatment. When Pam refused, he suddenly got up and moved to leave the room. All of a sudden he was very busy and had other appointments waiting for him. He apologised for needing to end their meeting so abruptly and left the room immediately.

When she came home Pam filled me in on every detail of her encounter with William Porter. I was glad I had not gone. When somebody is diagnosed with cancer they are entering one of the most terrifying episodes of their lives. To think other people would try to exploit their state of sheer desperation is deplorable. It ranks, for me, as one of the cruelest acts one human being can do to another. If you are mugged on the street the crime is transparent. The mugger has no money and needs some for drugs, drink or food. It is an unpleasant and unacceptable experience for the victim but at least, as a crime, it is honest!

When you are given a major cancer diagnosis and standard treatment is not available to you, it is likely you will pay any amount of money to be cured. Vulnerable people will pay anything they have for a chance to be cured. You just need to convince them that you have that cure. Desperate people are easy to convince. They are looking to be convinced.

Deception of this kind is considerably worse than the offence of the street mugger. In this instance the mugger is disguised as a saviour.

I will cure your husband's cancer uninvasively, William Porter told Pam. His face will be perfect so his three boys will not be taunted by their friends. You should consider postponing his assment in Liverpool. Had I opted for his services my face may well have been perfect, but it probably would have been a perfect face on a cold, lifeless corpse. We would also have been about €30,000 poorer for the sake of that posthumous perfection.

The Porter scam eventually made the headlines and he fled the country. Pam went on national radio to tell our little bit of the story. Many people were left with the devastation that was caused by the promise of his false hope. They were burying loved ones that he had assured would live. As well as being swindled, many patients had the quality of life of their final months annihilated by the dreadful medications that were prescribed. The devastation reached into the very core of personal family bonds. Mothers and fathers, and sons and daughters watched their nearest and dearest die in distress, during what were to be the last precious months of their lives.

People who survive a cancer diagnosis, to me, are some of the greatest in the world. People who profit from it, by inference, are some of the cruellest.

35 – Going Back to Liverpool

Time was of the essence now. Within a week John Fenton had arranged a consultation for me with two oncologists at the Royal Liverpool hospital. Simon Rogers was the top maxio facial surgeon at the university hospital in Aintree and David Husband was the senior radiotherapy consultant at Clatterbridge on the Wirral. Scans of my tumour had already been sent over to them so both men had a good understanding of my case even before I entered the room. Simon admitted to me later that they both got a shock when they first saw me. Head and neck cancer is normally an older mans disease. Mine was so severe they were expecting a man who hadn't looked after himself too well. They already had a preconceived expectation that the man about to walk through the door would be 16 or 17 stone and in his late fifties. The last thing he would have done on entering the hospital would have been to extinguish a cigarette. He was also likely to be a heavy drinker.

I had made a good start. I had already begun to not live up to their expectations.

My entire life was now in the hands of these two men. If they deemed that they were in a position to offer me treatment, I had some chance. If they did not, I was going to die very soon.

Simon would have the initial role so he spoke first. He proceeded to show both Pam and I a complete series of gory slides to demonstrate what surgery to remove a tumour like mine entails. Each slide just seemed to depict an explosion of blood and you could just decipher that a human face was located somewhere in the middle by the briefest hint of an eye or a set of teeth. The patient in each case looked as if they had their face split in two.

His later slides then showed us some of the incredible reconstruction work that can be done in putting these desecrated faces back together. The results that were achieved were amazing and Simon was very proud of these later slides. Their relevance however was a little lost on me on that particular day. We had a long way to go before re-perfecting my face would be our biggest concern.

He explained that the normal procedure for my condition would be to surgically remove the tumour itself and then take out a further centimetre of tissue all around its located area. This was a precaution against any cancer cells that would be missed. In my case however this was not going to be possible. My tumour was already backed up against my brain stem. It had taken control of all the soft tissue and was now eating into my cheek bones. This meant that surgery alone could not be relied upon to remove it completely. I would require radiotherapy to kill off anything that was left behind.

This situation was far from ideal he told me. Radiotherapy, for a stage four tumour, is generally intended as a back up, secondary stage of treatment rather than being part of the primary treatment itself. Ideally all of the tumour would be removed surgically with radiotherapy used as a follow up. This was not going to be possible for me. My chances of survival, even with a good surgical prognosis were slim. Everything was against me. Both men agreed that I was not in a good position.

David Husband then explained to me what radiotherapy would involve. I would need to attend hospital every day, as an out-patient, to receive my treatment over a period of five to six weeks. After the surgery he would evaluate the exact strength and duration of the radiotherapy I would require. To do this he would have to assess where any remaining tumour was likely to be. Then he would need to calculate the specific angles the rays would need to be directed to hopefully eradicate it. Due to the likelihood that the surgery could not be relied upon to remove all the tumour, this was going to be the most essential part of my treatment. My radiotherapy would kill or cure me, depending on its success rate. But as a treatment it is based on a calculated attack of the tumour, rather than its physical removal, and therefore contains risks. When it is being relied upon as a primary source of treatment, that risk is very high. This was the reason that my chances were so low.

Radiotherapy, he told me, is extremely precise. A plaster cast of my face would need to be made, from which a clear plastic mask would be moulded. Every day when I attended for my session I would be fixed in position on the treatment table. This was the only way of ensuring that my head was in exactly the same position each time. Only then could they be certain that the rays were hitting their exact targets for each treatment.

All of the time whilst each of these two consultants were addressing us I was under the impression that the decision on whether treatment was possible or not was entirely based on an assessment of my condition. I did not appreciate that they were also assessing Pam and I as an integral part of making that decision. Surgeons for this kind of work have many factors to take into account before a decision on an expensive and dangerous surgical procedure can be made. Quality of life was a phrase that was continually referred to in these discussions. These men and women will not wish to keep you alive just for the sake of being alive. They will not bring you through very complex surgery for the sake of having you spend the rest of your life on a life-support machine. They want you to return to the world, when they are finished, as close as possible to the condition they found you in. Their decision is not black and white. It is not based on keeping you alive just for the sake of not being dead.

Having initially examined the inherent risks of the procedure they then must also establish if the patient, and their family, will be able to cope with the likely outcome. This can range from death or poor recovery at one end of the scale, physical disability, disfigurement or the loss of one or more of the senses in the middle, to complete recovery at the other end.

Years later Simon Rogers admitted to me that on that day, when he first met me, he did not think I was going to make it. He said that if I had given him any opportunity to cancel the surgery by expressing hesitation or doubt, he would have taken it. He would have advised against going ahead with the massive operation. The risks were huge. It was likely to be unsuccessful and take away whatever quality of life I had left in the remaining months I had left to live.

But he then told me that as I had shown such clear determination to go through with it, he felt he could not let me down. I had convinced him that I fully understood the position I was in. I wanted to take my chance of the surgery if a chance was open to me. I could deal with the consequences, whatever they turned out to be. If he would give me a chance I would take it, even if it was to take away the last six months of my life.

In that room in Liverpool therefore, in May 2002, the major dictating factor that the treatment should take place was not the tumour itself, it was actually Pam and I. If the decision was purely based on the tumour then surgery would not have been recommended. We had both convinced them that we fully understood what lay ahead of us. We had the mentality to deal with the consequences, no matter what they were going to be. For Pam the worst case scenario would have been my death or years dedicated to my care. For me it could have been severe disability, disfigurement, blindness, deafness, dumbness or any combination of all five.

Death, ironically, was the one option I didn't have to worry about. If I were to die then whatever happened afterwards would be out of my hands. In that room on that day Simon Rogers and Dave Husband came to the conclusion that we were tough enough to take on what was coming towards us. Ultimately that was the basis on which the decision was taken.

All of the details of this decision making process were only revealed to me years later. Once again it has been great to have lived long enough to have been fully exposed to them long after they happened. Simon Rogers and I have become very good friends in the intervening years. Every time I meet him now I glean a few more little details of my case.

When he eventually revealed the full extent of their criteria in the making of their decision to approve me for treatment, I began to see this initial assessment completely differently. I realised then I was effectively attending a meeting and the main issue on the table was not my cancer, but me. My cancer was so severe that neither Simon Rogers or David Husband believed I would survive. If the decision was purely based on the tumour I would not be here today. The very final decision would be made on how I could cope with the high risk treatment that they could offer me. It was as if the likely decision had already been formulated and I had one last chance to convince them otherwise.

Supposing I had fluffed my lines? What if I had expressed fears or doubts? I had just been at the biggest assessment that anybody could have had. Now, years later, with the benefit of knowing the exact agenda for that meeting, I could look back and see that it was the biggest interview in the world. I was effectively being interviewed for my life. And I got the job!

Having approved me for treatment and described all of the risks to the procedure, I was determined that Simon and David gave me some idea, in lay mans terms, as to what my chances were. They both agreed that my chance of getting out of this alive were about 5%. Simon Rogers has since admitted to me that my actual chances where nowhere near as high as 5%! He couldn't give me 0.5% or 1.25% so he rounded it up to 5%. He didn't really believe I would survive. But having convinced him that I possessed the necessary fighting spirit to take it on, he felt he had to give me something to fight for. Yet again, this was another beautiful statistic to discover five years later.

So they had given me a five percent survival chance. That's one in twenty. In a group of a hundred people only five will be chosen. Those are big odds. At this point they moved to leave the room to give us time to decide. Our options were stark. I could go ahead with the surgery where the chances of death or non-recovery were 95%. If I did survive the treatment there was a good chance I would only recover sufficiently to have a very poor quality of life in return. The 5% survival chance also included the likelihood of a recovery that encompassed being deaf, dumb, blind or mentally impaired. Or any combination of all four. Even if I did survive the level of ability I would have would be very questionable. Nobody could know for sure. Buried deep somewhere in the 5% was the hope that I could come through and be able to live the remainder of my life to a curtailed but acceptable standard. I would come through all of this and be able to function in a human capacity to some degree.

The other option was to simply do nothing. I would just live out the rest of my life, as best I could, for as long as I could. They predicted that would be six months. If I opted to go for the treatment I ran the risk of losing the only guaranteed few months of my life I had left. The bird in the hand was six months. The birds in the bush were 95 skeletons, a couple of blind pigeons, a few decrepit jackdaws and hidden around the back, a single, beautiful dove.

As they reached the door I told them there was no need to go. The decision was already made. I had managed to scan across my entire life before they even got to leave the room. At the age of 40, with three small children, the youngest of whom was only one, six months were of little use to me. A period of six months would hardly even register on the lives they were going to have.

I also, very briefly began to think what I would do with that six months. What would you want to do with the last six months of your life. Would I go on a round the world cruise. That appeared to be the most desired luxury that sprang to mind. In a split second I had a very brief vision of myself on the deck of a big ship. But in the vision I didn't see myself admiring the Sydney harbour bridge or table mountain in Cape Town or the Christ the Redeemer statue in Rio de Janeiro. Instead I saw somebody who didn't want to be there. I saw somebody who had been given a chance and was now running away from that chance.

I knew then I wouldn't have enjoyed a single minute of that cruise. How could I be sipping champagne and effectively toasting the end of my life when my family needed me to fight this all the way. This was not the time to fiddle whilst Rome was burning. It was time to grab a helmet, an oxygen mask and a fire extinguisher. How could I live out those six months as if they were just for me, knowing I had never tried. I had been given a chance and never taken it. It was now my job to take that chance.

If I was going to die I was going to die fighting. My cancer had laid down the terms and was expecting a walkover. But for a walkover it needed me to concede. So it was time to surprise my opponent. It was time to climb into the ring and tell him the fight was on. It was time to ring the bell and beckon him to come and slug it out. There was going to be no walkover here. This fight was just beginning.

If this was the challenge I had been given, then bring it on. I was ready. Ready to fight to the very end. I was going to give this everything I had until there was absolutely nothing left. Before they reached the door I told them there was no need to leave the room. The decision was already made. I asked Simon to make all the arrangements for my surgery as soon as he possibly could. The operation was going ahead.

We left the hospital that evening with the very daunting figure of 5% ringing in our ears. I would later receive a telephone call from Paddy Hynes, my old work colleague, from Athlone. Paddy was to be the man who would completely reverse my attitude towards this figure. This was six months after Paddy had informed me he had beaten bowel cancer. Now I was beginning to understand what he was telling me.

On hearing that I had been given a very small chance of survival, Paddy phoned me. "I hear they have given you a 5% chance, Liam" he began. "Yes Paddy that's right" I replied tentatively. "Great Liam, that's fantastic news!" "Ahem…sorry Paddy, what was that you said." Over the next five minutes he proceeded to completely turn this figure around for me. "If it is one in a hundred, Liam, it is you. You are young, you are fit, you are strong and you are not going to let this beat you. If I was asked to pick one person out of a hundred I wouldn't pick anyone but you. The one hundred percent will include people who are frail, who smoke, who are un-fit, who will give up but none of those are you. But it is not even 1% Liam, it is 5%. You have five times more chance than you need. This is great news. Now it is just your job to make sure you get yourself inside that percentage. There is absolutely no reason why you can't. You are the man! You will merely be knocked sideways for a year or so, after which you will be busy getting on with the rest of your life."

Wow! Absolutely unbelievable! What a call. And it worked. Suddenly I didn't see the 95% anymore. I just saw the 5%. I had been given a chance. That was the big thing. Now I had to make sure I took it. It was as if I was in an Olympic race. All I had to make sure was that I finished with a medal. Why should there be any reason why I could not make that happen. Somebody had to win the race. From now on I could only let myself believe that that person was me.

The next day I was due to break the news of my diagnosis to my four friends soon to be minders, Ian Connolly, Bernard Kennedy, Geno Reynolds and Bob Noonan. We met up for a drink in Mills pub in Ballina. Munster were playing in the Heineken Cup and I was desperately hoping they would win to cushion some of the blow I was about to land. They lost. I waited until the game was over and then for an appropriate gap in the conversation. "Lads there is something I want to tell all four of you" I began sombrely. "I have cancer. It's very serious and I am going to have a very tough road ahead of me over the next few months." They were all visibly shaken and I remember Bernard, the youngest of the four, taking the news particularly badly. It was a bolt from nowhere. It was their equivalent of John Fenton's "This is serious" line to me two weeks earlier. But now I was just after receiving my call from Paddy Hynes. I quickly followed up with "But wait, I have some great news. I have been given a 5% chance of survival. Isn't that fantastic! I'm going to take this on and come through. I am the man to do this."

At that point I just got up and went to the toilet. Years later I discovered that as soon as I left the table all four of them, still stunned at the news and believing I really had very little chance, just put their heads in their hands. They said "Oh my God, not only has he got cancer but now he has gone mad as well!"

The moral of Paddy Hynes wonderful phone call is that if you have a chance you grab that chance with both hands. He also delivered the message such single minded conviction that it was indisputable. Paddy knew what he was doing. He knew that I would do it in turn for somebody who was going to come after me. That is how the club works. The patients of the present are the inspiration of the future.

The real difference is not between 5% and 1%, it is between 1% and 0%. I would later meet many people who were not given a chance at all. They were beyond treatment. I could then see that was the worst place of all to be. There would be nowhere for your fight to go. No channel for your bravery or your immense pain threshold to be directed towards. No chance to get a crack at your opponent. The fight was just not going to happen. A walkover was being declared without you being given any option to enter the ring.

Paddy was right. I had a chance and that was indeed great news. It was now my job to make sure that chance was taken.

When we had driven out of the hospital after that very first encounter with Simon Rogers and Dave Husband, Pam and I went for a drink. We needed to collect our thoughts. We wanted to try and make some assessment of this news that we had just been landed with before returning to her mother and the boys. We parked the car and walked through Williamson Square in Liverpool city centre. As we passed the Playhouse Theatre I just happened to glance into a dark corner. I witnessed something I had only ever before seen in films. I saw a man, about my own age, with his trousers down below his knees and he was injecting heroin into his thigh. I stopped to show Pam what I could see and she was equally shocked.

For the remainder of our walk to the pub I thought about that man. How strange it was that I was to see him then, just after I had received the confirmation that the remainder of my life was now in jeopardy. I began to compare our scenarios. At that point in time, like for like, his chances were better than mine. He was more likely to keep living than I was. For the first time however I began to see that it may not be the length of your life that is the most important issue, but the type of life that is lived. If he went to hospital nobody would really care. He wouldn't have any visitors, or cards or flowers. He wouldn't have friends coming over from Ireland or student and work colleagues dropping in on their lunch hour in Liverpool. Even the hospital staff, who would do all of the necessary duties for him, probably wouldn't make any real connection with him. I realised that the man I had just seen was practically anonymous. Very few people would actually care whether he lived or died. At that point in time I felt lucky I was me rather than him.

36 – Run for your Life

We returned to Ireland. The very first hurdle had now been cleared. Treatment was available to me. Whether imagined or not, I was now convinced I could feel the tumour growing inside my cheek. Now that I knew it was trying to kill me, I was anxious for it to be removed as soon as possible. My operation however was to be so big it would take at least a month to prepare.

Ironically, having been made aware of the odds that were against me, I was now more at ease with my predicament. Once I knew I had cancer I was in a better position to start taking it on. I was just completely focussed on what I needed to do now. I had four weeks to prepare for the biggest event of my life. My role, I believed, was to become the best patient I could possibly be. I wanted to be in the best possible shape, both mentally and physically, when that trolley came to collect me for surgery. This was my end of the bargain. The medics would do their job and our families and community would look after whatever needs Pam and the boys had but the cancer patient has a role too. I had to facilitate, as best I could, all the work that would be going on around me. I needed to make sure I did everything possible to help everybody else help me.

In assessing my situation I concluded that my preparation needed to address two distinctive areas. The first was my physical condition. I resolved to get myself as fit as I could to provide the surgeons with the best possible specimen for their work. Running, to me, has always been the greatest source of fitness of all. I was going to run as much as I could right up to the operation.

The second, perhaps more important, area was my psychological state. I believed I needed to have my head ready for everything that lay ahead. This was likely to be a more difficult area to conquer and control. My mentality needed to be in the best possible state so that it would assist my prospects of survival in every way it could. There would be no room for doubts or fear.

I knew only one escape door existed. The common denominator for all who beat cancer is a positive attitude, no matter what. They retain a will to live regardless of what is thrown in their path. They never lose sight of the destination they are convinced they will reach. That was the zone I now had to move into. I had to adopt a positive mentality without question.

The very first step of your preparation to combat cancer is a complete acceptance of your disease. The sooner every patient does this, the better. Apart from the few hours after the news broke I found I performed well here. Cancer is not a disease that conforms to any rules when it comes to seeking out victims. It pays no heed to circumstances, age or family history. To dwell in the "why me" phase for any length of time is therefore not only futile but also damaging. The very first stage is acceptance.

Cancer has never pretended to be a disease we can predict or cure with any certainty. To be surprised that it should strike me rather than you, or you rather than me, is therefore illogical. After I was diagnosed people who smoked asked how come it came to me rather than them. I would reply that I know people who have smoked all their lives and lived to 95. The exception destroys the rule. There is no rule here.

Certain activities will increase your chances of getting cancer but this disease will not be pinned down. Cancer is part of life and as such, just like life itself, is unpredictable. From getting out of bed in the morning to returning to it at night most of us can't say for sure what will happen on any given day. We equally don't know who will get cancer.

I love the uncertainty of life. I delight in the element of surprise that can happen at any time. I wouldn't have it any other way. How poorer our lives would be if we couldn't be surprised by meeting an old friend on holiday or be told you have won first prize in a local raffle. Just as these surprises are good, we must also accept that sometimes they will not be good. That is the life that we have. We have known that from the very start.

When I speak to cancer patients in recent years about acceptance of their disease I would often remind them that they never question when good things happen. If they won the lottery or their aunt gave them her car they don't then ask "why me"? They don't say it shouldn't be me because I already have a car or it should be him because he has no money. We don't tend to question our good fortune. We all know that life is comprised of both ups and downs. Just as the roller-coaster goes up, so too must it go down. Why then should we feel we can question our bad fortune. We will never be bigger than our lives.

So, for me, just as you accept the good things in life that happen to you, you must also be prepared to accept the bad. As soon as you achieve this acceptance, you have reached point zero. Zero in this instance means not questioning why. "It's not fair" and "It shouldn't be me" will only take you away from your starting point. It will only take you backwards into minus territory. You need to get to the start line at zero and get ready to run. You must accept the fact that you have cancer and now your fight can begin. When the gun goes off you will leave point zero behind and not look back. You must only run along the positive side of the scale. You must run all the way knowing you are going to cross the finish line. When you do your disease is beaten.

On practically all of the days before I returned to Liverpool I went out and ran at least five miles. Initially I didn't really know why I felt compelled to do this. In time it was obvious. My survival mechanism was already kicking in. We have lovely country roads around Ballina and Killaloe. It was into those expansive spaces that my head needed to go. I needed to get away, but get away with a purpose. I was getting fit but my mind had begun its training too. I was about to embark on the toughest challenge of my life and it needed to prepare too. Running was the one activity that I found could satisfy the two key areas of my preparation. It got me out of the house for exercise and fresh air. But it also got me on my own so I could mentally begin to prepare the thought process required for what lay ahead.

Running is a purely personal confrontation. It is you against the one mile or the six miles you have to run. There are no short cuts. It will require a few thousand strides, with each one equally essential. The first one just as much as the last. If you play a team sport you can have a bad game but score the winning goal in the final minute. You will receive all the congratulations for winning the match for your team but you will know you didn't play well. Running doesn't offer you such luxuries. If you have six miles to run there is nowhere to hide. It will begin with the first stride and not end until the last one. There will be no teammates to carry you if you don't perform.

Running is also never easy. It is never routine. It will always involve a certain degree of pain and discomfort. The fitter you are the faster you will run so it is never automatic. Every time, before you run, a little bit of your head will work against you. "Do you really need to do this today"? "It looks like rain. Why not leave it until tomorrow?"

I found that this daily uprising, somewhere in my brain, was the best possible mental preparation I could have had for what was coming down the line. My mind was teaching me how to override annoyance and discomfort. It was teaching me that once a plan was in place nothing should be allowed to deter the mental focus required to ensure that plan gets activated. It was teaching me to be strong.

The mini insurgence would soon be quelled. The remainder of my brain would take control and declare "Look, this body runs and will do so every day until the surgery starts. Get used to it"! It could just have easily been saying "Look, we have cancer so now we are going to get stronger and tougher. That is our job now" The running piece of my cancer survival jigsaw was not just putting itself in place. It was insisting it be put in place.

My great friend Ian Connolly was instrumental to me at this time. Ian, without any invitation, adopted the position of fitness trainer and psychological mentor all rolled into one. We ran together just about every day. The terms were different now but just as before he knew the role he needed to fill. If he suspected that my daily run was ever vulnerable through a weakness on my part, the call would be made. The run was always enshrined. Equally, he also had the wonderful awareness to recognise the days when I wanted to run alone. He was sensitive to when I needed to be on my own with just my own thoughts. His companionship, as a result, was never forced.

Ian was so much more than just a running partner for these runs. We talked incessantly as we ran. We talked about things that men generally don't talk to each other about. We talked about health issues and about cancer. We spoke about our marriages and our children. We looked at our lives, how we had got where we were and what we might change if we were to do it all again. We talked about life and we talked about death. We became ultimate soul mates. Ian Connolly's friendship and wonderful support was to be a very significant piece in my survival jigsaw.

As I ran along those charming country lanes, I had a buried awareness that I might be viewing them for the last time. Their outstanding natural beauty and great sense of place were probably all the more powerful as a result. This was my home. I could not have imagined wanting to be anywhere else at that point in time. The panoramas over Lough Derg that these roads were providing me with were both beautiful and inspirational. For the hour or so that I left the house for these runs I had a great attachment to where I was living. This was Gods country but now it was my country too. He had given it to me to live, work and run in. He had given it to me to get ready for what I now needed to do. He had given it to me to come back to.

Of all the scenery on the Tipperary side of the lake, one feature dominates above all else. Our local mountain in Ballina is Tountinna, standing at 460 metres above sea level. It looks down over everything below, the lake, the two towns and the surrounding countryside. If this was Gods country then Tountinna was the high altar. Most of the runs Ian and I would do were through the valleys and foothills of this great mountain. It had always been there but right now I seemed to have an association with it like never before. It was tall and strong just like I was going to need to be. If the lake was choppy or the two towns filled with hustle and bustle, Tountinna was always calm and serene. I was going to need a cool head too. It was quietly formidable. It just sat there like a great big gentle friend to our town. Now it was almost as if it was calling me. It wanted to become a beacon of strength for the beginning of my journey. I had a mountain to climb and it was telling me that it was my mountain. It wanted to show me the way I needed to go.

One of the reasons the people of Ballina feel so connected to Tountinna is due to its accessibility. It can by reached on foot from the town but also has a tarred road all the way to the summit. The very top is therefore available to all. Apart from running underneath Tountinna, I would also drive to the top in the last few weeks before I left for England. I often had one, two or all three of my boys with me. As they played I would just sit there, watch them and soak up the tranquillity and outstanding beauty of this great place. The world down below was beginning to accelerate to a point where all routes were leading to Liverpool. It was now offering me a final place of solace and refuge before my ordeal began in earnest. It had guided my running and prepared me physically. Now it was taking me up to induce calm before the storm.

It was an icon to me now. Like Paddy Hynes, Tountinna knew what it was doing. It knew I needed a mountain in my armour. It was giving itself to me. It knew my icon needed to be strong. It needed to be calm. It needed to be silent. Tountinna was all of those things. I formed a beautiful bond with that mountain. It was my mountain. It was as if it was there to inspire me. It knew that it was always going to be a place that I would want to come back to. By doing that alone, it had put a piece in my jigsaw.

37 – Community Support

When we returned home from Limerick with my cancer diagnosis we were not sure who to tell. It was a bit like struggling to carry a time bomb into your house and wondering who to ask to help you carry it through the door. Our three boys had all gone to a little country primary school in Boher village under the wonderful stewardship of the principal there, Una Kennedy. In all our years of knowing her, Una has run this lovely school brilliantly with her unique blend of determined but discrete focus on one hand and great compassion on the other. She was the kind of woman that no matter what you told her, you would only receive supporting words of wisdom and encouragement in return.

Una Kennedy was the very first person in Ballina and Killaloe that we revealed my cancer to. Her reaction was befitting of the esteem we held her in. As we spoke she listened calmly. Then, with a warm matter of factness, she told us that nothing was yet for certain. My cancer was not terminal until all avenues of any possible treatment had been gone down. Until then we would all need to carry on as normal, especially for the sake of our three boys. This was not going to get the better of us. Life should go on as normal until all possibility of hope was gone.

The following Sunday Christy was making his first communion in Boher church. Her advice, that we remain in place as a normal family, as least in the immediate term, was well founded. This was to be our first big family occasion and for Christy's sake, we needed to rise to the challenge of masking the news Pam and I were carrying inside us. We did but if you examined the photographs taken on the day, you could probably make out an invisible black cloud stationed above our heads. I was beginning to look a little gaunt by then. With the secret knowledge of what was looking like a death sentence hanging over me, it was difficult to maintain a normal appearance. There were lots of family photographs taken that day. Deep down I wondered if they were the last ones that I would ever be in.

After we told Una, I told Ian, Bernard, Geno and Bob. We didn't want to withhold the news from anybody living around us but we felt we needed to carefully select the people best able to handle it. In many rural areas still, especially among older people, cancer only means one thing. For many the equation is absolute, no matter what the diagnosis. Cancer equals death. My equation was one where it looked as if the figures could not possibly add up any other way. But I was now determined to go to the greatest lengths I could to find a different solution to the equation that had been set for me.

Anybody who spent any amount of time with either Pam or I didn't take long to figure out that something was wrong. It was difficult to keep a screen in place. We knew that friends and acquaintances who were unable to accept the news would only weaken my resolve. I wouldn't have been able to cope with people coming up to me and bursting into tears. We could not know how each individual would react. Ian, Bob, Geno and Bernard now stepped forward to fill this breach. They became my screen. The screen that ensured my positive focus to beat my cancer was not undermined in any way. They became the minders who were to shield me from distressed sympathisers.

The overwhelming response of the community in which I lived however was not negative at all. It was simply unbelievable. All manner of things just suddenly started to arrive at our door. Get Well cards, Mass cards, flowers, religious items, food and gifts all began to appear like some sort of community avalanche. Some people who either didn't wish to disturb us or were perhaps too upset to see me didn't even let us know they had called. As you were putting on your coat to go out the front door you would almost trip over the hamper of food that was anonymously sitting on the step below you.

All of the attention wasn't just directed at me. The phone rang constantly to know if Pam needed anything or if the boys had to be taken anywhere. If the answer was yes a queue of cars would immediately begin to form outside our door. Veronica and Liam Molloy were especially good to all of us as a family at this time.

One of the greatest gestures of all came from Michael and Irene Fenton. They arranged for both Pam and I to spend two nights at Ballymaloe House before we left for Liverpool. They also made sure that no stone remained unturned for the duration of our stay.

Ballymaloe is one of the great dining experiences in Ireland. Set in the rich pastures of east Cork it is famous for the quality of its local produce and the cuisine of its renowned chef, Darina Allen. It is a beautiful old country house in a majestic rural setting. We went there shortly before I left for my surgery and by then the illness inside me was beginning to make its impact. My energy levels were low. The last breakfast was served at ten so when I was too tired to get up for it, I decided to let it go. My sleep was more valuable to me than food so I slept on. I eventually came down the stairs at 11.30 only to find that a place had been set for me in the conservatory. The chef had not been allowed to knock off that morning until Liam Ryan had his breakfast. These were the lengths that the people in my community were going to, on my account.

Living in a rural community has many benefits at a time of family crisis. In so many ways less is more. We would have had many more people living around us in Liverpool but known far fewer of them. A cancer diagnosis invades every corner of your life. Our community knew that. The people of Ballina and Killaloe were trying to make sure that the only thing we had to worry about was the treatment itself. I put this great community response down as another essential piece in my jigsaw. Little old ladies that I hardly knew would stop me in the street and give me a religious relic or a prayer. They would tell me that they were now praying exclusively for me. Not only were these lovely encounters a great source of uplift for me but also, in the nicest possible way, they were putting implied pressure on me. People were coming up to tell me that hundreds of candles were being lit for me, everyday, all over Ireland. I wasn't to let them down. All of a sudden it wasn't just my fight anymore. It had become theirs too. I was also now representing the loved ones that many of these people had lost to cancer. It was as if I was now offering them a chance to get something back. This campaign had become a lot bigger than just me now.

The people I met were only the support I was aware of. Behind the scenes the fund was being put in place. Plans were being made for whatever needs Pam and the boys would have in the event of my death or severe disability. I had always known and appreciated that I lived in a great community. But this was a phenomenal response to the news of my diagnosis. The magnitude of the help and support they showed for all five of us at this time was truly overwhelming. Without being asked to, they had climbed aboard my campaign. This now meant that if I ever stopped fighting for myself, I would stop fighting for them too. I knew that meant that even if I could stop fighting for myself, I could not stop fighting for all these people. They took their places behind me and would remain there to the very end.

I was to have one famous final night in the midst of this community before I departed for Liverpool. All of my family and friends would be there. I was due to leave on Tuesday July 2nd and on the Sunday night we decided to have a farewell celebration in Liam O'Riains. Mid Life Crisis were assembled one more time to provide the music. In their short career I am honoured to say that every gig they performed was for my benefit. This one however was special.

It was always going to be an emotional night. There was no hiding the fact that it was seen as a final gathering by most. Many of the people in the room that night were expecting that this was going to be the last time they would ever see me. I was aware of this and did not want the night to become a "wake". I did not want anybody to feel I was unapproachable or that this was to be a sad occasion. I wanted everybody to have a great night. I wanted them to share my enthusiasm that I was going to take this on with everything I had inside me. I wanted them to believe that I would not stop until there was nothing left. As long as there was a chance I wanted them to know I was going to be the man who would take that chance.

For myself I wanted to fill that room with all the wonderful people I had in my life. I wanted all those people around me just before I left. I was conscious that everybody was going to be wondering what to say to me. I didn't want anyone to feel awkward. This was a night for all of us. A special night. I needed them to know that there was nothing they could not say to me. I was strong. I wanted them to be strong too. I wanted to show them that I was ready for what lay ahead. I was ready and I wanted them to be ready with me.

On two previous occasions I had written a witty poem about all of the various characters in Liam O'Riains. Liam himself tricked me into the first one. He held an amateur poetry evening in the pub during the summer festival and led me to believe that everyone who came had to write a few lines. I read out what I had written and it went down very well. I followed it up with a second one the following year. Now I thought it is time to write No. 3. I will use it to set the right tone for how I want this evening to run.

Mid Life Crisis warmed up the crowd up with a few lively numbers to get the proceedings underway. Then I stood up in front of the band. I told the crowd that I had written a poem. It was a special poem for a very special evening. I wanted to read it to them now . . .

Liam O'Riains (No. 3)

It's a Sunday night, and I'm afraid I just have to go

When I'll be back, I don't quite know

I'm off on a bit of a journey, it's going to be a bit of a plight

But I'm a Munster man now, so I won't be afraid of the fight

By the time that I come back, the new bridge may well be there

Fr. O'Rahelly will be a bishop, and Noel O'Brien a millionaire

Mike Larkin will have extended, and will now own all Birdhill

And Liam will have finally worked out, what goes wrong with the till

The Sullivan's will be at No. 1, much to Westlife's woe

Ballina will win the Heineken Cup, under coach Piers Devereux

Jack Quigley will be elected, as Ballina's first Lord Mayor

And thanks to a new Sean Collins invention, Ian Connolly will grow hair

There'll be a new Brian Boru theme park, with Irelands tallest tower

And sure while you've got me going, Fine Gael will be in power

Sadie Scanlan will be ordained, and she'll be bossin Fr. O'Rahelly around

But her plans for midnight Mass in Liam's, will never get off the ground

Mick Healy will win Wimbledon, with a set or two to spare

And when the customs come for Geno, the wine just won't be there

Prince Faisal will be impressed, with Danny Ryans great new shed

He'll offer Trudy all his camels, but she'll take three oil wells instead

Ted O'Connor will open a heliport, and Cora will be the director

He'll send a hit team out in the middle of the night, to deal with a planning objector

Bernard Kennedy will still be waiting, for a Limerick All-Ireland crown

They'll miss out again in 2003, losing the final to Down

I'm going to miss so many things, that I see in this room tonight

The pubs in England just aren't the same, the Guinness can be shite

I'm going to miss Pat Grace, and all the injustices he curses

And all the lovely women here, I just wish I could bring you all as nurses

I'm going to miss John Clifford, showing me the cards to play

And John Minogue and Padraig Gough, telling me how to make good hay

I won't have Martin O'Connor, to tell me who's going to win the match

Or Paul McCormack explaining, about the trout he just didn't catch

And Bobby Reynold pints, with their heads on them so high

I'll now just have to swop, for steak and kidney pie

I realise now as I leave, and with all these things I'll miss

That for all the places to live, there are very few better than this

For all the incredible support I've had, I just want to say thanks to you all

It's going to really stand to me, when my back is against the wall

And all your best wishes and prayers, and the goodwill from all your homes

Will have me back in Liam's in no time, writing more of these bloody poems!

Just, as on the two previous occasions when I read out my poem to a packed Liam O'Riains, the house came down. This one however was different. Just about everybody I knew and loved in Ireland was in the room that night. We all knew that the chances were high that we would all never be in the same room again.

There were some tearful embraces through the night but in the main the poem had done its job. As I looked out over the crowd after uttering the final word every face looking back at me had a big broad smile on it. I had managed to capture the mood that I wanted for the remainder of the evening. This party was a celebration of life. A tribute to the fact that our lives had brought us all together. For that night we were all together again, in that room. We had all been lucky enough, in the course of our lives, to meet and get to know each other. That was a cause for celebration. This night was not to be a sombre curtain raiser to a possible death.

As a night, it was truly memorable. For those hours the overwhelming appreciation of simply being there easily outweighed any tendency to worry about what might be about to happen. I hugged and kissed just about everybody at least once. We all danced and sang the night away. If it was to be a final farewell, then, once again, I couldn't have wished for any better.

One encounter in particular stands out. In my time in Ballina Jack Quigley was one of the finest men I came to know. Although he was more than 30 years older than me we became good friends and regularly had a drink together. Jack was a great source of local historical knowledge and had an endless collection of funny stories to entertain us all. He was there that night too and picked his moment to catch me on my own. "Liam I want you to do a favour for me". "Of course Jack" I replied a little puzzled at his timing. "We have been good friends for a number of years now and there is something I'd like you to do for me". "Yes Jack, of course" I replied again, still puzzled. "I want you to say a few words at my funeral".

The line simply blew me away. What a line it was. This was Jack's way of telling me to go over to Liverpool, do what I needed to do, come back and in 25 years time, when he was ready to go himself, fulfill the promise I had just given. It was a beautiful way to put pressure on me to survive. He had got me to make a personal promise. To deliver that promise I needed to go and beat this cancer I had. Now it wasn't just group pressure. Individuals were handing me wonderful obligations not to let them down. We embraced and he gave me a broad smile before returning to his family at the bar.

Before the night was over I said my last goodbyes. I wanted to slip away out the back door and just be gone at the end. As I was heading down the lane behind the pub I heard my name being called for one last embrace. When I turned around John Clifford was standing outside the back door. John Clifford and I, in a short space in time, went back a long way. A few years after we moved to Ballina Pam and I bought some land about a mile from the town. It was only then did I really get to know the sixty year old man who owned the 22 acre farm beside us. John Clifford was a great big gentle man. When he spoke, he tended to speak wisely. He loved his pub and his pint. He loved a sing-song and a game of cards. In spite of the age difference he formed an unlikely alliance with both myself and Bernard Kennedy. We became great friends. I went in to his house many times for a few minutes for a cup of tea only to come out hours later having drank a lot more than tea.

We got a difficult planning permission for him for a house on his farm for his son Sean. Sean would tragically be killed in a car accident a few years later. So, on that memorable night, the tragedy that was looking to befall me would be deferred, only to return to his own doorstep. If I was to have one last final farewell with anybody from Ballina and Killaloe that night, it seemed only fitting that that person was to be John Clifford.

We clenched our arms around each other in that lane for three or four minutes with tears in both sets of eyes. In many ways I didn't want to ever let go. When I did I knew I would be letting go of not just John Clifford, but also the safety and the care of this wonderful community that I had become part of. I would be leaving my well loved, safe harbour. Tomorrow I would be sailing my little boat out into the deep and dark waters of the unknown. But I knew that was what I had to do. Now was the time and I was ready. I had said goodbye to Tountinna. I had said goodbye to Ballina and Killaloe. I had said goodbye to my community. Now I was at the base of the mountain. It was time to start climbing. The next chapter was about to unfold. It was time to look forward and not look back. Bring it on!

38 – The Longest Road to Liverpool

We left Ballina/Killaloe with a fully laden car. We didn't know how long our trip would last so we brought enough possessions to cover all eventualities. The three boys had been packed away to my sister Carol's farm in Co. Offaly. They would remain there until it was appropriate to bring them over. We were headed for the ferryport in Dun Laoighaire. From there we would sail to Holyhead and then drive to Liverpool. My very last Irish well wisher would see me just as I was about to board the ship. Jack Naughton has been a great friend of mine since our days together in primary school in Horseleap. He had gone to great lengths to get his hands on a religious relic that he wanted me to have. The only suitable rendezvous we could arrange before I departed was at the ferryport itself. He was there waiting for us when we arrived. We were late setting off so didn't have much time to spare.

Jack and I had shared many adventures over the previous twenty five years. He was one my longest standing friends. The relic was exchanged, as was another prolonged hug but this time there were no tears. I hadn't time for them now. I was too focused on the job in hand. I was ready now to leave most of my emotions in Ireland and be a different man by the time I got to England. I had cancer to beat. I had been given a five percent chance and now I was going to take that chance. I was in fight mode. Nothing would stop me now.

As the ship pulled away I was surprised at how little remorse I had on leaving my homeland. I now just wanted to get to the country that was giving me an opportunity to take on this disease. As much as I love Ireland I will always be indebted to Liverpool. If my progression through life was like walking along a corridor it was as if Liverpool was always where the doors were. When I discovered I wanted to be an architect my own country would not provide me with the stepping stone I needed to fulfill my dream. Liverpool did. It also gave me my wife, my career and my first two children. Now I was very sick and just about every other place in the world had given up on me. Liverpool didn't. It was calling me back once again. "Liam, when you were in trouble before, you knew where to come. Now you know where to come again". Last week I was running around Ballina and Killaloe on my roads. Now I was setting sail across the sea to my city.

The surgery was scheduled for Monday July 8th. Before it could take place I needed to have a peg tube inserted. I had never even heard of such a thing before. When your mouth is unable to function, as mine would be after the surgery, a peg tube is used to feed you directly into your stomach. I went to the hospital on the Thursday before my operation. I would need to stay in for one night to recover after they inserted it. It seemed to be a relatively straight forward procedure and went fine. When I came around on the ward I had acquired a new part to my anatomy. I now had a twelve inch length of plastic tubing sticking out of my stomach. This was going to supply me with food over the next few months. It was an ugly looking thing but this was not the time to be judgemental. I needed to embrace it rather than reject it. It had now become part of my fight. It was now part of me. It would be another little important piece of my jigsaw. This "thing" was going to provide my body with the fuel it would need to keep me fighting. I needed to respect it for playing that role no matter how inhuman it looked.

A young lad, probably in his late teens, was in the next bed to me on the ward. His right eye was heavily bandaged. I got chatting to his Mam and Dad when they came in to visit that evening. It transpired that he had been the victim of a serious assault. He was coming home on his moped when three thugs pounced on him as he stopped at traffic lights. They then set upon him to steal his bike. Not content to limit their attack to just theft they knocked him to the ground and proceeded to kick the living daylights out of him. After several minutes they made off with the moped leaving him badly injured on the side of the road. One of the kicks connected directly with his eye socket. It was delivered with such force that it completely squashed his eyeball. He was now being admitted to hospital to have the damaged eye removed. A replacement false eye would be put in, in its place.

As the story was unfolding I was beginning to see how every case in that hospital could be viewed as better or worse than mine. It depended on which way you wanted to look at it. I began to see that perspective was waiting for me everywhere I turned. All I needed to be able to do was recognise it. I realised this was going to be a powerful weapon that I would need to avail of. It would help me maintain a positive focus no matter what was to come along.

My disease was obviously much more critical than what this young lad was going through. My life was in grave danger. His was not. But my affliction had come through natural causes. It wasn't brought about by three brave morons who decided they didn't like the look of me. A cancer diagnosis is dreadful but how does it compare to a family who must cope with a murder or violent assault. Which predicament is worse. In the first instance the trauma has occurred through nobody's fault. In the second it should never have happened in the first place. I now had the capability to see that it was impossible to distinguish between a forty year old getting a serious cancer and a seventeen year old getting stabbed on the way home from a nightclub. Both events were terrible. But it was impossible to say one was worse than the other.

When I found out that the patient beside me was also about to have his eye removed, I began to chat to him. I wanted to console him and give him a lift. Up to then he had been very quiet. He was still traumatised from what had just happened to him. I offered him the solace that I was just about to have my eye removed too. He wasn't on his own. As soon as I uttered these words of encouragement however, I realised how little weight they carried. I was forty, with a wife and three children waiting for me. They were going to welcome me home again, if I survived, no matter what I looked like. I was still going to be the same man to them. No facial disfigurement or loss of an eye would change my status in the slightest. I was still going to be Pam Teese's husband and Christy, Lowell and Abe Ryan's dad. They would only be too happy to have me home alive, in any form. Anything beyond that would be a bonus.

This poor lad on the other hand had all of that still ahead of him. He was going to leave this hospital and go out to begin his twenties. He would want to be just like every other twenty year old. Now that was not going to happen. He would want to socialise and meet girlfriends just like all his friends. But now he had a major handicap compared to everybody else. He was going to be missing an eye. He was returning to a generation that can be hostile and cruel if you are different from the norm. I would go home to people who would just be delighted to see me, no matter what I looked like. He would be released from the hospital into the hands of a social group who's aspirations are to be beautiful, indestructible and perfect. A social group who's role models are film stars, pop singers and catwalk queens. A social group preoccupied with fame, wealth and good looks. He was going out to a generation where perfection was everything. I was going back to one that knew it didn't exist. One that would just be happy to see Liam Ryan still alive.

So we weren't the same at all. The loss of an eye was going to have a much more dramatic impact on his life than it was on mine. I felt stupid then. I had tried to cheer this boy up but he knew, long before I did, that I was trying to compare apples to oranges. We were both going to have a similar appearances after surgery but everything else in our lives was different. The surgery was our only base line. After that our worlds were completely different. The treatment for your ailment is one thing. The impact it will have on the rest of your life something completely different. You will have to cope with that for a lot longer than the surgery itself.

So I had cancer and this boy did not. It was likely I would die and he would not. Yet I could see the advantages to my case that he didn't have. I could see the disadvantages to his case that I didn't have. The ability to be able to find perspective was already there, even before my surgery began. I could look at any other patient and feel lucky I wasn't them. Perspective was going to be a huge piece in my jigsaw. I could now see that it was already in place.

39 – From First Life to Second

The very final social gathering of my first life took place on Saturday July 6th 2002. It was the day before I went in to hospital. I already had my final Irish farewell so this one was for the friends I had in Liverpool or elsewhere in the UK. These would be the very last people to see me before my operation.

When the International Garden Festival came to Liverpool in 1984 a new waterside pub called the Britannia Inn was built. It was roomy, had plenty of car parking and was pleasantly located overlooking the river Mersey. It seemed to be the ideal choice for what potentially, could have been my very last social outing. Brendan Kilpatrick and Barry O'Neill had come up all the way from London. Many of my Liverpool based ex-college friends and old work colleagues were also there. My first cousin from Clara in Offaly, Mary Naughton and her husband Brian, who were now settled in Liverpool, were there too.

It was a beautiful sunny day. For three hours we just commandeered half of the outside tables, overlooking the sparkling water. This was our territory for a final social gathering. A final get together in the first life of Liam Ryan. It was hopefully not to be the final social gathering of his entire life.

Everybody was very upbeat. Whether they were feeding from the enthusiasm to get on with the battle I was now showing or just putting on a brave face, I'm not quite sure. Either way, I was ready now. They didn't need to have any concerns over my state of mind.

Just like my final night at Liam O'Riains I wanted this to be a happy occasion. We all began to reminisce about our time together. We recalled the many funny incidents that had happened over the years. As each story was told, the rest of us all laughed along as the specific details were revived.

It reminded me of the wedding scene in the Deerhunter. We all knew some unpleasantness was on its way, but all of that was set aside for now. It was only time to celebrate and remember fondly. I managed to get a great laugh out of Pete at one point when I pulled up alongside him at the urinals in the toilet. After unzipping my jeans I took out my peg tube rather than the normal piece of apparatus for the task required. He never knew that such a thing existed. We laughed and laughed. It was good to laugh.

And so that was it. All of the final social formalities had been dispensed with. It was now time to put on my blinkers and get down to business. I had two wonderful celebrations with just about all of the friends I had in both Ireland and England. These events were now going to become one of two things. They would become the moment when most of these people would see me for the last time or the landmark gatherings that would launch to my successful fight against cancer. I was fully committed to making sure that the latter scenario was the one that would prevail.

On Sunday July 7th 2002 I was admitted to the University Hospital at Aintree. I was taken to ward 29. This was going to be my home for the next few months. Again I felt I needed to regard this ward as my friend rather than my foe. It was there to help me. I needed to adopt it from the very start rather than regard it as somewhere I did not want to be. It too was an important part of the jigsaw.

This hospital was my friend. It was the only hospital that would take me in and give me a chance. Consequently I didn't just embrace ward 29 but became proud of it. It was immediately incorporated as an integral part of my campaign plan. I was glad it was there for me. It had eight beds, all with patients requiring surgery to the head area to varying degrees.

Pam's brother Paul dropped me in. He was going to be the last person to see me before my surgery. Possibly the last person I knew to see me alive. I was glad it was Paul. We had always got on well but because we were on opposites sides of the family and located in different countries we rarely got the chance to chat alone. He is solid and calm and was probably just the kind of company I needed as I waited for my bed to be prepared. He stayed for about an hour and I believe on leaving, felt he was saying goodbye for the last time.

I lay in bed that night realising those last hours of wakefulness were very precious. They could have been my last hours of clear thinking for quite a while. They could have been my last hours ever. I felt I needed to use them as a last chance to run through some of the bigger issues going through my head. The topic I have barely touched on in this account to date is my faith. This has not been by accident. This is an area, I believe, that is very personal to every individual. In many ways, is not easily shared. When you begin to share it, it can start to lose its personal integrity.

I would never wish to impose anything I believe in on anybody else. For me any faith you possess is exclusively just a two way relationship. It is only between you and whoever or whatever you believe in. That relationship is the very core of the individual you believe yourself to be. It is private and sacred. Your beliefs and your conscience are as specific to you as your personality. When you begin to discuss them with a third party or even within a religious movement, your personal connection can begin to lose its uniqueness. Your beliefs are not just for you anymore.

I am not here to tell anybody what to believe in. For me, you have to find that for yourself. Just like my roads and my city, my God is for me and I, no matter how unworthy, am for him.

I will say, as a cancer fighter, that I found my faith to be a huge advantage to me at this time. Through it I found I was literally able to remove myself from everything I had to face, if I needed to. It made me incredibly strong. It gave me the strength to be not afraid of anything I had to do, irrespective of what the end result could be.

No matter who you are it is difficult to go to the very precipice of your life without wondering what will happen next. Cancer brings you to that point. If I am to die now, is that it. Or is there more. Am I just to be put into a wooden box in the ground to feed the worms. Or will I return next week as a tree or a book or a wolf or another human being. Is there a heaven and a hell. If so, which one has now been advised to expect me. Will I be able to look down on my family and see everything they do from now on.

Many of these questions must be common to anybody who fears that they are close to their death. In my case I was born and raised an Irish catholic. In my teens and late twenties I graduated to being an Irish lapsed catholic. My religion returned to me or more precisely I went back to it when I went to England. Initially the draw back to it came through cultural reasons rather than anything deeper. I saw it as a big part of my Irish identity. I also then began to see however that there was nothing in my belief in God that didn't fit in with the life I was trying to lead. The message of trying to be the best person you can be, and trying to love everybody and everything, is universal to making this a perfect world. It cannot be argued with. If we all adhered to the basic principles of any sensible religion we would have a perfect society.

The philosophy of any half decent religion is that we should all try and live exceedingly good lives and evil should not exist. There would be no need for locks on doors, or courts, or prisons, or police. Crime would not exist. But God is one thing and man, the church, religious movements and the world we all have to live in something completely different. It can be difficult for all of us to tie the two together. In two thousand years different philosophies have evolved, different interpretations have emerged and different religions are claiming to be the correct one. People have become confused. Even within the same religion there are differences and contradictions. How can a priest that I saw an hour ago terrorise a pupil for not knowing his maths now get up in Mass and preach to me about loving your enemy. When I get confused I go straight back to my personal two way relationship. I don't need a middle man or a third party. I just go to God with what I have done, what I have not done and my conscience. That was where I needed to go now.

The trolley arrived for me at eight o'clock the next morning. It was a long run to the operating theatre. I distinctly remember measuring the length of the journey by the amount of white suspended ceiling tiles I could register as I was pushed along. I didn't count them but it was a big number.

I was clean shaven now for the first time in thirteen years. The surgeons job was going to be difficult enough trying to put my face back together without asking them to knit my beard back in to place too. Aintree hospital has a tiny little multi denominational church buried in its bowels. I had already sought its refuge on previous visits. It was on my route to the theatre. On passing it I remember clenching my fist. I promised that if I was granted the liberty of coming this way again, it would be my first port of call.

Simon Rogers was waiting for me when I arrived at the theatre. I was very familiar with this scenario now. You get to exchange a few pleasantries with your surgeon before your lights go out. I forget what we spoke about but I'm sure it was something encouraging and reassuring. Those were to be the very last words of my first life. The anaesthetist said hello as the needle moved towards my arm. I smiled back as I clung to my last few seconds of reality. Within seconds my senses began to blur into a fuzzy haze. And then I was gone.

I opened my eyes again about eighteen hours later. Both of them. They had unexpectedly managed to save my right eye during the surgery. I was optimistically under the impression that this meant it would function just as it did before, but this was not to be. I had a poor quality, blurred image from it for a while but, by the end of radiotherapy all sight from it was gone. If I was an airplane, one of my two sight engines was now gone. However at least the eye itself was still in place. This would save me further surgery to have it replaced.

I was very grateful to be able to see at all at this point. It meant that two big milestones had already been achieved. I had survived the surgery and I had done so without going blind. As I scanned down along my arm I could see that Pam was on the end of it, holding on tightly to my hand. My cousin Mary was with her. I then broadened my viewfinder to acquaint myself with the remainder of the intensive care unit. It seemed to be like a space ship. I remember it being completely dark, as dark as night but with tiny shiny lights everywhere. The room was full of commotion with people constantly on the move and many voices talking at the one time. I was to be in that room for two days and don't remember it being anything other than dark with lights on so I can't be sure how accurate these recollections are. I also remember conversing with the nurses which would have been impossible as I now had a tracheotomy.

However my recollections of what Pam and Mary were saying to me were correct so my level of understanding appeared to be somewhat intact. The conversations I thought I was having with the nursing staff were centred around compliments they were paying me on how good all my readings on the monitors were. They were amazed at my condition after such a major operation. Pam and Mary were also using this as a source of encouragement for me.

I was proud of all of these comments. They meant that I had made a good start. I had completed steps one, two and three. I was alive, I could see and I was in good condition. These were essential little building blocks that were already in place within the first few hours. I deemed the good monitor readings were due to my level of fitness and strength. This was one of my own pieces in the jigsaw. All of the running work on the roads around Ballina and Killaloe had paid off. I had gone in to the operation in a good, strong condition. Now at this first point of reference after the surgery, I was still strong. This gave my spirits a huge lift. If cancer and I were playing tennis I felt I had scored the first point. I was leading fifteen love. It was very little in the context of a five set match and was no indication of who the eventual winner would be, but on that day, in that intensive care unit, it was a very important first score to me.

I was obviously on morphine at this time because I don't remember feeling any great pain, but I was boosted greatly by the fact that my awareness was so good. It would be a full week before I would get to see myself in a mirror. The swelling to my face had greatly reduced by then. I can only imagine therefore what I looked like at that stage. Nobody referred to it. Pam and Mary, to their credit, didn't give me any hint that I looked any different than normal. I assume I must have looked something like the Elephant Man.

This didn't concern me in the least. My entire focus in those early weeks was just to be alive. I was still critical and I knew it. I just needed to get to the first base on the mountain. First base was having come out of the surgery alive. All of the other specific climbs would be tackled individually on route to the top. I was just delighted to have come around and be able to coherently communicate with both the staff and the few visitors allowed in to see me.

I did very well for my stay in intensive care. After forty eight hours I was deemed to be stable and strong enough to return to the ward. Now I had a much better appreciation of the condition I was in. Apart from the main wounds to my face they had punctured my neck for the tracheotomy. I also had a long eight inch scar to the top of my right leg where they had accessed my hip. I managed to view down the length of my entire body. It was in a poor state. From my legs up it was bruised and scarred in most locations. I was able to count about twelve tubes that were coming out of me. I wasn't in acute pain but I was in what I would describe as 24 hour discomfort. Many of my unpleasant experiences from my ordeal have faded with time but I remember this discomfort vividly. It will always remain with me. These moments are the exclusive domain of the hospital patient. Only we know what they were like. As a consequence I now no longer trust the hospital that I have telephoned when they tell me that somebody is comfortable. They may be stable but only the patient themselves can tell you for certain if they are comfortable!

40 – The Will to Live

Up to this I had believed that my cancer battle needed to be entirely founded on my ability to fight to stay alive. Now, in an ironic twist, I discovered an unlikely ally to strengthen this mindset. A component that would upgrade it from strong to indestructible. At this point in my campaign not only was I prepared to fight tooth and nail to stay alive, I was also not afraid to die.

It is impossible to seriously consider any cancer diagnosis without acknowledging that the possibility that your demise exists. The old adage that cancer equals death is impossible to ignore completely. No matter what the diagnosis is, or how remote the possibility, the prospect of dying is at the back of every cancer patient's mind, at some stage. Many people try to ignore it, make it go away or pretend it just won't happen. If this mentality goes unchecked however you are handing an advantage to your cancer. You have a weak spot that you are trying to conceal. The key to me is not to ignore it, but to control it. If the possibility of your death is in your mind it needs to be exposed and dealt with. It will not go away by itself.

This approach again may appear to conflict with your positive dynamic to focus single-mindedly on beating your disease. But rather than ignore it you merely need to turn it to your advantage, just like every other component of your campaign. You need it to be able to put it on the right side of zero. Then, when even the worst case scenario can't undermine your overall fight, you become stronger still. There is nothing that can touch you now.

With my diagnosis being so poor I knew I would have been foolish not to have addressed the likelihood of my death. Initially I didn't want to contemplate it because I believed it was negative thinking. It would take me in the wrong direction from my starting point. It would weaken my gung-ho, win at all costs, battle campaign. But, deep down, I always knew that if I didn't overturn this one remaining stone my fight would always have an Achilles heel. I knew I would have a little corner that I was afraid to shine a light into. The foundation of the cancer fight I was about to construct would have an inherent fault line. So one night in hospital, when I was waiting for my operation, I decided I was going to shine a light into this corner. I was going to expose my Achilles heel. I said to myself "Liam, you're not going to be here next week. How do you feel?"

The first thing I did was take a very deep breath. This was uncharted territory. An area where nobody really wants to go. I began to look back over my life as I lay in my bed. My first reaction was "Forty, it has been short hasn't it?" The first people I saw were my mother and father. They had been wonderful. I could see that as parents go, how privileged I had been. From there I began to see my three sisters, my cousins and the great extended family I have. Then I saw my school and my education, my friends and all the things I had done as an adolescent. After that it was off to Liverpool and college, a career and a profession. Next I saw Pam and how grateful I was to have met her and be given the chance to spend 15 years with her. Then came my three boys, Christy, Lowell and Abe. I had lived long enough to see my own three children come into the world and start to grow. Finally I saw the wonderful community in rural Ireland that I live in. I had lived to set up my own business in that community and enjoyed many years working with some great people. Now I could see that although short, my life had been both beautiful and fulfilled. I had reached the summit and was beginning to go down the other side. I could tick most of the boxes of life that many people aspire to, family, education, travel, partner, career, children, business, with perhaps only grandchildren missing.

I then began to think of all the people who hadn't ticked half the boxes I had. The people you read about in the newspaper everyday. The stories that made no impact on you until now, because you had nothing to relate them to. The three year old diagnosed with leukaemia. The seventeen year old who comes off a motorbike. The young people all over the world who leave their homes everyday only never to end up coming back.

Suddenly I wasn't sad anymore. How could I feel sad when I had been so lucky. I had got to do so many more things than any of these people. I had lived a life. I had lived a wonderful life. It now looked as if it could be a short life, but it had still been a complete life. Now the tables had been completely turned. My mind had made me go where I didn't think I could and turned it into something positive. In contemplating my death I only ended up appreciating my life. It didn't weaken my fight. It only made me stronger. If my death was to come I would be ready. It would bring nothing that I would be afraid of. I now knew there was nothing I could not face.

I didn't need to take this analysis any further. I knew I had the mindset to deal with the worst case scenario if I needed to. But now was not the time. I immediately brought a halt to this self examination. I put all of these thoughts into an imaginary glass box. I would only open that box again when there was only one road left to go down. I could do this because unlike an accident or a heart attack, my demise would not be sudden. I would have time at the very end to return to these sentiments after every single battle had been fought. I would only go there when there was nothing else left. For now I didn't want anything in that box to dilute the ferocity of my fight against my disease. Now, with my mind happy that it was there, it needed to be sealed tight.

From that night I was immortal. Death had no power over me. I had no dark corners. I had caught my Achilles heel and chopped it off. Nothing daunted me now, not surgery, or pain, or disfigurement, or invalidity. They were all less than death and now, I wasn't afraid to die. Cancer had no hold on me anymore.

41 – Life 2, Week 1

That first week I had after my surgery was probably the worst I am ever likely to have in my life. I still had the form of a human being, but with most of my primary functions disconnected, it was hard to feel like one. I was more machine than man. I was unable to eat, drink, talk, walk, sit or sleep. The tracheotomy was doing my breathing for me and the peg tube was feeding me. I remember being awake for every second of the first three days with nothing to break the timeless agony. I was unable to sleep because of the tracheotomy. My lack of sleep was tortuous in itself but unfortunately I was also within view of the clock on the ward opposite my bed. This only further inflamed my exhausted frustration.

I began to hate that clock. It was almost as if it revelled in its power over me. It became like some kind of cruel time torturer. It knew it could command my attention and having secured my gaze it was as if it delighted in informing me that time was no longer passing as I knew it. What I had previously known to be five minutes now passed as slowly as an hour. An hour on that clock seemed to be twelve hours in real time.

I literally spent these days just wishing a week away. "If you can just get yourself through to this time next week" I kept telling myself "All of this pain and discomfort will then be gone. You will be a normal person again. The only enemy you have right now is time." Carmel O'Sullivan knew my pain at this stage. She sent me a text every night at this point of my treatment. She was just extraordinary. She was also the only person I felt who could understand what I was going through then. Her care for me was now travelling well beyond the limits of Ward 2C in Limerick.

My running experience was a great source of strength to me at this stage. The day after I was brought back to the ward one of the nurses removed the first of my tubes. It was an anaesthetic feed in my foot. When she did, I just clenched my fist and thought, one gone, eleven more to go. It was just one little tube but its significance did not go unnoticed. Just as every long run is made up from thousands of individual strides, my recovery was going to begin with this one little tube being removed. Every marathon must begin with the first step, the first hundred yards, the first mile. I had started running. I had taken the first stride of the marathon of my recovery. All I now had to do was keep running. If I did the finish line would come by itself.

This was going to be my tactic for my recovery. All I wanted was some small bit of progress for each day that came. This could be the removal of a tube or to sip from a glass of water or to sit up. All of these small steps would eventually take me to the point where I would be able to get out of bed and talk, eat, drink and walk for the first time again.

I hated the tracheotomy. It was the worst part of all. Apart from being physically uncomfortable it had the psychological affect of tying you to the bed like a noose around your neck. I appreciate that with my mouth out of action it was keeping me alive, but it was not pleasant. Its greatest infliction of pain came when it made me cough. Coughing was the one thing I did not want to do at that early stage of my recovery.

When the tracheotomy discharged air down my throat it moistened it. This moisture would then collect on my chest. I would not be able to withstand the build up for long and would need to cough to relieve it. However the most painful part of my body at this time was my newly re-shaped hip. The stomach contraction that each cough generated sent a searing pain across all of my lower abdomen. I was trying to avoid coughing at all costs.

I would resist for as long as I possibly could but eventually the moisture build up would be too much to bear. I would then just brace myself for the acute pain strike. The tracheotomy was also lodged in the middle of my throat so the coughing was also largely ineffective in any case. I was caught in a vicious circle. The most painful vicious circle I have ever experienced.

The nursing staff were obviously aware of the distress the tracheotomy generates. They would also relieve the moisture build up with a suction tube. They came at intervals to do this but unfortunately, this was also extremely painful for the mute patient. You welcomed their intervention on one hand as the suction tube provided a longer relief between coughs but on another, you dreaded it even more. The discomfort of having the tube steered down your throat was excruciating. It was even more painful than my sore hip.

All of this pain was now being laid at the feet of just one culprit, the tracheotomy. Saving my life and part of my jigsaw or not, we were never destined to be good friends. Its insistence on inflicting pain was never a basis from which a friendship could form.

For that first week of recovery I was stripped right down to the very basics. I felt as if I was alive but not much more. Most of my senses had been inactivated and I was effectively cocooned in my own little world of tracheotomy, tubes, exhaustion and silent discomfort. My only line of communication with the outside world was to write some hand written notes when visitors came but I would tire easily.

This was now to be the first great test of my mental ability to deal with extreme states of pain and senses depravation. This was the marker for how I would perform when the going was to get even tougher. I needed to know now that I had in me whatever it was going to take. I needed to know that my strength and my resolve could be depended upon right to the end. The time had now come to go deep inside myself and see what was there. It was time to see what I had in my reserve petrol tank.

I was now going to need to visit every part of my body. Parts that I had never called upon before. Every inch of the body matter that was uniquely known as Liam Ryan would be relied upon for this challenge. There was no piece of me that could not afford to respond to the call.

When I did venture into this territory I was pleasantly surprised with what I found. I am now convinced that we all have a secret store of resolve. You will never really know what is in there until you need to go looking. It is as if a little part of you remains sealed until it is absolutely necessary to be called upon. When you tap into it you may find new depths to yourself that you never thought were there before.

I was thinking at this time about all of the stories of true resolve that you can read about every day. The people who survive a tsunami, or an earthquake, a flood, or a mudslide. The people who get on with their lives, in spite of enduring some of the greatest hardships known to man. These are the real people who find resolve. These are the people who show the rest of us what the human spirit can really do. I had been reading the stories about people with wonderful resolve every day in the newspaper. They simply passed before my eyes without registering. Now I read them all again. This time I put myself in the shoes of the man in Afghanistan who goes home in the evening to find his house with his wife and four children blown up. Where does he find the strength to carry on with the rest of his life. Where does he find the resolve to open up his market stall again on Monday morning. But he does. Thousands more like him do every day too. These people are the real heroes in this world. They carry on with their lives having suffered tragedies the rest of us can only imagine.

With my body in meltdown I began to recognise all of the fundamental activities it had been performing for years. Rather than mourn their temporary loss I was now appreciating how fortunate I was to have had them in the first place. I now, probably for the first time in my life, realised all the wonderful things my body could do.

Up to this I had been able to walk, I could see, I could run, I could talk, I could eat, I could swim, I could hear, I could taste, I could sleep. I was able to do so many things that many people throughout the world could not. These were only the simple things. I could also drive a car or fly in an airplane, climb a mountain or ride a roller coaster. All of a sudden I realised I wasn't one of the unlucky ones anymore. I was one of the lucky ones. It was only now, when I was denied these wonderful attributes that my body could perform, did I begin to appreciate how fortunate I was to have had them in the first place. Now, when it would have been very easy to slip into disgruntlement due to my condition, I discovered I was never more appreciative of my place in the world.

In assessing my predicament all of my thoughts were turning into positives. For that to happen all I needed to do was dig deep enough. Although I was in a swamp, my mind was always able to find the only solid path that would get me out. It was telling me that it was not the time for fear, or regret, or bitterness. Now was the time for appreciation and strength and resolve. Only on that rock would my survival be built.

With this newly found re-appreciation, my promise to my wonderful body was to restore it back to its original condition. That was all I needed to focus on. Then I could start to re-appreciate its great abilities all over again. I vowed that I would never again take them for granted. I would never become complacent again about all of the amazing gifts I had been given as a human being. We do not realise how incredible it is to talk or walk or see, until they are taken away.

Now I was strong. I was grateful to my body for what it had been before and at ease with where it was now. We would tackle this recovery piece by piece, day by day. I was prepared to accept whatever condition we got it back to, even if I had to let go of some of the powers it had before. Both body and mind would do their very best. This mindset was to be a big watershed in my cancer battle. At that point I knew for certain that I had the resolve within me to withstand anything my recovery was going to throw at me.

Two days after I got back to the ward Simon Rogers came and sat on the end of my bed. He began to describe all that had taken place during the course of my operation. He told me they started by cutting my face from just below my ear across to my nose. Then they broke my jaw and cut right down to beyond my chin. At this point they folded the lower section of my jaw away to give them direct access to my sinus and beyond.

Before they could start to remove the tumour they had to sever all of the nerves that were running through the middle of my head. These were all blocking their path. This was very intricate work and each one had to be carefully positioned for later reconnection. He described this part of the procedure as similar to taking the engine out of a car. Before you can remove the engine to begin to work on it you must first disconnect all of its many connections to the remainder of the car. There is nothing wrong with any of these connections in themselves. They are merely in the way of the work to be done. Their disconnection however brings extra risk to the success of the work that needs to be undertaken.

When the engine is fixed the work is far from complete. All of the connections must then be put back in place before the car will go again. In my case the connections were all of the nerves travelling from my brain to my eyes, ears, nose, mouth and down my entire body.

Once that work was done the way was clear for the removal of the tumour to begin. They began with the base of the sinus and removed half of the roof of my mouth and half of my top set of teeth. They then removed all of the soft tissue in the sinus area. Because my cancer was so advanced it had already began to attack my cheekbone. So after all of the soft tissue had been removed they had to cut away all of the damaged bone that they could see. He explained to me that they then had to follow the tumour in around my eye to my brain stem. This is where the top of my spine connects with my brain. This was the most difficult area because they were working only millimetres from both my brain and spine. One slip and the result would have been a brain injury or paralysis.

When they were satisfied they had removed all of the cancerous tissue they could see, it was time to begin the repair work. The removal of substantial tissue and bone to my face meant they were now left with a large cavity that needed to be filled. This would be too big to heal naturally. The structure of my entire face had been undermined by the amount of material taken away.

Their next job therefore was to cut me open at the top of my leg and to saw a slice of bone off my hip. They then took tissue from my stomach to fill the void created by the cancerous material they had removed. Whilst they were salvaging filler material from my stomach they also took some lining tissue. This was to be used to attempt to reseal the roof of my mouth. This is called a flap. He told me that this is the most effective way to carry out this particular piece of repair work because as natural body material it has a chance to bond to form a perfect seal. This is important in the mouth area especially. If it was successful it would mean that every time I drank I would not have any leakage from mouth to nose. If the flap did not take, the only other option would be to use an artificial plate, called a bung. This is effectively a type of denture. It would however not seal perfectly and I would always have a certain amount of discomfort, between nose and mouth, as a result.

Simon told me it would be a lot more beneficial to me if the flap eventually settled and took to its new home. He assured me that it was a 95% chance that this would happen. Great, I thought, that's reasonably certain. Then I realised that was the figure he quoted against my chances of survival. "You can't be doing that Liam," I thought to myself, "picking and choosing percentages just to suit yourself" "Yes I can!" I immediately replied. "Whatever the percentage is, I'm going to get inside it. Big or small, it makes no difference!" A 95% chance in one scenario is good news and a 5% chance in another is still just as good.

Once they had extracted what they needed from my hip the rebuilding of my cheek began. The piece of hip bone had to be shaped to suit the area it needed to fill. Then it was screwed into position with two metal screws. The stomach tissue was then used to try and fill some of the excessive hole to my cheek. A smoother section of this material was shaped and carefully placed in position to become the flap to the half of the roof of my mouth that had been cut away.

At this point all of the tumour they could find had been removed and the necessary rebuilding work had been completed. The engine had effectively been repaired and put back in place. Now it was time to reconnect all of the various pipes, sparks plugs and hoses that were required to make the rest of the car work.

They were now well into my operation but everything was still critical. The re-connecting of the nerves was very delicate work and just as essential to a successful recovery as the removal of the tumour. I briefly amused myself with the possibility of the surgical team getting some of these connections wrong. I imagined myself making a full cancer recovery only to blink my eyes two weeks later and discovered my ears twitched instead!

When all my nerve connections were back in place the next job was to put my jaw back together. This was always going to be the most uncertain element of the reconstruction work. Simon had always warned me from the outset that this part of the procedure was going to be impossible to predict. He could not know exactly how much bone would need to be removed and therefore could not be sure how well my jaw would go back in place. He wouldn't know the extent of this work until he could see the cancer-attacked bone. As this part of the surgery was indeterminable he had always made a point of preparing me for the likelihood that I might not be able to talk or eat once the surgery was completed. The jaw was not going to be able to go back to what it was before. How good it would be, nobody could be sure.

All of these issues were going to have a huge impact on my future quality of life but, at that time, they were practically irrelevant to me. It was one hurdle at a time. The first one was to stay alive. I was solely focused on overturning the major odds that were against me. I just wanted to beat my cancer. I didn't really care what I needed to do to achieve that goal. I would have accepted blind, deaf, dumb or a wheelchair as a consequence if necessary. At that point the likelihood of my death was so big on the horizon that nothing else really mattered.

This singlemindedness was the right approach at that stage of my ordeal. I could not have afforded for anything to dilute my conviction to survive. Ten years on however, I now hugely appreciate all of the abilities that have been restored to me throughout my recovery. I have an entirely new sense of value about being able to see, hear, speak, eat and drink.

Survival is one thing, recovery and resuming a normal life is another.

In the end when my jaw was put back in place I found I was only able to open my mouth about half an inch. Remarkably this appears to be just enough for me to still speak perfectly. I can also eat every food type that I ate before, except, in some cases, I have needed to devise new methods to shuffle them in. Perhaps however the greatest accolade to the surgical team who reconstructed my mouth is that I can still sing! My singing has never been exceptional but the standard doesn't seem to have deteriorated between the old mouth and the new one.

When the work to the lower jaw was done most of the major reconstruction surgery was then complete. All that now remained was the 130 stitches it would take to close the wound to my face and whatever stitching was required to the cut at my hip. Due to it being a facial operation the surgical team wanted to minimise the possibility of any permanent scarring to my face. They had been working on me for ten or eleven hours and were nearing the end. They were all tired. But the stitching work was just as intricate as much of their earlier, risky surgical procedure. The stitches needed to be very small and frequent so that both sides of the wound would have maximum contact to enable it to heal seamlessly. Each stitch consequently was laborious to insert.

I got first hand knowledge of this myself about a week later when a nurse came to remove them. She told me that removing my stitches took her about six times longer than normal. The stubble on my face had started to grow back by then and the little stitches bore a remarkable resemblance to each one of my many facial hairs. She had to find each stitch first before it could be snipped for removal. In the end she had no option but to use a magnifying glass to determine which was thread and which was hair.

When the last stitch was put in place in the operating theatre it was 8.30 p.m. Simon told me that it had been a twelve hour operation. He explained that as surgical procedures go, it was as big as they get. My operation was on a par with anything that would be carried out after a major traffic accident. I had all of my original blood replaced during the course of their work.

He told me that by the end they were all exhausted. They needed maximum concentration right to the end. The work they were undertaking in the last hour was just as precise as what they were doing in the first. The work around the brain stem was especially critical. Any slip could have been catastrophic. He said to me that I was in danger right up to the end and would remain in danger for two or three weeks. He then reminded me that even now, I still had a long way to go in recovery before the success of the surgery could be determined. The flap on the roof of my mouth was very delicate. It needed to be inspected with a small torch four times a day and could be rejected at any stage.

He concluded by saying that from his point of view, as the surgeon, he felt all had gone as well as he could have expected. Everybody was satisfied that all of the tumour they could see had been removed. It was over to the radiotherapy now to hopefully destroy anything that may have been left behind.

For all of the time whilst Simon Rogers was speaking at the end of my bed I was just in awe of this man. The more he spoke the more and more embarrassed I became about what I did for a living. Up to this point in my life I had no appreciation of the incredible work that surgeons do. These unbelievable people had just spent twelve hours in the middle of my head.

A twelve hour day is a long day for anybody. It is a long day for a waitress in a café or a construction worker on a building site or an accountant in an office. But these people weren't serving coffee or drawing up a tax return. They were deconstructing the head of another human being. Your head is your computer. It contains your brain, your eyes, your ears, your nose, your mouth and your spine. They were delicately removing a vigorous cancer tumour from the very middle of the most complex part of the body, the head. Then they had to re-build all of the deconstructive work they had just done. They had to carefully reconstruct and reconnect everything again. On completion their concerns not just limited to how well the tumour had been removed but also to how well this head would ever function again.

That head belonged to me.

I just felt so guilty as this man at the end of my bed was describing what they had all done. Surely there is no greater work than this.

Then I thought of the 5% chance I had been given. That meant that I am only one out of twenty people who will survive an operation like this. There are 19 more people like me, who will undergo the exact same exhausting procedure. But they won't make it. How do these wonderful medical people go home to their families on those days as if it had been a normal working day. They will have carried out twelve hours of the most important work that you will find on this planet, only for it to have been in vain.

I was simply spellbound as he spoke. These were the most incredible men and women I had ever known. I was humbled by the extraordinary work they do. I was also acutely aware, for the first time, of the consequences of that work. Sometimes it will not go to plan. The rest of us can have a bad day but a bad day for these people means somebody dies when they did everything they could.

I needed these men and women much more than they will ever need me. But I had no awareness whatsoever of the work they did until now. My need from them was the ultimate need of all. It was the need to be kept alive.

I realised I had no understanding or appreciation of hospitals or the health industry up to this point in my life. Many of us suffer from this lack of awareness. As a consequence health cuts in governmental budgets are often seen as more palatable compared to sacrificing a major road building program or a new bridge or factory. In one case only a few hundred people will be affected but in the other a few thousand will be impressed. However it is only in the case of health cuts where you can be certain that people will die. All of this comes home much more clearly to you when your surgeon sits on the end of your bed and begins describing the work he has just done.

Now that I have started my second life, post cancer, I realise that the people who daily inhabit the mini-city that every hospital is, perform the ultimate work of all. It just doesn't get any bigger than saving or improving people's lives. From the porters to the managers, everybody in a hospital plays their part in the greatest form of human work of all, man looking after his fellow man. After the people who find the resolve to survive great tragedy these are the greatest human beings in the world. Without Blathnaid McCurtain, Carmel

O'Sullivan, John Fenton, David Husband, Simon Rogers and all of their wonderful staff and assistants I would not be sitting here now writing these words. I am forever indebted to all of them for every day I shall live from now on.

42 – First Word and First Drink

After a week the tracheotomy was taken out. I detested it so much by then that its removal gave me a huge lift. A few minutes later I uttered the very first word of my second life. I forget what it was. Soon after this a glass of iced water was brought to me. I didn't feel hungry when I was fed through the peg tube but I did feel extremely thirsty. After my pain, the sensation of wanting a drink was my next greatest agony. No matter how much I tried to remove it from my thoughts it became a permanent craving. I used all of my previously unfailing running mindset to help me ignore it. All you have to do is keep running until the end of the tracheotomy and then you can drink to your hearts content. Just keep going until then. But this time it was to no avail. This particular desire refused to be blocked out.

It did worse than that. It became almost like an unfed addiction. It got bigger and bigger. The more I tried to stop thinking about wanting a drink, the thirstier I got. My mind, rather than succumb to the discipline of my running mentality, began to play tricks on me. It started to send me flashes of the most alluring drinks I have ever enjoyed throughout my life. It presented them in their most irresistible form. Drinks in long, tall, ice cold glasses with warm sunshine, golden beaches and sparkling seas in the background.

All of these images eventually merged to become a billboard sized, glass of Coca Cola. The more I tried to stop thinking about it, the bigger it got. It was like some kind of torture. I was in my very own, one-man, week long, silent, thirst craving, prison camp. I have heard of torture through sleep depravation. Now I had a new method to offer to the despots of the world. You can drive a man crazy by denying him a drink if you supplant images of sun kissed cocktails into his mind.

The tracheotomy was my torturer. It was stopping me from relieving this craving. If it wasn't in place I could drink. I hated it even more now. I vowed that if I ever escaped from its clutches I would come back one day and exact my revenge! I would return and somehow work out a method to hurt that tracheotomy!

I raised the glass of iced water to my lips. It is genuinely difficult to describe how good it tasted. Maybe, if you imagined yourself having crawled through the Sahara desert for twenty days and somebody handing you your favourite drink, just before you die of thirst, it might come close. But I doubt it! That simple drink was one of the greatest sensations of my entire life. In a life span that now covers 50 years, it was six seconds of pure heaven.

I promised from that day out I would always fully value every drink I ever had again. I would cherish the fact that I could drink and that I had a drink to drink long before whatever liquid it was, reached my lips. I vowed that I would never again complain that a drink was too hot, or too cold, or didn't have enough ice or was in the wrong glass or cup. I will never again moan if the café only has ordinary coffee when I want a cappuccino. Every drink I would ever have from now on will definitely be sipped from the section of the glass that is half full.

I never want to let myself forget the sensations of that week. I know now how privileged I am to still be able to drink and especially to be able to speak. I don't want to forget how good that first drink tasted. That day I rediscovered how fortunate I was to be able to drink at all. I must never let myself forget that appreciation. That glass of water was one of the first major milestones of my recovery. I was able to drink again. No drink for the rest of my life will come close to how sweet it tasted.

It was now, only in the second week, after the tracheotomy had been removed, that the rehabilitation element of my recovery could begin. The physiotherapist came to see me as soon as I was sitting up in bed. My body had virtually been in the exact same position for two weeks. His job was to reintroduce it to some form of activity again before it started to think it was destined for rigor mortis.

The physiotherapist was a pleasant but determined individual. The nursing staff had all nicknamed him the "physioterrorist" but I assume that's an old hospital joke by now. He had a series of exercises to be achieved each day and would work with me until they were completed, no matter how long it took. He began with simple arm, neck and shoulder movements, whilst I was still sitting up in bed. Eventually he progressed to getting me standing again initially, before being convinced I had the strength and the confidence to start learning to walk again. Very, very slowly I began to take the very first steps of my second life.

To his delight he found me to be an equally determined pupil. This was a body that had run six marathons. It was almost an embarrassment for it now to be precariously treading across the floor of ward 29. It had reached the dizzy heights of crossing a finish line with thousands of people cheering it on. Now its achievements were only witnessed by my fellow patients on the ward. The top of the range running shoes had been replaced by a pair of slippers. It had fallen a long way from having run in the same race as two of the greatest long distance runners in Ireland and England, Sonia O'Sullivan and Paula Radcliffe. But that didn't matter now. Running would come later. Now it was time to try and walk what I could see. You have to crawl before you can walk. You have to walk before you can run. These were very early but essential pieces of the jigsaw. If they didn't go in place, vast sections around them would never be completed.

Once again I was able to apply my running experience to maximum effect. I could relate how I was feeling to the twenty mile stage of a badly run marathon. I still had 6 miles to go with nothing left but I knew that as soon as I started to dig deep, I would find something. It was time to go into my reserve petrol tank. This body of mine had simply never let me down before. It always responded to whatever demands I made on it.

This time however the goal wasn't to run 200 metres to the top of the hill. It was to have the strength and confidence to place one foot in front of the other. One foot in front of the other foot, without holding on to anyone. This wonderful body of mine, as always, would not let me down. This time I was going to go all the way to the toilet door.

My recovery had now become like one big long run. All I wanted to achieve was some progress for each day that came. This could have been just to sit up in bed or complete a new exercise with the physiotherapist. As I progressed it could just have been to eat something small or wash my face. Now it had reached the stage where I was going to be able to walk unaided for the first time again.

By the end of the week the physiotherapist was amazed with my progress. His final exercise was for me to go up and down a flight of stairs. I achieved this, exactly as he asked, at the first time of asking. Of all of my body parts, my two legs were the limbs that could be most relied upon. They had often carried me when just about everything else had given up. When the top step of the stairs was reached my physiotherapy was complete.

To be back on my feet so quickly was one of the key early pillars of my entire recovery. I could look out the window again. I could use the toilet unaided. I could walk over to chat to the other patients. Just like being able to drink again I uncovered a whole new appreciation as to what the word mobility actually means.

The ability to be mobile and independent was a huge factor in steering me back towards a normal life again. I was convinced I had my running to thank for this rapid early progress. I had always regarded my legs as the strongest part of my body. This was the great reward I was reaping for all the miles I had put in before leaving Ireland. Running had not just provided the mental stamina I needed to get me through recovery, it had also put the strength in my legs that I needed to get me back on my feet. In marathon terms I was past half-way now. I was turning for home. Nothing was going to stop me now. Not pain, not discomfort. They could throw what they liked at me now. I knew I had the capacity to cope. I had my rhythm and my stride and my pain threshold was unshakable. Nothing would knock me off course. First the tracheotomy had been removed, now I was walking again. After three weeks my recovery had reached an incredible level.

I was well able for all of my visitors by now. Pam was an unsung hero at this stage. She came in at least twice a day for every day I was in hospital. Carol, Dolores and Eleanor, my three sisters, were all taking turns to disrupt their lives in Ireland and come to see me too. The word was now spreading that I at last had the stamina for anybody who wanted to come. I am delighted to say that come they all did. People reappeared from all corners of my life again, just as they had before. Jack Naughton and Hugo Gaynor represented old friends from Horseleap. Simon Cushing, Dave Rudkin, Mike Cunningham and all of my old college friends took turns to give me a surprise boost by appearing at the end of the bed. Steve Quicke, Angie Boardman, Dave Colley and the F.S.P. staff from both the Liverpool and London offices came. Even two of my clients from Ryan Teese Architects made the journey. Denis Cooney and his family were returning from a tour of Europe in their camper van when they heard I was ill. They made a special detour to Liverpool just to see me. I was proud to be able to tell the nurses that the singular, conspicuously lost looking camper van they could see in the enormous hospital car park was there on my account!

Denis was the main instigator of our return to Ireland. He gave us our first commission for the design of his new house. That single project eventually culminated in us setting up our own practice. Now here he was going to great lengths for me again. Another client,

John Flynn from Ennis, like Ian Connolly before him, would not be content until he had got over to see me. John and I had become great friends during the previous couple of years when he asked me to design a scheme of houses on his land overlooking Ballyalla lake.

The two parish priests I had known in my time in Ballina also came to see me. As it turned out, both came separately on the same day! Fr. John Beatty was in charge when we first moved to Ballina and we became great friends. He arrived off the morning flight from Dublin. The plane that came over to bring him back later that day, brought our current parish priest, Fr. Ted O'Rahelly, also a great friend. Two parish priests on the one day. That can't have been good for the morale of my medical team!

I was amazed that such excursions were being made on my behalf. People were rearranging their lives and going to expense just to come and see me. But the lift that the visit of each of these distant visitors gave me was immeasurable. Pam, to her immense credit and my eternal gratitude, seemed to be at my side at all times. She tended to my every need on a daily basis. Unfortunately the familiarity of her visits could never match the impact of seeing a surprise face. This, sadly, is often the lot of the carer of the hospital patient.

The three boys were allowed to see me for the first time at this stage too. It was to be a dramatic encounter. It was difficult for both them and me. Up to the point of my surgery it was not easy for them to appreciate how ill their dad actually was. There was no blood to be seen. He appeared to be functioning much the same as he always did. We hear he is sick but we can't really see how he is. Now they realised that things had got a little more serious. I was in hospital and they were told I had undergone a big operation. Nothing however could really prepare them for what the implications of that operation would be.

As soon as they saw me for the first time after my surgery, they were just completely shocked. Two of them, I forget which two, immediately burst into tears. This hideous looking creature in the bed in front of them could not be their dad. Where had the man, who used to be their father, gone. And then I spoke. After hearing my voice they tentatively began to accept that this patient was indeed their dad. He must have been very sick after all. So sick that he had to have half of his face transformed.

Children, I believe, have an inherent sense of self preservation for situations like this. This is a good thing. You are very small and the world is very big. When the systems you have become accustomed to appear to malfunction your first instinct can often be to protect yourself. Perhaps a little bit of their reaction that first day stemmed more from "Oh no, how will we survive with a dad that looks like that" rather than "Oh no, our poor old dad"!

But if that was the case, it was perfectly fine.

The people from Ireland who didn't manage to come over made their connection by sending all kinds of gifts, cards and get well wishes. The funniest of these was sent by Malcolm and Clare Bell and Brian Byrne in Ballina. These three, I assume after a good night in the pub, decided to send me a sort of "Irishman abroad survival kit". It was a surprise package to lift my spirits. Three days later, Pam arrived in to see me. I was sleeping at the time. To her horror a very foreboding looking clinical box was placed beside the bed with my name on it. This mysterious container had all the appearances of being an authentic and very serious piece of medical kit. It was securely sealed up with tape and was emblazoned with intimidating warning signs. "Handle with care", "Right way up only" and "Very fragile" appeared to affirm its importance to anybody brave enough to glance in its direction.

Pam was stopped dead in her tracks. "Oh my God, not only has he cancer but now he has to have a heart transplant as well"

I came around a few minutes later and we jointly unwrapped the mystery box. It transpired that the nurses had left it for me while I was sleeping. After negotiating our way past all of the warning signs we discovered an inner cooler box. This only seemed to reaffirm the possibility that we might unearth a pumping heart or a pair of lungs! We carefully removed the lid and found a sea of polystyrene padding chips waiting for us. We plunged our hands below the surface, still puzzled as to what we were going to find.

When we had removed the last item from the box the table across my bed contained six cans of draught Guinness, a Guinness pint glass, a "Guinness is good for you" T-shirt, a Guinness pen, a Guinness key ring, a bar towel, two beer mats and various other bits of paraphernalia from the famous Dublin Brewery. The card inside simply read "All of these will keep you going until you get home".

We had attracted quite an audience by this stage. The nurses and even a few of the doctors had gathered, eager to discover if yet another surprising Guinness object could emerge from our rummage through the magical pool of polystyrene chippings. How we all laughed. The "Irishman's survival kit" had nearly been responsible for giving the Irishman's wife a heart attack!

One of the major factors that every hospital patient has to contend with is the passage of time. A hospital stay will be one of the few occasions in your life when you will have more time than you can use. Filling this time appropriately can be crucial to maintaining a good state of mind to aid your recovery. Many people will use spare time like this to read. Reading however requires a relatively high level of concentration. This may not make it an appropriate source of distraction to patients with low energy levels. Any kind of sustained book reading was certainly well beyond me at this stage. Besides, as I said from the outset, I have never been a good reader. It was never going to be my preferred choice for making time disappear.

The situation you now find yourself in is unorthodox. It is not part of your normal life plan. The solution to keeping your mind occupied may, as a result, need to be unorthodox too. Almost all regular pastimes, walking, fishing, cards, chess, etc. are unavailable to you. Rather than a standard off the shelf activity, you may now need something more tailor-made. Although I have never been a good book reader I have always loved newspapers, reading only the parts that interest me and skimming the rest. I also have the sort of brain that has always enjoyed the challenge of a puzzle such as a crossword, quiz or Sudoku. If I could, I needed to find something that would combine both of these interests, but in a manner that would not require extensive brainwork.

I found exactly what I was looking for in a most unexpected part of the newspaper. A section of the newspaper that previously I would barely have noticed. The newspaper pages that I found were best suited to whiling away the long hours of my hospital recuperation were the racing pages.

Every day of my hospital stay I would do the horses. I would do every race, at every meeting. This was the one activity that I found not only appealed to me, it could also be adjusted to suit my varying levels of stamina. It was a challenge of judgement if I needed it to be, or a lucky dip if that was all I could manage. It could be adjusted to soak up as much or as little time as I was able to throw at it. If my energy levels were high I could spend twenty or thirty minutes on just one race. If I was completely exhausted I could just select all the second favourites or all the number 5's or just the horses whose names I liked. It appealed to my fondness for calculation, statistics and methodology but my input could be varied to suit what I was able for. I could calculate my own selections based on intense scrutiny of the form of each horse or I could just employ a system and select on the basis of the jockey, the trainer, the favourite, the name or the number. I could then compare all the various systems. Yesterday I would have made more money by backing all the number sevens than all the favourites.

The greatest appeal of my racing conundrums however was that horse racing is part of the real world. Unlike a crossword or a Sudoku these were real race meetings with real horses and real people in attendance. My past-time was real. The results everyday were part of the news in the newspaper. I wanted my activity to also help reintroduce me to the world beyond the hospital walls.

All of this could take me hours. It required a certain amount of judgement and memory so I felt it was a good early mental exercise for me. When the following day's paper arrived I would first spend an hour or so checking the results. I would evaluate my success rate or otherwise from my combination of selections the previous day. I would establish which system, if any, would have been the most successful. All of the horses with the word "house" in their name, all of the horses ridden by Tony McCoy, all of the horses who had won their last race. And all of this took up time before I even got started on that days racing.

My daily racing selections were just another invention my mind had conjured to keep itself busy while it was restricted to a hospital bed. It knew I liked newspapers and statistics. All it did was found a combination of the two that I could manage. It knew it had to put this piece of the jigsaw in place for me. It had to keep my mind occupied and contented whilst the rest of my body was incapacitated. It was aware that my mind needed exercise too. It needed to be kept occupied to stay on the right track.

Now that the jigsaw has been completed and my newspaper reading is back to normal I don't think I have ever read the racing pages in the same way since then!

The two easiest mediums for passing time at this early stage of my recovery were television and music. Every bed at Aintree University Hospital had its own paycard television monitor. If used continuously this proved to be expensive but with selective viewing it became an affordable essential. For a patient in my debilitated condition I found it to be an indispensable distraction.

Television can sometimes get bad press. It can be accused of encouraging idleness in normal life. When a state of exhaustive idleness is forced upon you however, through no fault of your own, there are few better sources of entertainment. Television is not intrusive or demanding. It does all of the thinking for you. You are only required to relax and observe. That was not only what I needed at that time but also it was all that I was capable of. I was in a permanent state of tiredness and I needed my pastime to do all of the work for me.

Television addressed that requirement perfectly. It again also offered a flexible and varied menu to suit the fluctuating levels of my ability. When my brain was completely flat something superficial and unchallenging was selected. As my strength began to return I could select programmes with more depth that provided greater mental stimulus. Television, in my opinion, is a quintessential element of a productive hospital stay for every patient.

The only item I bought for myself before I was admitted to hospital was a compact disc player. I have always been a big music fan. I knew the right kind of music would play an important role in keeping me contented through rehabilitation and recovery. Before I set out for Liverpool I lined up all my old favourite C.D.s and bought some new ones. I thought it would be an opportunity to run through my entire back catalogue of the music that I had been playing for years. To my surprise however only one band emerged from this personal selection process. One band emerged to the complete exclusion of all others.

The only music I could play for the entire duration of my illness was that of the Smashing Pumpkins. I made an exclusive connection with them for my entire hospital stay. They were the only band I found that could cover all of the emotions I was experiencing. They had songs on every album that connected directly with my anger, my hope, my despair, my joy, my love, my pain, my faith.

The Smashing Pumpkins are from Chicago. They are led by their enigmatic front man Billy Corgan. As a band they have always remained true to their principles. At the height of their popularity they could have opted to travel a well trodden route to megastar fame and universal popularity. They refused. Instead they continued to write edgy but incredible songs about life as they saw it. As a result they attracted a devoted cult following rather than an unlimited one. The more I discovered about them the more attached I became.

Their songs varied from raging anthems filled with fury and desolation to beautiful, delicate love songs of innocence and purity. In any one night all of these songs would tune perfectly with the range of emotions running through me. I could be silently screaming "let me out" (of this cancer ravaged body) whilst listening to "Cherub Rock" one minute and declaring that "today is the greatest day of my life" from "Today", the next.

Billy Corgan himself also appeared to have many attributes I liked. It was as if we had become friends. We were waiting for each other at the end of the day. I was alone on my bed by then. All of the daily activities had ceased and the visitors had gone. His lyrics seemed to portray him as something of a tortured soul, a frustrated genius. Somebody who wrote songs in accordance with his feelings. As a result, his music connected with you personally. A man who wouldn't sell out on the standards he wanted to achieve. He refused to compromise his art for the sake of maximising commercial opportunities.

I knew he would understand just how I felt lying on that bed at that time. A body that had run six marathons now lay crumpled and devastated. Billy Corgan and Co. put the music piece of my jigsaw in its place. So, just as the roads around Ballina and Killaloe became my roads and Liverpool became my city, the Smashing Pumpkins became my band. I refused to play the music of anybody else.

My progress by week four was simply extraordinary. The physiotherapist was long gone. I was back on my feet, looking, remarkably, as if I could soon start to think about being discharged. I was on the verge of setting a new record for recovery from major surgery. Surgery that was as big as it comes but this wonderful body of mine had risen up to defy it. It all seemed to be too good to be true. That is exactly what came to pass.

43 - Meningitis

With Pam seeing me at least twice a day she was becoming the best person to monitor my condition on a regular basis. She began to notice that my remarkable progress had not only stalled but now appeared to be regressing. Over a few visits she found me to be more drowsy every time she came in. I was clearly not as bright and responsive as I had previously been.

She brought what she saw as a deterioration in my condition, to the attention of the nurses. Initially they assumed it was still extreme tiredness after the surgery. For the nursing staff you are just one of many patients they have to oversee. Unless you are in visible distress on their snapshots of you through the day, they may not immediately pick up a more sedentary change to your condition.

Relatives perform a vital role in this area of patient care. They have only one person in the hospital that they care about. They also care about that person more than anyone else does. Your visiting carer will often become the most important and immediate assessor of a change in your condition. I was very lucky to have one of the best there is. Pam is thankfully extremely thorough when it comes to all matters medical. In fact she goes beyond thorough to the point of being obstinately persistent.

Dissatisfied with the nurses response that I was just tired she insisted that a doctor was called. When the doctor came I was examined. Within minutes the alarm was raised. All was not well.

By now I was in a state of semi-consciousness. The immediate suspicion was that I had hydrocephalus. Hydrocephalus, to the lay-man, is water on the brain. It is a very serious condition. Fluid build up, caused by the trauma of major surgery, gets trapped in the skull. It will cause permanent brain damage if not released quickly.

When I was returned to the ward after my operation many of my tubes would have been drains to relieve excess fluid and damaged blood. The worry now was that all of this fluid may not have drained away. Some may have found its way into the cavity between my brain and skull. This fluid now needed to be released immediately. If it remained in place it would apply pressure to my brain. If I did have hydrocephalus I would require to have a shunt fitted as a permanent valve to prevent any future build up.

This was a very serious setback. Everybody was very worried. My chances of getting through this without brain damage were slim. As I was whisked out of ward 29 pandemonium was breaking out all around me. By now I was in a deep coma and was blissfully unaware of this latest twist that my story had taken.

I was rushed to the neuro wing of the hospital. In the next few minutes I went somewhat from the frying pan to the fire. I didn't have hydrocephalus. That was great news. What I did have however was an even greater threat to my life. A lumbar puncture revealed that I had acute bacterial meningitis.

One of the downsides of my extensive surgery was that it opened up all of the major channels between my brain and the cavities to my nose, mouth and ears. My immune system had effectively been pushed aside. It was like a goalkeeper who returned to the pitch for the second half only to discover the goalposts had been replaced by tower cranes. All of the routes to my brain were now wide open for any infection that chose to let itself in. Unfortunately the one that took up the invitation was meningitis.

It was to be two days before I would get back to my senses. I was apparently out of danger by then but had come very close to losing my life. Meningitis is an infection that attacks the lining to your brain. It can kill you within hours. Mine was intercepted just in time.

I scanned down along my body, just as I did when I came around after the surgery. I became very dejected with what I saw. All of those tubes were back in place and I was strictly confined to bed. All that seemed to be missing for a complete déjà vu was the tracheotomy. I was about to discover a whole new compartment of my fight plan. A compartment that, just now, I found to be bare.

Up to this I had fully accepted my cancer. Everything had been geared to fighting that cancer all the way. Unexpected setbacks however, had not been included in the calculation. The cancer alone was such a massive enemy that I had made no allowances for it joining forces with an ally. Suddenly I found I had been wrong footed. I had only one battle plan. I had nothing in place to take on the meningitis or any other side effect.

If my mind had been missing in action for the first days of meningitis at least the rest of my body carried on the fight. It had taken the necessary medication to suppress the meningitis attack without any instruction from head office. The control tower had been taken out for the first few days of combat through unconsciousness. This was probably just as well for my ill-prepared mindset. It would have had to scramble back to zero before any clear instruction could have been given.

Now that I was beyond danger and conscious again I needed to re-focus. I needed to get my mind back on track. This was a setback and I needed to accept it and deal with it. I needed to keep running without breaking stride. I had to get my mind to rejoin my body so that they were both fighting side by side again.

Within hours my disappointment was dissipating. I was being fed the necessary medication intravenously and the meningitis was under control. All I needed to do was lie there and see it through. Then I would just get ready to move on to the next stage after it was done. I needed to switch my thinking from marathon to triathlon now. I had just completed the run. Now I needed to cycle through meningitis.

The greatest setback was a mental one. I now needed to deal with the psychological impact of appearing to be right back to square one. I was completely exhausted. I seemed to have fallen a long way since impressing my physiotherapist with my stair exercises. It had been 12 steps forward and now 11 steps back.

But by now, my mind was back in harness. It was strong again. It would go wherever I needed it to go. It had readjusted to the fact that a new, sub-challenge had been thrown in its way. The radio wasn't broken. All that had happened was the station that was playing had slipped off its wavelength. It just needed to be retuned and all would be fine again.

Now it was merely a case of retracing steps that I knew I had previously achieved. I just needed to focus on them again. There was no need for fuss or complaint. All I had to do was run what I could see. Even if this was a section of road I had already run before. The danger of the meningitis had now passed. I just needed to learn to sit up, stand up, eat, drink and walk all over again.

With the right frame of mind restored I began to make steady progress. The remainder of my treatment in the neuro wing passed off without any further incident. My strength returned and I replaced all of the little recovery blocks that had gone missing. Two weeks later I reached the biggest milestone in my treatment to date. I was deemed to be well enough to be discharged from hospital. If opening my eyes after my surgery was winning the first point in my cancer tennis match, this was the equivalent of taking the first set.

44 – Back Out in the Real World

David Husband, my radiotherapy consultant, did not want that essential part of my treatment to begin much later than six weeks after my surgery. Because of the meningitis almost a month of that interval had now passed. It was now imperative that I became strong enough to start radiotherapy within two more weeks. When I left the hospital, Pam and I moved in with her mother for a few days and then with my first cousin Mary Naughton. A semblance of normal life was beginning to fall into place for me again.

Mary and her husband Brian lived in the attractive leafy Liverpool suburb of Grassendale. It was about four miles south of the city centre and a short distance from the shore of the river Mersey estuary. My fondest memories from this period were every evening when Pam, Mary and Brian would take me for the short walk down to the river. I would rest through the day and by evening time would have enough energy accumulated for the 300 metre stroll to the water and back.

The reward for my endeavours was a splendid view across the river, which by that time of the evening, was bathed in a beautiful palette of twilight shades. It was fitting that I was in the company of the three people who had done so much to get me to this point. This little walk every evening was like a microcosm of all their assistance, along the journey, up to then. It was as if the front door represented my initial diagnosis and they helped me from there to the river which was like the new horizon awaiting me after my release from hospital.

It was early Autumn. I distinctly remember the crispness of these atmospheric evenings. To this day I still have a vivid recollection of rustle of the leaves underfoot as I walked along the pavements. I can remember registering, like never before, how beautiful this season is. In the calendar year it heralds the end of the growing season but it was my renaissance. It marked the very first meaningful activity of my second life.

These beautiful evenings were the birth of that second chance at life. Because of this I have a tremendous appreciation for every Autumn I have enjoyed ever since. This was the season I was to be re-born into. Every year it registers that I have survived yet another year. It announces that I have a whole new one about to begin. I have always loved the Autumn. Now I love it even more. It is my season.

Whilst I was recovering at Mary and Brian's a remarkable event took place in Ballina. Fr. Ted O'Rahelly and the local community organised for a special Mass to be said for me. This Mass was videotaped and a copy was sent over to me. It took place on a Tuesday evening and just about everybody I knew in Ballina attended. At this stage of my recovery I was still prone to an occasional bout of dejection. Now I was equipped with a powerful new weapon to combat this. All I had to do was pop this video into the machine and my spirits were lifted immediately. How could I feel downcast when all of these people had gone to such lengths for me. They had arranged a Mass just for my benefit. They were fighting for me and now I was not fighting for them. It was time to stop feeling sorry for myself and re-focus. I had to resume fighting because if I didn't, I was letting these wonderful people down.

The camera recorded everyone as they entered the church. Then it panned around the congregation as Fr. Ted said Mass. These were great people. These were my people. For his sermon Fr. Ted spoke directly into the camera. He told me everybody in that church was rooting for me. Everyone was praying that I would make a full recovery and come back home. They would all be waiting for me when I did.

That Mass was a wonderful celebration of hope and spirit dedicated just to me. It was a wonderful gesture and gave me a huge lift. In many ways it was an appreciation and amusingly all that seemed to be missing was the coffin at front of the altar!

I had a famous day out with Fr. Ted soon after I returned home. We drank many bottles of wine together in a pub in Birdhill. I jokingly asked him that day if I was the only person in Ireland with a video of my own funeral!

I never got the chance to tell all of the people in that church how inspirational that video was. Any time I was low all I had to do was put it on. I could let myself down but I couldn't let all of them down. No matter how much pain or despondency I was feeling, it always worked. It was an incredible thing to do and its impact was immense. I would like to take this opportunity to thank all of them now.

I was now gaining in strength with each passing day. The fragile daily walks were just the beginning. Before long they propelled me towards a more recognisable daily lifestyle. For the first time in two months I began to rejoin the human race. I was beginning to return to the everyday world that exists beyond the walls of a hospital. My second life was starting to vaguely resemble the one I had known and loved so much as my first.

I was still on very heavy medication, including a high dosage of morphine, but I was now starting to do what normal people do again. I was able to have the occasional meal in a restaurant. I was able to go with family and friends for a drink in the local pub. All of these little milestones were a huge boost to the restoration of my humanity. I was beginning to dip my toe in the real world again. Little things became big for me like ordering a meal from a menu or paying a barman for a drink. They were a long way from designing a new football stadium or running a marathon, but in the infancy of my second life, for a man given a 5% chance to live, they were huge. I was no longer a house bound invalid who only moved between the bed and the sofa. I was a man again. Just like the progress I had shown after my physiotherapy, it all nearly seemed to be too good to be true. And once again, it was!

45 – Deep Vein Thrombosis

One of the medications I was on at this time was warfarin. This was a blood thinning agent. I was prescribed it to prevent any clotting that could occur as a result of the surgery. This information was likely to have been explained to me at some point along the way but it probably got lost beneath the bigger issues, like life and death. When I woke in Mary's one morning therefore with a visibly swollen right leg I was not in a position to self diagnose what it might be. I naively just assumed that it was a slight swelling, probably caused by my lack of exercise. It would soon pass. I also did that "man" thing again. I neglected to inform either Pam or Mary, who was a qualified doctor. As the day wore on the swelling got bigger rather than reduce. I eventually got back to bed in the certainty that all it needed was a good night's sleep. It would probably be gone in the morning.

When the morning came my leg was almost twice the size it should have been. Pam and Mary only needed one look at it before calling an ambulance first and scolding me for ignoring it for a full 24 hours second. It was time for hospital number three and I was rushed to the main hospital in Liverpool, the Royal, in the city centre.

When I hobbled in to A & E with my new "balloon" leg I was immediately ushered to a bed and connected up to a drip. I had a deep vein thrombosis. Just like with meningitis time was of the essence. I had ignored this potentially lethal situation for a little too long. If the clot had travelled to my heart it would have killed me long before the cancer got the chance to. Yet again I had just been caught in time. I needed to improve my tactics with the non-cancer issues. Everything could not be accounted for as a side affect of my extensive surgery that would just pass. It was time to cut out these near miss setbacks. My luck would eventually run out.

For those few hours I was a sorry looking state. Here I was having to tackle another blow that had come from nowhere. I had been so proud of being able to walk to the river and now my freedom was gone. I sat discontentedly in a chair of yet another hospital. I felt like an old man. These self pitying sentiments did not even recognise the real danger. The true facts were that I had escaped yet another threat to my life.

All I was able to see was that the mobility that I had become so fond of again was now gone. I sat there very dejectedly taking the necessary medicine. I was more fearful that I might not walk properly again, rather than realise how lucky I was to still be alive.

In time I would come around. I would get my fight plan up and running again. I began to joke that most people who got a D.V.T. had earned it by taking a long haul flight half way around the world. All I had done was catch the Seacat from Dublin! My mind was quicker now at getting back on track. It could shake off any new despondency before too long. It started to ensure my spirits were lifted by finding humour somewhere in the in midst of my latest disappointment.

Of all the days to have a very special visitor, that had to be the one. My great friend John Clifford had never been on an airplane before but he wanted to come and see me. Bernard Kennedy persuaded him to take to the skies just for me. The two of them flew in that morning. I am very proud to be able to say that I was the person responsible for John Clifford taking his very first flight. I am also glad to report that has hardly stopped flying ever since. He has been a frequent visitor to see his relatives in America since we managed to get him to break his duck by flying from Dublin to Liverpool.

John and Bernard were due to come and see me at Mary's house but Pam redirected them to the Royal. I got the shock of my life when the two of them walked in to the day ward. At most other times I was ready for my visitors but not that day. In hindsight it was probably just the shot in the arm I needed. I didn't want them to see me in the middle of another despairing setback. I sat up in the bed and pretended nothing was wrong. I was trying to make it look as if they had just come on the day of one of my routine visits to the hospital. If I thought however that I was making a good impression on them, I was greatly mistaken.

Bernard admitted to me months later that in their assessment of me on the flight home, they both reached the conclusion that they had seen me for the last time. He said I looked terrible that day. They both got a huge shock when they saw me. They were convinced I would not survive to make the return journey back to Ireland. He said they both found it difficult to conceal this assessment from me for the duration of their visit.

It is great to hear honest details like this when you have reached the safety of a successful recovery. If I had been aware of these sentiments on the day I am not sure how I would have reacted. You depend heavily on your family and friends at times like these. If two of my best friends were feeling I was going to die I'm sure it may have punctured my fighting armour. Especially on a day like that when my spirits were already low.

By the end of the day I had completed the medication. I was deemed fit enough to be released and did not require an overnight stay. I was dragging my right leg for a little while but within a couple of days the swelling had gone. I was properly back on my feet again. Now I had run the cancer, cycled the meningitis and swam the deep vein thrombosis. I had to hope now my ordeal was just a triathlon. I would not survive if it became a decathlon.

46 – Chemo-Radiotherapy Begins

By now my time limit for beginning radiotherapy was almost up. Dave Husband confirmed that he did not wish to postpone it any longer than August 28th. Radiotherapy ideally follows as soon as it can after surgery. This is to give the tumour as little chance as possible to begin to regenerate itself. Any remnants, missed by the surgery, need to be radioactively destroyed before they can conspire into a stronger force. It was critical now that nothing else went wrong for me. However, one final twist was still to be faced.

We were now staying in a nice apartment overlooking Sefton Park. Sefton Park is a beautiful old Victorian park just south of Liverpool city centre. It covers 269 acres, complete with lakes, bandstands, a cafe, an aviary, a palmhouse and hundreds of majestic trees. It is to Liverpool what Central Park is to New York.

The apartment was owned by Aileen Flavin from Cork. Aileen was not just a very good friend of Mary's but coincidentally was also an oncologist in Clatterbridge, my radiotherapy hospital. She was going to be away for a few weeks and we gratefully accepted her offer of the apartment to give Mary and Brian a break. They had given over the top floor of their house to Pam and I for two months at this stage.

On the weekend before I was due to begin radiotherapy I began to experience severe headaches. This was grim news indeed. I had already rebuffed meningitis and a D.V.T. but headaches could only mean one thing. This story had begun with headaches and their return now brought me right back to the day I was told I had cancer. All we could believe was that this was the return of my tumour. All of the delays had permitted it to resurrect even before I got to begin radiotherapy.

We were now very worried. I was in great pain. These headaches were not like before. For the first time in all of my treatment I momentarily did lose heart. The boxing gloves were lowered. I began to believe that this was now the end.

We tried to call a doctor but it was a holiday weekend. All of the regular doctors were off duty. All we could get was a locum on temporary cover. Our frustrations grew when it very difficult to convey the details of my case to him. He just kept trying to prescribe normal medication for me assuming these were normal headaches. In the end all we could do was hold out until Monday and make direct contact with Dave Husband. All through the weekend the headaches refused to relent. I was in constant agony now. My mind was oblivious to everything apart from the pain and the words Simon Rogers had said to me "If it comes back, there is nothing we can do".

When Dave Husband heard about my new predicament he summoned me immediately to Clatterbridge. I was sent for a C.T. scan. Our fears that this was the reoccurrence of the tumour were proved accurate when he confirmed that this was the likely cause. The scan should be able to tell him for sure.

The C.T. scan, as it transpired, was not entirely conclusive. It did indicate a new area of concern where tumour re-growth was the most likely explanation, but it was not definitive. New alarm bells were now ringing for Dave Husband. He had to assume this was the return of my tumour and needed to make last minute adjustments, to counteract this, to his intended treatment.

Just like John Fenton and Simon Rogers before him, I got on very well with Dave Husband. I was more than happy to be in his hands. Whatever call he felt he needed to make at this late juncture was fine by me.

The one thing he was certain of was that my radiotherapy could not afford any further delay. Whatever changes he needed to make would have to be based around that. He decided that if this was a fresh re-growth of tumour it was likely to be at an early stage. His impromptu rearrangement therefore was to upgrade my treatment to a course of chemo-radiotherapy rather than just radiotherapy alone. This involved interspersing three separate chemotherapy treatments whilst my radiotherapy was taking place. Each of these treatments would require me to stay overnight in the hospital, at two week intervals. Having attended for my normal radiotherapy session that day I would just go upstairs to be admitted for the night. I would then be hooked up to a drip and fed the chemotherapy drugs until the next day. The following day I would just go down for my regular radiotherapy session and return home.

This combination of treatments would hopefully work together. The chemotherapy would target any new tumour growth and the radiotherapy would be aimed at anything that was possibly left behind after the surgery. Between the two it was hoped that any possibility of the tumour re-establishing itself would be eradicated.

In hindsight, given the change in circumstances, I believe this last minute switch was probably a long shot. I was lucky to have a radiotherapist of the quality of Dave Husband. It was a radical decision to switch from radiotherapy to chemo-radiotherapy at the very last minute.

When I look back over my cancer treatment I always feel a little guilty that I tend to concentrate on the surgical aspect of what I went through rather than my radiotherapy. The extent of the surgical element of the treatment is much more understandable to the patient. Its impact is fully visible. I had a twelve hour operation and, to a large degree, have a good understanding of the work that was done.

The radiotherapy work, on the other hand, is much more abstruse. It is more of a silent assassin. In its administration it doesn't appear much different than a series of daily x-rays. It is generally both non intrusive and invisible. It is also undertaken while you are a day patient. You are free to come and go rather than being confined to a bed in a ward. It does not require tracheotomies, peg tubes, 130 stitches or physiotherapists. If both treatments were films, surgery would be "The Texas Chainsaw Massacre" compared to radiotherapy's "The Usual Suspects".

Simon Rogers has always made a point of reminding me that my radiotherapy was just as crucial to my survival as my surgery, if not more so. His work, although extremely intricate and delicate, had a physicality to it. He had to find and remove as much of the tumour as he could see. Dave Husband's work in comparison was much more abstract. It was more science than medicine. He didn't have the luxury of being able to look his enemy in the eye. He had to work out where his target was likely to be hiding. Then he had to calculate how much ammunition would be required to finish him off. But he couldn't just fire at will. If he did his patient could die. He had to carefully balance the amount of radiotherapy that could be withstood, with the amount needed to get the job done. In my case he also needed to make a last minute adjustment to his battle plan. He needed to add chemotherapy to his weaponry.

Simon Rogers also informed me, years later, that chemo-radiotherapy treatments were still at an early stage at that time. Dave Husband may well have needed to go into uncharted waters in his final calculations for my treatment. I had radical radiotherapy and may not have survived if I was not in his hands. John Fenton sent me to Liverpool, Simon Rogers removed my tumour but Dave Husbands role may well have been the most important of all.

I began my first chemotherapy session immediately. I was now on my fourth hospital. Clatterbridge was also my first non-city hospital. It is located in a pleasant rural setting on the Wirral peninsula, south of Birkenhead, about fifteen miles from Liverpool. It was generally a low slung development, with no buildings more than two storeys high, all sprawled over a large area. All of the treatment stations and daytime facilities were located at ground level with the admission wards on the floor above.

After assessing my headaches and recalculating my treatment he sent me upstairs immediately to be allocated a bed. In all of my preparations chemotherapy was the one thing I had not allowed for. I was familiar with the stories about your hair falling out and feeling very sick but by now I just didn't care. My fight plan had a last caught up with all possible setbacks and diversions. Now it was ready to take anything in its stride. It was as if somebody had just thrown a hurdle on to the track in a race I was running. Rather than raise an objection I just wanted to jump it and carry on. My high pain threshold was still there and I was already bald. Neither sickness nor hair loss would have any impact on me. This chemo medication had now just become an extra piece in my jigsaw. It was just a case of taking it to put that piece in place. Then I would just continue with my search for the remaining pieces to complete the puzzle.

My three chemotherapy treatments turned out to be very straightforward. They didn't have any impact on the normal quality of life I had now returned to. I didn't experience any sickness or additional hair loss. My headaches never returned so, as a treatment, it worked perfectly. It appears that Dave Husband's intuitive decision to add chemotherapy to my program was a masterstroke. He had successfully eradicated whatever was causing the headaches I had been experiencing.

Before I could begin radiotherapy I was sent to the lab. I needed to have a mask of my face made. Every day for radiotherapy it was imperative that my head was in exactly the same position for each treatment. This was to ensure that the angles for my radiation, which had been so expertly calculated by Dave Husband, would always be precise. The only method of ensuring this was to fit my face with a mask and literally bolt my head to the treatment table. That was the only way to guarantee that I was in exactly the same position every day.

Clatterbridge had a specialist lab technician. His job was to make these unique masks for each head and neck patient. First he needed a mould so wet strips of plaster of Paris were placed all over my face. For a few minutes I felt as if I was in some kind of French art studio rather than a hospital. I lay on a table as the wet plaster was smoothed into place with two small uncovered areas left for my eyes and a larger opening for my mouth and nostrils. I then had to remain motionless for about half an hour while it set. This was now the mould from which an exclusive mask would be made. It would be a mask that could not be found anywhere else in the world. That mask would be of Liam Ryan's face. It would take two days to be ready.

As soon as my mask was made my radiotherapy began. As a cancer patient, radiotherapy was, in many ways, the best period of my entire treatment. For surgery it was as if I was a patient first and a person second, especially when the tracheotomy was in place. Now I had returned to normal life and my treatment had become just a small part of my normal day. My strength levels had returned to a recognisable level. I was feeling fully human for the first time in three months. Apart from my lunchtime radiotherapy visit to Clatterbridge, the rest of my day was free.

My radiotherapy would run for seven weeks. I had to attend every day from Monday to Friday with each treatment lasting no longer than fifteen minutes. Clatterbridge had an entire fleet of radiotherapy treatment stations, each with their own designated team of radiologists. You were assigned to one of the stations for all of your treatment and given an hourly slot during which you needed to turn up.

In spite of the gravity of this treatment for all of the patients concerned, radiotherapy has a lovely social dimension to it. Every day when you arrived, you met the same staff and got to know the other patients in your slot. My time was between 12.30 and 1.30 every day. I had four other patients in my group. We could turn up at any time within our designated hour and were then treated on a first come, first served basis.

The treatment room was effectively a concrete bunker. This was to ensure the radioactive rays were limited to the patient they were intended for only. Each staff member had to adhere to a very strict system of checks before the machines were switched on.

All of the staff I met in radiotherapy were absolutely wonderful. They greeted you every day as if you had just walked in to a cake shop. Yet, concealed behind the warm smiles, they were all dedicated professionals. They were all fully aware of the gravity of the work they were performing. They were skilled and efficient without ever making you feel anything but relaxed and reassured. They got to know us all personally but I assume each case history must have been impossible to ignore. They must have wondered, from time to time, how many of us would still be alive in twelve months time. If they did they never showed it. They greeted you every day as if they had been an old friend you had known for years.

When it was my turn I was taken inside the treatment room. I was placed lying face up on the treatment table. My very own unique clear plastic mask was then produced and applied to my face to fix me in position. On the first day that this was done the three boys were allowed in to see me before the machines were switched on. Their dad had just become the man in the "plastic" mask. Once the mask was secured to the treatment table and everything was ready the staff would leave the room. The radiation danger light would then be switched on. Now it was just me and the machine. We had a good understanding between us. I was providing the tumour. The machine provided the radioactivity.

The treatment that followed was like a scene out of Star Trek. The table would spin to whatever position it required me to be in. All of this had been programmed by David Husband in precise detail. The radiotherapy device would then hover over my head like a miniature space ship on a robotic arm. It was controlled by the staff beyond the safety of the thick concrete walls. A light on the wall would indicate when the radiation had been switched on. It then silently emitted its deadly, invisible rays. It travelled to two further positions to repeat the procedure. If the film Rollerball was the human equivalent of pinball, this was the human version of Space Invaders. My cancer cells were the lines of little aliens on the screen that were getting blown to bits.

Dave Husband had to meticulously calculate and indeed predict all of this treatment. Where was the tumour likely to be. How advanced would it have become. What amount of radiation would be needed to destroy it. How much radiation would I be able to withstand. This part of my treatment was more about engineering and science than it was about medicine. If Simon Rogers was my surgeon, Dave Husband was both my engineer and my scientist.

I didn't feel anything during the course of each radiotherapy treatment. When it was finished the machine and the treatment table returned to their original positions and the lights came on again. One of the staff would appear and unfetter me from my captive mask. I was then simply free to go.

This was easy. I just had to come in, have convivial conversations with both my fellow patients and the staff before undergoing what seemed like a completely benign process for 15 minutes. Then I could return to relaxing for the rest of the day.

But of my two treatments, radiotherapy was always going to be the sneaky one. Behind its short term cloak was a very long term dagger. It masqueraded as benign in its application but it concealed its repercussions for a later day. The payback for its annihilation of my inner body tissue was yet to come.

47 – Visitors & Taxi Drivers

I was really beginning to live again at this stage. I had many visitors coming over from Ireland and I now had the energy to show them many of the great sights around Liverpool. I began to revisit all of the places that I had known and loved so well from my student days. My three sisters Carol, Dolores and Eleanor were also with me for much of this time. Everybody stayed at a small budget hotel near Mary and Brian's house. Cousin Cora came over from Dublin, as did Mick Dolan. Jack Naughton and Hugo Gaynor came from Horseleap, Philip Brady from Cavan and Ian and Geno came back again from Ballina. My life was becoming a social whirl, even if the swirl was turning very slowly.

I was only too happy to show "my city" off to all of these visitors. I became their guide for tours that included the two cathedrals, the Albert Dock, Matthew Street and other famous Beatle locations, the Pier Head and Speke Hall. I was also able make return visits to many of my old favourite student pubs. The Philharmonic, Ye Cracke, The Roscoe Head, The Beehive and The Albert on Lark Lane all went down well when my visitors grew thirsty. I wasn't overdoing it of course but my first glass of water after the tracheotomy had now progressed to an occasional pint of beer or Guinness. I appreciated them like I never had before.

I also went to see the three football teams on Merseyside. Christy, Lowell and I went to see Liverpool at Anfield when they beat Spartak Moscow 5-0 in the Champions League. With the girls and Jack and Hugo I saw Everton beat Middlesborough at Goodison Park. We "discovered" Wayne Rooney that day. It was his last home game before he scored his famous goal against Arsenal that catapulted his recognition well beyond the Everton faithful. I also popped across the river to see the team that probably became my favourite Merseyside team of all. The team that bore the closest resemblance to Athlone Town, Tranmere Rovers. Six of us went over to see them that night when they lost 2-0 to Wigan Athletic.

I still had my peg tube but it hadn't been used for weeks. Instead I was now dining out with family and friends in all of my favourite restaurants. I became a regular visitor to the Casa Italia on Stanley Street, Eureka in Myrtle Parade, Est Est Est at the Albert Dock and to see our good friend Keith Haggis at Keiths Wine Bar on Lark Lane. I was not just alive now. I was alive, well and dining out. These were lovely weeks for me. I was embracing life and all the people I knew in that life, to the full.

My other, less obvious, social outlet at that time was my daily run to the hospital. This journey was fundamental to my survival but also became a surprising opportunity to spend quality time with all of the volunteers who drove me. Clatterbridge, due to its rural location, was difficult to reach by public transport so an essential personal taxi requirement materialized. All kinds of people came forward to offer to step into this breach. I had immediate family members on both sides, friends living locally in Liverpool and visitors from Ireland who came by car, all offering their services. Of all of my personal taxi drivers two of the most prominent were Pams dad Alan and her sister Diane with her boyfriend Steve Hadden. These were people that ordinarily, in the course of normal family and in-law gatherings, I would not have the opportunity to spend time with on a one to one basis. Now we were isolated together on the roads to Clatterbridge to talk about whatever we chose. For all we knew these could be our last journeys together and we were conversing now, not as relatives but as friends.

My cancer was putting a new twist on all of the relationships I had established with people during my first life. It was greatly enhancing them. The parameters were changed now. There was no time for role play or diplomacy. Now was the time to speak from your heart. It was time for open friendship and appreciation. You may not get the chance to say these things again.

With Diane and Steve the journey was never just a routine trip to a hospital. It was always used as an opportunity to create an eventful day, of which the hospital visit was only a small part. It became an excuse to go for a late lunch in Parkgate or have a drink in a pub in one of the lovely little villages on the Wirral. These journeys gave me an opportunity to have precious time with all of my many taxi drivers. In Diane and Steve's case especially, this was something I didn't get a chance to do in all of my previous years as their in-law. We had always been friendly but for those weeks we became true friends.

The first four weeks of radiotherapy passed off straightforwardly. The only impact the treatment was having on me was a welcome social one. Every day I really looked forward to my trip to Clatterbridge to see my fellow patients. We all became great friends. The lovely staff only added to this harmonious mix. My trip to the hospital was no more than a pleasant distraction in my wonderful, how good it is to be alive, day.

Radiotherapy is extremely powerful. Over time it will begin to aggravate and damage the skin and tissue area through which it must pass. My skin began to show signs of stress from the fourth week on. It was expected that this would escalate to a point where my mouth would swell. I would then need to be readmitted to hospital and fed through my peg tube again. One of the angles of radiotherapy was also through my damaged right eye. I had a blurred image from this eye after the surgery but this was now beginning to deteriorate. Initially I felt losing the sight completely from this eye would be a big blow. It offered some kind of back-up should anything happen to my good eye. In reality however the image it gave me was so poor that it would not have given me any worthwhile vision. I could only barely make out shapes and colours with it. I could not recognise what the details of those shapes and colours were. When I realised that it didn't really have any worthwhile sight to offer me I was happy to let it go. If losing the sight from one eye was the only sacrifice I had to make in return for being alive, that was a price I was more than willing to pay.

Now that my life was back to some kind of normality again I would have regarded being re-admitted to hospital as the worst setback of all. If it had to happen I was ready to accept it. My mind had learned its lesson from previous set backs. Deep down however I desperately hoped I would be able to retain my independence and my daily social life. I had grown very fond of the real world again. My skin did burn for the final weeks and it became quite sore and uncomfortable but I managed to hold out. The swelling did not progress to a level that prevented me from eating normally and I was able to complete all of my treatment as an out-patient.

The staff were amazed at this. They claimed I must have had very good skin to begin with for it to have withstood my extensive dose of radiotherapy. The treatment I had been subjected to was a lot longer than all of my fellow patients. They were delighted for me. It was mid October and a huge milestone had now been achieved. I had completed my radiotherapy.

48 - Join the Club

When you get cancer there is very much a feeling of joining a club. Firstly you discover there are many people in the same situation that you never knew about before. Then you realise that you have an incredibly strong bond with all of them. These are your fellow cancer sufferers. At lunchtime in Clatterbridge hospital every day this universal club, that we had all just joined, microscopically reduced to our own little group of five patients. We were the 12.30 to 1.30, machine no. 4, Clatterbridge radiotherapy patients. We were five strangers, brought together for one hour every day and our only common currency was our cancer.

The people in my group were mainly older women with breast cancer. Every day we would meet and chat, support and entertain each other and get to know each others families. We were all united by the greatest bond of all. We had all been joined together by the fact that we all wanted to stay alive. Even though we had only met through the gravity of the situation we all found ourselves in, our conversations were laced with lightheartedness from the outset. We began to find black humour to laugh at in places where I never believed humour could exist. The first revelation was that we all had, what I now discovered is regarded as the ultimate disease of all. Cancer is the Rolls Royce of diseases. We were almost proud to have it. If you are going to get a disease, then you might as well get the big one.

Suddenly, after having had the most devastating disease there is thrown at us, we were all laughing and joking. Then, having compared our individual cases of this ultimate disease, a bizarre pecking order began to emerge. Soon we were teasing each other about which version we had. Those of us with head and neck cancer felt we were the king of kings. We surely had the most serious version of all. We especially began to frown on people with breast or testicular cancer. "Just go and chop them off!" we told them nonchalantly. "We can't chop our heads off!"

I learned from this time with my little group that no matter where you are, humour will always be there too. It will be there for the sole purpose of providing a welcome distraction. We were the only ones who could crack these jokes to each other. Coming from anybody else they would have been disrespectful. That is because we were all in the club. The humour we exchanged, however, never took away from the depth of warmth and respect we all had for each other. I had never met these people before and probably would never see them again but for those few weeks we were all the greatest friends we could possibly be.

I had now completed my radiotherapy program. I had no idea how it had gone. The very last hurdle to be cleared was a final review meeting with Dave Husband. Only after that could I begin to allow myself the possibility of considering that the end of my treatment was in sight.

It had now been four months since I had left Ireland. I was in such good form that I began to long for home like never before. Given the severity of my case and the many pitfalls that had already befallen me I was reluctant to start thinking about going home just yet. My protective mindset now had a once bitten, twice shy policy. Although the two main procedures, surgery and radiotherapy, had been dispensed with, I was certain another twist could be lying in wait. Perhaps Dave Husband would now insist on a few more radiotherapy sessions. Maybe I needed one final dose of chemotherapy, just as a final precaution. As I entered his office therefore I was braced for him to prolong my stay for a further week or two. If he was insisting on anything longer than that I was going to be very disappointed.

I sat down in front of him expecting the worst. "You've done very well." he said to me. "That was a very heavy program of radiotherapy I had you on. You have come through it excellently. I'm done with you. You are free to go."

To my complete surprise he gave me an outstanding review. He said I had taken everything he could throw at me, including three sessions of chemotherapy. I could now walk out of his office, walk out of the hospital and not come back. I was free to go home!

Wow! It was all over. I was all done. After four months, four hospitals, two major treatment procedures and three serious setbacks I could return to Ireland. I had completed my cancer treatment.

My predicament now was that I had taken all the treatment that was available to me. My body had been sent to the extremes of what it could withstand. The surgery was so extensive and so complicated that it could never be repeated. My radiotherapy program was also taken to its very limits. I would not be able to undergo radiation ever again. If I did, my bone and tissue structures would simply decompose.

If cancer ever returns to me therefore, there is nothing left. I have had all of the treatment that I can have. There is nothing else that can be done. They had thrown everything they had at me. If war breaks out again, we have no bullets left in our guns.

The hope therefore was that all of this treatment had either removed or killed my tumour. If it had not, it would soon return and have me all to itself. But even if I survived now, this was just the first battle. Victory now would only buy me time. Cancer had made its mark on me and consequently would always retain a spell over me. Cure now would not be cure forever. My tumour would return one day. The spoils of this victory would be an indeterminable and unexpected extension to my time on earth. It also gave me the satisfaction of having beaten one of the severest forms of cancer that anybody can get on this occasion. It will eventually return however and will not be beaten a second time.

By selecting me as a victim, no matter what the outcome this time, cancer always knew it would have the very last laugh. It would be responsible for ensuring that my death arrived prematurely. The only question mark would be the length of the truce between the first battle and the unwinnable second.

I now have to live in the shadow of this knowledge for the rest of my life. But at that point in time, it didn't matter. Given the chances that were put in front of me, just completing my treatment was a huge achievement in itself. As well as running what I could see I would also only worry about what I could see. Each stage would only be tackled once it presented itself in front of me. For now I had completed my treatment. That was an amazing hurdle to have cleared in itself. That was all I needed to focus on.

Simon Rogers had told me that when head and neck cancers return, they invariably tend to do so quickly. He felt that if I could remain clear for 18 months I would have a good chance of getting through this episode without reoccurrence. John Fenton on the other hand was much more conservative. "Remission is remission" he said. "The cancer you have isn't beaten until you have five years clear."

I had no problem with accepting either of these projections. Simon's was optimistic so my heart was happy with that. John's was realistic and my head was more satisfied with that. They took one each.

Considering the odds that had been placed against me I was doing very well just to be alive at all at this point. Long term expectations were still well beyond my concern. Eighteen months or five years both seemed like a lifetime away at that stage. I still had my blinkers on. I had retained my focus to just wanting to be alive, in any form. Anything beyond that was still a huge bonus. For now it was just time to enjoy the moment. I had completed my treatment and I was about to walk out the door of Clatterbridge hospital for the last time.

Everybody faces danger everyday. You are in danger when you cross the road, or drive a car. You are in danger when you play a contact sport or fly in an airplane. As I assessed the possible future return of my tumour I was happy to bundle it in with all of the other unforeseen dangers that are faced on a daily basis. I decided that when it eventually comes back I will just start to address it then. There was no point in worrying about the future. For now it was done. I had completed my treatment and even that was against the odds. I had won the first round.

As I left the hospital I thanked Dave Husband and all of my radiotherapy staff. Just like my surgical team they had all done incredible work on my behalf. A milestone had been passed and I had a great sense of appreciation on still being alive as a result. It was a wonderful sensation driving out of the car park and heading back towards Liverpool. I felt I must have been the luckiest person in the world that day.

The very final event of my four month sojourn in England was a celebratory meal. Pam and all of our friends in Liverpool booked an Italian restaurant in the city centre for the following evening. We had about twenty people in all. It was to be the first memorable night at the other end of my ordeal. I felt a great sense of achievement. That night I had lived to repeat the get-together we all had almost four months earlier at The Britannia Inn.

Everybody took turns to relate their individual accounts of their experiences over the previous months to me, as we dined. One by one they told me what I looked like just after the surgery and how they felt at that time. I wasn't a pretty sight and many of them did not expect we would all be sitting down to eat that night, three months later. Pete Morgan, of course, was the only person who confirmed that my post surgery appearance was actually an improvement on how I looked beforehand.

This night was a great release for all of them. It was when many of them could tell me how they really felt and what they really thought. All of them thought they would never see me again.

It was a night full of appreciation. Appreciation for our lives and our friendship and the length of time we had all known each other. Appreciation for our health and our families. It was a pinnacle night when we all rediscovered our gratitude for the important things in our lives. We appreciated that we were all there, in that place, at that point in time. It was the opposite of the Last Supper. It was the First Supper. The First Supper of the rest of our lives. The First Supper of my second life. These great freinds had all been my apostles. They had all done so much for me over the last few months.

The following day was Sunday. We packed up all our stuff and had our last night with Mary and Brian. So many people had played pivotal roles in getting me to this point but Mary Naughton and Brian Boyle had been two of the most essential. They had invited me into their home for as long as I needed to stay. There was nothing they would not have done for us. Their piece in the jigsaw was one of the biggest of all.

49 – Going Home

On the morning of Monday October 14th 2002 Pam steered our station wagon car out of Mary and Brian's driveway for the last time. I was beside her in the passenger seat. All of our possessions filled the remainder of the car. We were making the short trip to the ferry terminal at the Pier Head to catch the 11.00 a.m. sailing to Dublin. We were going home. In my entire ordeal this little journey was probably the most significant one of all. It was the one many people thought I would never make. This was my biggest day since the day I was told I had cancer.

As the ship pulled away I steadfastly remained out on deck. I wanted to stay there until Liverpool disappeared into oblivion. That was my city and I didn't want to let it go until it was gone. I owed it my life.

I arrived back to a wonderful welcome in Ballina and Killaloe. The new bridge may not have been built but the most essential part of my Liam O'Riains poem had come true. I had lived to come home. For the next few weeks just about everybody I knew came to see me. These visits were the perfect culmination to the incredible support they had all given me throughout my entire ordeal. These were my people. People who had sent me cards, flowers, texts, prayers, C.D.s, mystery Guinness gift boxes and Mass videos.

My days needed to be carefully managed now. I was still extremely tired and needed about fourteen hours of sleep a day. I managed two periods of social interaction within this. The first was late morning after I got up. The second was in the early evening after I got up again!

Pam had now gone from fulltime hospital carer to fulltime home help. Over the previous four months I had been granted an exclusive insight into how a major illness impacts those near and dear to you. My job was easy. All I had to do was what I was told. I didn't have any decisions to make. "Your surgery will be on July 8th", "We're sending you down for a colonoscopy tomorrow", "You need to take two of these and drink this".

Pam on the other hand had nobody to tell her what to do. She had three small children and the likelihood was that their father was going to die. What would or should she tell them? What would we earn if I died? If I didn't die what would she be able to earn if she had to spend all her time looking after me. She had to come to the hospital every day and be my hand maid. Some days I would not be in good form. Some days I would be in pain or dejected or both. She may not have been in good spirits some days too, but for my sake she would never show it. There were bills to be paid in Ireland. She needed to ask Mary and Brian if we could move in. The kids were homesick for their friends back home. She could lose her husband at any stage.

She had all of this and much more to contend with. But every day when she was at my bedside she would only be in good form. I was allowed to be in bad form but she, as my carer, was not.

All of these thoughts actuated a whole new appreciation for the wonderful work Pam had done for me. Like my new found recognition of the health industry, I began to recognise another group of people that I had never considered previously. Carers and everybody who looks after sick relatives at home. All of these people are more of the unsung heroes of this world. Yet their remarkable deeds are rarely acknowledged beyond the walls of their own homes. Your family is everything to you at a time like this. I knew now, how lucky I was to have mine.

50 ~ Lanzarote

I took things very easy for the first few weeks. My body had been through the mill. I needed to be very gentle with it as it tried to restore itself back to what it once was. By mid-November I was getting back to something like my old self. My strength was gradually returning to a point where I felt confident enough to begin to increase my level of activity. I was now getting out for a short walk every day and I required less sleep. I had reached the stage where we felt a family holiday could be considered. It wouldn't be anything energetic, just a gentle break somewhere relaxing and warm. As a family we could start doing some nice things in life again. Everybody had been part of this ordeal and if ever a holiday can be deserved, we felt we must have been close to the head of the queue.

We booked to go to the Canary Islands for two weeks. It seemed like the perfect thing to do. Pam and the three boys had been through so much since my original diagnosis in April. They all needed a break. For me it also seemed to make good sense. Rather than recuperate in the cold and wet of November in Ireland, I could relax in the warm winter sunshine off the North African coast.

We flew to Lanzarote on November 14th. It was one month from my last day of my radiotherapy. At last my life was heading in the right direction again. After all we had been through we were now going to draw an end to our year with two weeks of relaxation in the sun and by the sea. Then we would return for the run-in to Christmas.

The three boys were all excited. It was just what they needed. Their lives had been completely disrupted over the previous seven months. They had stayed with each of my three sisters in Ireland and in four different locations in England. The only common thread linking each place was that they were only there because it was uncertain whether their Dad would live or die.

Pam was happy too as she boarded the plane. She had always been a sun worshipper. It was going to be a good ending to what had been a very tough chapter of her life. This was to be our first ever family holiday as a complete family. We had only one expectation for it. It was simply going to be the greatest holiday we would ever have.

We arrived to a nice apartment in the pretty little resort of Puento Del Carmen. Our first full day was as perfect as we all considered we were entitled for it to be. We spent most of the afternoon strolling along the lively main street at the seafront, casually window shopping and stopping for ice cream or coffee whenever we chose. In the evening we dined in a nice little seafood restaurant down at the harbour in the older part of town.

On our second day it was time to hit the beach. Pam and the three boys had been waiting for this for a long time. Early that morning they sprang from their beds like greyhounds out of traps. It took them another hour to assemble all of their necessary aqueous paraphernalia. Then they made the short journey to the sea looking like some kind of giant inflatable armadillo. Eight little legs trundled along under a colourful canopy of lilos, parasols, beach balls, snorkels and buckets and spades. They had every possible accessory required for a fun-filled day by the sea.

My progress was a little slower. I was not yet at a stage where I could just hop out of bed. Dressing was still a slow process for me. I didn't want to stall their excitement so I told them to go on ahead. I would catch up as soon as I could. I didn't want to miss out on too much of their fun.

I was just ready to follow when I decided I would have one more cup of coffee. I would just sit and relax to ease myself into the day ahead. During the course of that cup of coffee, somewhere between making it and finishing it, I began to feel unwell. I assumed it was just a bout of delayed tiredness from the flight. There was no reason to start worrying about anything more serious just yet. A couple of extra hours sleep would sort me out. I returned to bed for a while, safe in the knowledge that the beach enthusiasts would hardly even miss my non arrival.

I got up again later in the afternoon. I still didn't feel well. I made my way down to the promenade that evening and met up with the four of them. We were all going to go for something to eat. By now I had become very quiet. I was not in good form. I was conscious that I was beginning to put a damper on what should have been day two of our dream holiday. I just clung on to the prognosis that rest was all I needed. A good night's sleep and by day three I would have returned to my normal self again.

We went back to the apartment after the meal. I was just in the door when I started to become violently sick. Pam called for a doctor immediately.

A young female doctor arrived after twenty minutes. With a mixture of her broken English and Pam's broken Spanish, we were able to communicate the details of my medical history to her. She began to look more and more distraught as my story was unfolded. Her usual calls at this hour of the night were for tourists who had too much sunburn or too much sangria or both. My symptoms and case history were well beyond the scope of her normal day's work.

We were all convinced that this was the return of my tumour. Her sombre demeanour did little to allay those fears. Any reassurance that we were not once again of the periphery of yet another huge drop on the roller coaster of my life was not forthcoming. At one point she almost tearfully turned to Pam and said "Well at least you have the children. They are beautiful".

I was taken to the tourist hospital on Lanzarote. Shortly after my arrival it was evident that my case was even too big for there. The main hospital for the Canaries is on Gran Canaria. An air ambulance was summoned. I was completely unconscious by now. I had never been on a helicopter before and now when I got my big break I was not in a position to know anything about it.

When I arrived at the main hospital my condition had become critical. Once again I was arriving at a hospital with nobody quite sure what was wrong with me and, once again, pandemonium broke out. A flurry of doctors rushed to the scene to try and evaluate what my condition was. Communication lines were difficult because I was comatose and now we also had language difficulties to slow down the diagnosis process. They were relying on Pam for the exact details of my case. She did all she could to relay my medical journey to this point in time. When she mentioned the word "meningitis" they at last had a disease that matched the symptoms I was presenting. I was taken for a lumbar puncture immediately and, once again, a case of bacterial meningitis was confirmed.

This time I was more critical than before. With island hopping, language difficulties and general diagnosis confusion I had trimmed my survival chances to the absolute minimum. I was now in intensive care and very critical. Carol, Dolores and Eleanor were summoned. The three of them caught the first flight available from Ireland. This time it really did look as if this was the end. This seemed to be one setback too many. I had used up all of my lives.

I eventually came around, three days later. Once again I had missed out on the main drama. I had been unconscious through all of the "will he live" or "will he die" commotion. I was now stable and out of danger. This was familiar ground. Somewhere I had been before. Once again I had gone to the very edge of the cliff between life and death and had a good peer over. Once again I pulled back at the last minute.

This was meningitis again. It had been caught in time again, just. For a second time I found myself waking up in a hospital bed hooked up to a drip. Meningitis had stole a march on its more illustrious counterpart. It was now Cancer 1 Meningitis 2.

It should have been straightforward from there. I was back on a road already travelled. The meningitis was now under control so I just needed to sit tight, take the medication and get out of there. I was about to discover however that a whole new series of mental challenges were waiting to ensnare me.

After my performance in Liverpool I was almost blasé about adopting a positive attitude towards recovery. I had no doubt that the right frame of mind was an essential component to beating any disease. I therefore could not understand why anybody would not automatically adopt a positive approach to help themselves get better. I became almost intolerant of patients who did not. This was surely a fundamental principle for everyone who was ill. It was obviously one of your own pieces of the jigsaw. If you want to continue living then it is your responsibility to do everything in your power to help yourself get better. If a positive attitude was a key element of this then why would you not adopt it straight away. I was to learn in Gran Canaria that this approach might not have been as straightforward as I thought.

This second meningitis setback caught me completely flatfooted. All of my previous derailments had occurred during the course of my treatment. Now that my treatment was over it was as if my mind had dropped its guard. It had gone on holiday like the rest of us. It had taken a break, safe in the knowledge that now that the treatment was over, no further setbacks would occur.

All of a sudden I had been caught out at my own game. Positivity is not something you can just reach up and take off the shelf. It is not something you can just "adopt". Now, when I needed them again I had lost sight of the core philosophies that had been my buttress to date. I had lost sight of my blinkered determination to bounce back, no matter what. I had stopped running to admire the view but the race had just been lengthened, at short notice. I needed to start running again. I needed to run without any complaint and just focus on the repositioned finish line. I just needed to "run what you see" and the only thing I should have seen was meningitis.

I was sick again. That was the only place my focus needed to be. I should have accepted my position instantly. All that mattered now was that I took it on again, got better again and got out of there as quick as I could again. Instead I had decided that I had come to this island for a holiday. I had now convinced myself that I was entitled to that holiday. Nothing would be allowed deny it to me. I started to complain rather than accept. All of this just wasn't fair. Why me? I did what I thought I would never do again. I went back past zero. I was in negative territory for the first time since they sent me down to the eye department in the Regional in Limerick.

I was not a happy patient for all of that first week in hospital in the Canaries. I was finding it very difficult to override the landslide of emotion I was now experiencing. I had gone from deciding which restaurant will we dine in tonight to now seeing a tray of hospital food coming towards me.

Many of the finer details also entwined to further fan the flames of my discontent. I am generally sociable by nature. In all of my previous hospital stays I both enjoyed and depended upon the interaction I had with those around me. I like to chat. In Gran Canaria I was denied this important distraction. Nobody spoke any English and I had no Spanish. Not only did I now find myself in a strange hospital in a foreign land but this inability to communicate heightened my sense of isolation.

I usually eat most things but for some reason I also hated the food. Maybe I still hadn't made the necessary adjustment from the restaurant menu to the hospital food trolley. Maybe, no matter what was on the plate, I would have rejected it. The combination of these two non medical items on their own, the lack of communication and the food, was enough to shackle me to permanent negativity.

Once again, from the meningitis, I was also somewhat delusional. I got it into my head that if I was not seen to be eating they would not allow me to be discharged. I decided to secretly dispose of the meals they were giving me so that they would think I was eating normally. I began to sneak the food I was being brought into the toilet in my room and flush it away. This continued until one day the toilet blocked. The staff came to me as soon as it was cleared and said "you don't have to eat the food but don't put it down the toilet"!

I was simply not a patient I would have recognised during this time. I was confused and angry and not thinking straight. Meningitis disturbed my normal mindset but I was also stuck in a negative rut. When I was in intensive care they kept sticking monitor tabs on my chest to record my heart rate. These were placed in several locations across my upper torso. In my angry confusion I was convinced they were plasters to cover wounds. I kept saying "But I haven't any cuts there. Why do they keep putting plasters on me". As soon as they had put them on I pulled them off again. When I persisted in continuing to remove these "ridiculous plasters" the nursing staff became angry. In the end they had no option but to restrain my arms on both sides of the bed. I had enough awareness to know I was being restrained but my thoughts and actions were not rational at this time.

Now that I was literally tied to the bed my level of frustration only increased further. On one occasion when Dolores came to see me I asked her for a favour. Expecting a normal patient request like a magazine or a bunch of grapes, she agreed immediately. She was taken aback however when my request was that she open a drawer I could see behind her and get me pair of scissors. I am fairly sure that the scissors and the drawer were completely imagined. I was going to cut my restraints and get up and leave that hospital. I didn't need to be there anymore. I was going to get dressed and go out and start my holiday.

Poor Dolores. She didn't want to refuse her sick brother anything but obviously, couldn't grant his request. I persisted, thinking on each occasion she simply hadn't heard what I was saying. To her credit she handled it perfectly. Every time I asked for the scissors she expertly deflected the issue without ever saying the word "no". My mind was definitely not in the right place for those few days.

After a week I settled better. I at last accepted my second bout of meningitis. My mind has relinquished its quest for all of the non-hospital delights that the Canary Islands had to offer. I had now given up on any hope of rescuing the holiday. My only duty now was to complete my medication and beat meningitis a second time. At last, I was a "good" patient again.

My spirits were also lifted by dozens of text messages that were coming through from back home. The news of my distressed state had reached both Ireland and England and many people took to their phones. I had a rejuvenated appreciation for mobile phone technology. Had it been ten years earlier I would not have had this important line of communication to lift my spirits. Michael and Irene Fenton went much further than just a text message. When they heard about my state of despair, they offered to provide an air ambulance to fly me back to Ireland. I may have been the fighter but this was the calibre of the people I had in my corner.

I was also back on my feet at this stage. This meant I could escape from my dreaded food tray at meal times. I was able to eat in the very swish public cafeteria on the ground floor. I now had a chance to look around this hospital that I had been so slow to embrace. I was impressed with what I saw. It was a spectacular modern building, with state of the art facilities. I'm sure I had received excellent care. It was a pity that I had been so slow to appreciate it due to my state of confusion. Its place in the story is just as important as the hospitals in Limerick, Aintree and Clatterbridge.

The trip to the Canaries, in its entirety, just goes down as a bad experience. The hospital in Gran Canaria can perhaps consider itself unlucky to have been so underappreciated due to my confused state. I learned the hard way that a positive attitude, when you need it, is not automatic.

For the duration of that first week, whilst I was both unconscious and delusional, Pam had to contend with the cancelling of our apartment in Puerto Del Carmen, the transfer of herself and the three boys to Gran Canaria, finding a hotel that would provide accommodation for as long as my treatment lasted and organising somewhere for my three sisters to stay. If I was feeling aggrieved that I was being denied my holiday, it seemed very little compared to her grounds for complaint. I was back to the position of not having any decisions to make. I was just taking the treatment that was coming at me. She however had not only lost the holiday that she was so looking forward to, she was parachuted into a complex labyrinth of reorganising her husband, her three children and herself, in a foreign country on two different islands. All of this had to be done within the parts of the day that were left after coming in to see me twice daily. The dream holiday in the sun had turned into a nightmare. How she would now have jumped at the opportunity to swop it all for an extra two weeks of recuperation back home.

The situation improved when Carol, Dolores and Eleanor arrived. They were able to lighten the burdens of coming in to see me and looking after the children. As soon as my condition stabilised everybody agreed that it was important that the holiday was restored, as much as possible, for Christy, Lowell and Abe. At eight, six and two they were still far too young to fully understand what was happening. It was as if somebody had promised them a holiday but really it was just another cover story for their Dad to go to hospital yet again!

The ratio between the helpers and those needing help was now more balanced. We now had four healthy adults, three children and one hospitalised adult. The dual tasks of taking the boys out for the day and attending to me were easier to manage. The four girls were able to split up the roster and alternate on who did what. If you picked the long straw you got you a ride on a roller-coaster with the kids. If you got the short one it meant a trip to the hospital to see me and be asked to go looking for a pair of imaginary scissors!

Families all over the world tend to find a new depth within themselves at times of crisis. Mine was no different. Each one of my three sisters were absolutely fantastic to me for my entire ordeal. They immediately dropped everything else in their lives so that they could attend to me in whatever way they could. They didn't hold back when the call came. This one had come from the Canary Islands. I appreciated and valued the three of them like never before. We had always got on well but still managed to retain our own independence and individualism within the family unit. For these seven months however that no longer applied. We were all in unison. The three of them made sure that they took every step of the journey with me.

I was on a steady path of recovery by now. After three weeks I had completed all of the medication. I was deemed to be well enough to be discharged. A two week holiday had turned into a three week hospital stay. The three boys had already returned home with Carol, Dolores and Eleanor. All that remained was one final non-hospital night in Gran Canaria. Pam and I would then fly home the following day.

I made a feeble attempt to enjoy our last night. We walked down to the seafront to a restaurant and went for a meal but to be honest, my heart wasn't in it. I'm sad to say the Canaries had been spoiled for me by then. I just wanted to go home and never come back. This was through no fault of the islands themselves or the hospital. It was just going to be filed as a bad memory and nothing within that memory could be salvaged.

The very final twist came the following day when Pam and I had boarded the plane. The flight attendants safety demonstration had concluded and I was just settling back into my seat. I was getting ready to look out the window for my last ever views of Gran Canaria. Just at the point where I was expecting the wheels to start slowly turning the pilot came down the aisle towards us. "Is there a Mister Liam Ryan on board" he asked in excellent

English. My heart jumped. The vision of being led off the plane to a waiting ambulance and back to the hospital was almost tangible. I just waited for his next words to turn that scenario into reality.

"Did a doctor deem you fit to fly before you boarded" he asked. "No" I replied. "I will need to phone the hospital" he said. "They will need to give their permission for you to take this flight". Now my heart sank. The Canary Islands had read the script perfectly. A last minute setback was needed to be thrown into the equation. I braced myself. Somebody was about to move the finish line again. This time I would ready to run. I wouldn't be caught out again. If I had to remain a little longer in the Canaries, then so be it. I was alive and well. That was all that mattered.

If Ireland had been superimposed onto the outer ring of Saturn at that particular moment, it couldn't have seemed any further away. After an agonising three minutes the pilot returned. The entire plane was now tuning in to its own in-flight soap opera. Who was this passenger? What had he done?

"You can fly" he said. "Prepare for take-off" he instructed the on-looking flight attendants.

Within the confines of my airplane seat, my seat belt restricted body concealed an internal explosion of ecstasy and relief. It was all over. I gave Pam a big, long hug. Once again we were going home.

51 – Writing it all Down

Ijust wanted to get out of 2002 now. I was in perfect health at the end of 2001 and I had convinced myself that if I could just get into 2003 all would be fine again. 2002 was to blame for everything. It was simply a year that needed to be erased from my history books. The sooner I could draw a close on it the better.

As if to reinforce this point we had one final crisis to face before the year was out. Two weeks after we returned from the Canaries our youngest boy, Abe, suddenly became very ill. He was rushed from our local doctor's surgery to the hospital in Limerick. Within an hour he was diagnosed with acute bacterial meningitis. Just like his Dad a few weeks before him, he went very close to losing his life but, once again, was caught just in time. The family hospital journey for the year had begun in Limerick and now it would end there too.

Pam spent a week at his bedside before he was eventually discharged. This remarkably was three cases of bacterial meningitis in the one house in four months. He came home two days before Christmas. Now, wholly convinced that 2002 was out to get us we just closed our doors. We dared not come out again until the year was over. Midnight, December 31st, 2002 – happy new year! – it sure was!

It was almost mid January before I renewed my acquaintance with the outside world. I was extremely tired at this stage and rarely ventured far from the house. We were invited to a late New Year house party by our friends. I decided I would have enough energy for a limited attendance and was keen to go. Whilst I was there I started telling little snippets of my story for the very first time. It began in conversation with whatever friends were around me but before long I had a attracted a captivated audience.

As I was relating one of the many little sub episodes that had been encountered along the way, I realised that everybody was fascinated with the detail of the scenarios I was illustrating. Health issues generally, and perhaps cancer specifically, attract universal interest. Health and disease are also unilateral topics. They connect with everybody, everywhere. Nobody is immune.

All of the people listening were completely absorbed in the description of the heroin addict after I was approved for treatment or the clock on the wall of the ward or the taste of my first glass of water. It was an ordinary human story they could all relate to. It just so happened that I was the ordinary human that the story was about.

They all knew, deep down, that it could just as easily have been one of them who was doing the telling and me doing the listening. Each of my little anecdotes, in their own way, connected with all who heard them in the room that night.

The next day I realised that if I didn't begin to write down all of these little details I would lose them over time. The finished garment would always remain but some of the smaller patterns of fine detail would begin to fade.

I was also now getting a little restless with full time convalescence. I was ready to tackle something a little more taxing. I needed something that would help me to start feeling I was part of the real world again. Writing an account of my story seemed to perfectly address this. Not only would it provide the mental stimulus I was looking for, it would also preserve all of the essential details of my ordeal whilst they were still fresh in my mind.

The best thing of all was that it was an activity that could be tailored to suit my varying energy levels. I could sit at my computer and write as much or as little as I was able to. There was no deadline to meet or timescale to be adhered to. I could drop back at any time and make revisions to correspond with whatever order my memory would feed the recollections to me. This very first personal account of this story ran to ten typed pages when it was finished. It took me two months to complete.

I wrote this record of my experience for myself. It was my account of my disease, for me. I have encouraged nearly all of the cancer sufferers I have met since to do the same. This is your own unique personal story and is the biggest thing that will ever happen to you. You deserve to have your own record of it for all time.

You will also have time to fill during your recovery. Writing everything down will not only help you fill some of this time, it can actually become an important part of your healing process. It will give you the strength of mind to go back into your ordeal. The strength to open doors you may have thought you'd prefer to leave closed forever. You can open them now because you have reached the safety of the other side. You are not the patient in the bed anymore.

Writing everything down will allow you to revaluate your experiences. It will help extinguish any fear you may still have to re-face any of the traumas that you have just been through. They can't touch you now.

It will give you an opportunity to have a better understanding and a greater appreciation of all the wonderful work that the medical staff, your family and your friends did for you. It will preserve forever all of the important little details of your case. It will ensure that all of the people, along the way, who have now left a handprint on the shape of your life, will never be forgotten.

Writing everything down also gives you control over your story. It will allow you to package it and draw a line under it. It will help you move on. Your personal account may never go any further than yourself but that doesn't matter. It is your own record, for yourself. In itself it will bring closure and allow you to start getting on with the rest of your life.

I had another, deeper motive for wanting to capture my story. At the time of my illness my children were very young. They were too young to know exactly how sick their Dad was. Too young to appreciate the great work their mother did, not just in keeping me alive, but also in keeping their lives as normal as possible. I wanted some way to pass it directly to them when they would be old enough to understand. Ideally this would happen in twenty years time, over a few pints, in a little pub somewhere. It would happen if and when they were ready to ask and I was still there to tell them. But just in case that it is not to be, I wanted an account that would preserve the story just for them. A personal account so that no matter what happens to me, it will always be there.

That original account, through this book, has now also turned into a memoir. Consequently, it has brought me full circle. In the end I had very few mature years with my own Dad. There were a lot of questions I didn't get to ask him. There were a lot of stories he never got to tell me. As we never got the chance for those exchanges I would now love to have a personal account of the things he did in his life. The things he did that I never knew about. He is part of me and there are parts of him that I never got to know. A little bit of this account is therefore also to close that gap. It is to ensure that those coming after me have the opportunity, if they wish, to know what I did in my life. What I went through. Just in case I don't get the chance to tell them myself.

When I had finished my account I passed it on to some friends who wished to read it. One of these, with my permission, sent it in to our local newspaper, the *Nenagh Guardian*. They were so taken with my story that they asked if they could publish it exactly as it was. They did so over two weeks. Those two articles generated an amazing response. It was at that point that I began to realise the power of the story I had to tell. I recognised it was a story that was bigger than I was. I was just the person it had been handed to. It was beginning to outgrow its original purpose. What had started out as a personal record just for its author was beginning to bring great encouragement to others.

In subsequent years I passed my script on to anybody I knew who had been diagnosed with cancer. I hoped it would be a source of inspiration to help them tackle what was lying ahead of them. Everybody who read it found encouragement. Through friends of friends it travelled to all parts of the world. I have received acknowledgements to that original ten page script from countries as far away as Canada and New Zealand.

The national press got interested next. Television and radio followed. Now, ten years later, my written account has culminated in the book you are now holding in your hands. This is the end of a journey too. My sense of duty to pass on this story as an inspiration to anybody coming along behind me is done. This book can now go wherever it wants without me. It can go to whoever feels it will give them hope. It can demonstrate forever that the odds, no matter how great, can always be beaten. It can inspire everybody who has been given a chance, no matter how small that chance is.

This book owes its existence to that personal record that was written three months after radiotherapy. Without that none of what followed would have happened. So if you can, write it all down. Keep a diary. Keep whatever form of record suits you. Then, somewhere in the middle of those long hours of recovery, you can put it all together. You can collect up all of those filaments of your story, those wonderful details that are the reason why you are still alive. Write it for yourself. Your cancer is unique and it belongs to you. You deserve to have your own account of your own experience. Something that will make sure you never forget. These personal reasons are enough to write everything down in themselves. But should your account go on to help even one other person, then that is a wonderful, worthwhile bonus.

52 – Early Recovery

I would be tired for three years after my treatment. This is the part of cancer that nobody really told me about. Tiredness is the hidden side effect of every cancer treatment.

In my own mind I had concluded that I must have been about 75% recovered when I was finally released from hospital. Three months later, when I was beginning to find my feet again, I was certain the figure must have risen to something like 85%.

At this point of your recovery the surgery and the radiotherapy begin to swop roles. The wounds from your operation are now practically healed but the effects of your radiotherapy are still emerging from the long grass. Your scars have been so visible they tend to dominate your perception of how much you have recovered. However you will spend the next three years recovering from the invisible effects of radiotherapy long after they have healed.

Extensive radiotherapy completely knocks the stuffing out of you. Just as my kids didn't fully understand my illness until they could see cuts and bruises, I, as the patient, did not comprehend the implications of radiotherapy until I experienced the extreme tiredness it causes. This is very much a personal cross you carry through your recovery. Nobody else can see or appreciate it.

The outcome of all of this was that although I returned to work, to some degree, by the summer of 2003 it would not be until 2005 before I could be considered a "serious" worker again.

I felt lucky I was self employed during this time. I could structure my day to suit my energy levels. All of my clients were also very understanding and accommodating with what I could achieve. I could do a few hours work in the morning and rest through lunchtime if I needed to. Then I could do a little more in the afternoon. Sometimes I would even manage a few hours in the late evening before I went to bed, if I needed to. I could work an eight hour day, if I really had to, as long I was given the full twenty four hours to get the eight in. I also needed not to be expected to work for a further eight hours the next day.

I began to wonder how employers must deal with this scenario. Cancer is the big disease. It generally commands good allowances and latitude within the working environment. But how long is your boss supposed to wait. If I had been working in a normal nine to five job I could not have expected the courtesy of being allowed to rest between midday and three o'clock and then make up the time in the evening. "But my shop closes at five"! my perplexed employer would exclaim.

But what could I do. These were the only hours my body would permit me to work. At this point of recovery a dilemma must occur for all cancer patients between what their employment requires and what their body can cope with.

I have no answers to this particular quandary. I can acknowledge that very few companies could afford to wait three years for an employee to return fully to work. Yet my sympathies will always lie with the cancer patient. Every cancer survivor is a mini-hero. They have just faced down one of the greatest challenges life can throw at them. I would hope they could all be granted all the support needed to re-take their position in the world before their diagnosis struck. I guess a good employer and good employee will work out a compromise. An arrangement that will work for both, somewhere in the middle.

If these are the issues that are now required to be dealt with, it is a measure of how far your recovery has come. Such details would have been a long way away when you faced into your treatment. The dilemma of when will I be able to work a full day again would have been buried for a long time, under much more serious concerns.

Self employment can have many risks and disadvantages compared to salaried employment but, when it came to my recovery, I was glad of it. It granted me the liberty of only having myself to deal with. I wasn't compromising an employer or disappointing a work colleague. It allowed me, thanks to my understanding clients, to reintroduce myself to work at my own pace and in my own time.

My remission clock was now ticking along nicely. Remission is further proof that cancer is the king of all diseases. With every other disease, first you get it, then, hopefully after your treatment, you recover from it. Then you are cured. It is a straightforward path.

Cancer doesn't work like that. Oh no, this disease has much more superior notions about itself. First you get it. Then you have your treatment to have it removed. But then, just at the point of recovery when you would normally be cured it grants itself an extra five year licence. Cancer will not let you use the word "cure" until five years after the end of your treatment.

This is remission. You have your opponent on the ropes and the ref is stepping in to stop the fight. Normally he counts to ten but cancer gets itself a special dispensation. The referee must count for five years before the fight is over. The result will only stand if it doesn't throw a punch back at you in all of that time. Oh yes, it's the special one this disease of ours. It thinks it is greater than we are. Surely there is no better motivation than that to want to put it in its place.

53 - Remission

You have some chance of trying to come to terms with what cancer is after you are diagnosed but getting to grips with the vagaries of remission is a different matter. It's a bit like limbo. The good news is that you are not in hell but the bad news is that you are not in heaven either. You are deemed to be neither sick nor cured but somewhere in between. The fact that remission is based on a fixed timespan rather than your actual condition only adds to this sense of intrigue. No matter what form of cancer you get, remission stays exactly the same. From my black humoured jousting with my fellow radiotherapy patients I am surprised that the head and neck division have not demanded that our remission is increased to ten years. A standard five year period completely disregards the highly prized cancer pecking order we had all been amicably fighting over.

For the survivor it is as if somebody has decided to invent remission to curb you jubilation after being released from hospital. You are just about to crack open the long dreamed of, and well deserved, bottle of champagne when someone takes it off you and puts it back in the fridge. They then tell you that the fridge won't be opened again for five years.

John Fenton had always said to me that no real celebration should take place until remission was over. That was the real finish line.

He was right. He had always managed to keep my feet on the ground. Consequently I was always going to be ready for remission when it came. Whether we like it or not, it is an integral part of our cancer. We need therefore to recognise it and adopt it, just like any other part of our treatment. You will know, in your heart, that any celebration of victory, prior to its conclusion, is a hollow one. Your cancer may be on the floor but the fight is not over until the referee has stopped counting.

I made sure I was fully aware of where I now was. The victory would not be declared until the challenger was counted out. That count is your remission. Having been caught by previous setbacks, I was not going to be caught out again. I was going to count along with the referee and pride myself with every second my vanquished opponent lay there at my feet. Only when the very last second was reached would my fists be raised in triumph.

The mindset you require for remission is different to what you have been using up to now. Remission gives you nothing physical to focus on. There are no tubes to be removed, no first steps to be retaken, no enemy in sight. Your only point of reference is the calendar. Your focus needs to be diverted from milestones and achievements to the passage of time. It begins on day one and ends on day 1825.

I quietly and calmly ticked off each year as it came and went. When all five had elapsed there was no celebration, no big party. That had all been done before. I found that this was a very personal, private day. I wanted to mark it on my own. It was the sixteenth of October 2007. In the middle of the day I made the time to take myself into Goosers pub in Ballina. I bought a whiskey and went over to one of its quieter corners. Without anybody noticing I just raised my glass and thought to myself proudly "That's it. I've won. I've beaten you.

Even if you come back now you can never take that away from me."

This particular match was over. The final result was in.

It read Cancer 4 Liam Ryan 5, after extra time.

54 – Reconstruction v Eyepatch

Ironically as soon as I began to feel well again one of the first things I started to think about was returning to hospital. Every patient who undergoes extensive facial surgery will have the impact of disfigurement to deal with. It will generally be well down the list of priorities until more fundamental, staying alive, issues have been addressed but, at some point, it will require consideration.

In certain cases your acceptance or otherwise of your new appearance can become a major hurdle to making a completely successful recovery. Basically the question every patient needs to ask themselves is if they are happy with the new modifications to their face. Or do they wish to try and return it to something more like what it looked like before.

Simon Rogers had always promised me that he would be only too delighted to get his hands on me again if I survived and recovered from all of his surgical work. He told he would spare no effort in attempting to return my face to its original form with the finest reconstruction work he could do.

He made this offer, I believe, on two genuine counts. The first was to ease any fears I might have had with disfigurement at that point in time. The second was to dangle the prospect of coming out of all of this as the person I was before, as an extra incentive to take on what I needed to do.

In later years he confided to me that this offer, although genuine and committed, was always perhaps a little over optimistic. The surgical work to my face was so destructive it would not have been possible to restore it to a replica of what it was before. His promise was aimed a little more at keeping my spirits up rather than a definitive guarantee of bringing me back to perfection.

My surgery was always going to be extremely complex. It required delicate and unquantifiable tissue and bone removal and replacement work. The outcome of any later reconstruction work was always going to be difficult to predict. My newly rearranged bone structure also required a section of transplanted hip bone with delicate screw fixings. Any later work to this area would also carry a high element of risk. Any new reconstruction work could potentially destabilise the entire structure of my face.

My right eye socket had also dropped down about an inch from where it used to be. It therefore would not be possible for my two eyes to ever align again. Even if the reconstruction work was a success surgically, the end result that could be achieved was always going to be limited. With a new false eye and plastic surgery to restore my cheek to its original profile, my face would still not resemble what it looked like before. Additional reconstructive surgery would really only tidy up my new look rather than restore my old one.

Three weeks after my surgery, Sally Lane, on ward 29 at Aintree University Hospital brought me my first ever eyepatch. Initially it was envisaged that it was to be a temporary measure. The main surgical damage was concentrated in the area around my right eye. The eyepatch therefore covered up most of my deformity until a decision could be made about reconstruction at a later date.

Sally knew however that the eyepatch had a much greater immediate function. It was going to be a big hit with the kids. Their dad was now a pirate. This was a nice turnaround from their initial shock of seeing him immediately after the surgery.

I soon grew to love my eyepatch. It gave me confidence about my appearance. Disfigurement was not an issue for me initially. I still had too many bigger problems to worry about. But as I began to return to a normal lifestyle I would not have wanted people to be shocked by my appearance.

The eyepatch also brought some much needed humour and notoriety to my recovery. I was now the only truly authentic pirate in Ireland! Every child in every supermarket reacted just the same as Christy, Lowell and Abe did. They would nudge their mums excitedly to tell her there was a pirate in the next aisle. The mother would generally try and subdue their exuberance, thinking I would be embarrassed by it. My response however showed she had nothing to worry about.

"Did you not see my ship out in the car park" I would ask the curious children. "Can you use a sword? We're setting sail for America on Monday and I'm looking for crew"!

I had an eyepatch and the kids seemed to love it. I wasn't going to disappoint any of the myths they wanted to create about me.

Disfigurement, I guess, means different things to different people. To some survivors it can become a huge issue. Others, less so. In the end I feel quite lucky with both the version I got and the stage of life at which I got it. Had I been a teenager rather than a forty year old I'm sure it may have had a more dramatic impact on my life. This was the lesson I had learned from the young lad in the bed beside me when I was getting my peg tube. But now I was a 40 year old pirate and that was fine by me.

If I had been younger I may have thought longer and harder about reconstruction. I may have felt under more pressure to do everything I could to try and return to a "normal" appearance. But I knew I was returning to a wife, family and community, who were going to reaccept me, exactly as before, regardless of how I now looked.

I suppose I also felt I was fortunate to be a man. It is probably easier for a man to wear an eyepatch than a woman. Some women do wear them and look fine to me but many would not. The female patients I spoke to during my treatment all admitted to me that facial disfigurement was one of their greatest fears. It would have been the one side effect they would have preferred most to decline. Had I been a woman I again probably may have examined the possibilities of reconstructive work a lot more comprehensively than I did, regardless of risk. In the end, in one fell swoop, the eyepatch generally covered everything.

I remember one day in Clatterbridge I shared the lift with a lovely young woman who had a similar tumour to mine. Hers was at the top of her neck rather than her sinus. The consequences of the surgery she had undergone was that her face was untouched but she would never be able to eat or drink again. She would require her peg tube for life. I, on the other hand, was well able to eat and drink but was left with severe facial disfigurement. As we chatted I could see how each mind was working for its own case. She was thinking "Well I'm glad I'm not him because as a woman I'm fussy about my looks. I really wouldn't like to look like that". At exactly the same instant I was saying to myself "Well I'm glad I'm not her because when I go back to Ballina and Killaloe I'm really looking forward to a pint of Guinness in Mrs. Reddans pub and one of Harry McKeoghs best steaks in the Cherry Tree".

A good cancer recovery begins with an acceptance of your condition at an early stage. At that time both that woman and I were so strong that even if our situations were reversed we would still have preferred our own case. We merely would have swopped scripts.

The eyepatch covers most of my disfigurement. All that is left is a hole in my cheek below it. I probably could have had cosmetic surgery to fill this in but I didn't want to. In many ways I am proud of my scars. They remind me every day of where I have been. To try and erase them would be disloyal. It would be trying to pretend that a huge event in my life had never happened.

Besides, the hole in my cheek plays an important supporting role to the eyepatch. In my pirate stories I can claim it came from a sword fight in the Caribbean or from a gun shot by a bad pirate just before I killed him. So the temporary eyepatch and the souvenir scars passed their audition. They were there to stay. Any flickering possibilities of seeking reconstructive surgery were extinguished at a very early stage.

I had second thoughts about this decision only once. My eye, since the surgery, can sometimes be a source of mild irritation. On windy days especially this discomfort can escalate to a point where it can only be resolved by lifting the eyepatch and physically closing the eye with my hand. I do this habitually now. It is not a problem. It has just become a seamless action in my daily routine.

When I began working seriously again however, this irritation was still new to me. I was in such a hurry to make a full return to the workplace that I found it affected my concentration. One day, in a fit of frustration, I said "That's it! This eye is coming out. I'm going to get the eyelid closed and get rid of this annoyance."

I met John Fenton shortly after this and mentioned my intention to him. With his usual eloquent style he prompted that I might think this declaration through. He politely suggested that it may be a case of "better the devil you know".

For all the incredible surgery I had been through this was now the only discomforting side effect I was experiencing. It was relatively minor, intermittent and easily relieved by the palm of my own hand. It didn't require any medication or doctors input. In time I would get used to it and I did. John said to me that if I was now to go and have my eye removed nobody could know what new complications I might induce as a result. I could solve one problem but perhaps end up with another, or others, of greater magnitude.

His words were very wise. My frustration was not well founded and was premature. It was caused by my eagerness to try to get back to the real world, too quickly. It was not based on a proper assessment of the actual inconvenience being experienced. A mild irritation that was easily rectified was not a problem at all. It was a very small price to have paid.

In later years Simon Rogers revealed to me that any further surgery was always going to be problematic. It could hold no guarantee of success. I had spent so long trying to get out of four different hospitals. How could I risk all of the great work that had been done by volunteering to go back of my own accord.

My recovery had just turned its final corner. I was now completely happy with both my appearance and my quality of life since my surgery. I accepted both without question. Everything was now complete. A happy pirate I was and a happy pirate I was going to stay!

55 – Looking Back

It was only when I reached the security of the post remission sector that I dared to look back. It was as if I had been wading across a river. The point of safety was not just on emerging from the water. It was only when high ground was reached on the other side, well beyond the flood plain.

When I did look back, what an amazing and daunting view I had. I had walked across the top of the Niagara falls without going over the edge. I could now clearly see that I should have been dead by that stage. But I wasn't. I was alive and recovering remarkably well. I had beaten one of the gravest forms of cancer anybody could get. Simon Rogers said to me in later years that I had boarded the bus to terminal cancer, with all of the doors locked and somehow managed to get off at the very last stop.

I alighted from that bus only to discover two more busses waiting for me. These ones had a different logo. They were from the Meningitis Bus Company. But they were both offering to take me to the same destination. I got on board both of those buses too and once again, managed to escape before they got to complete their journey.

From the higher ground I could now see that the journey entailed so much more than just reaching the end destination. There was much more to this episode of my life than just being dead or alive at the end of it. So many twists and turns had cropped up on route. I had met some incredible people along the way. My cancer journey had transformed into a lifetime experience rather than just being an illness.

Now, for the first time, I could begin to comprehend what that experience really was. It was part of my life rather than just a disease. In all of those twists and turns I could begin to recognise both positives as negatives. It was a story with as much good luck in it as bad.

Understandably the predominant finding of this retrospective evaluation was that it had been an extremely difficult and at times frightening ordeal. Amazing nuggets of brightness however, began to glow in the darkness of what I had laid out before me for appraisal. On inspection, the black cloud had sparkle all the way through it.

I had come across so many incredible people along the way. I simply would not have met them without my ordeal. I am now delighted to have my appreciation of them embedded forever into the rest of my life. I am only half joking when I say to Carmel O'Sullivan, John Fenton, Simon Rogers and Dave Husband that I am glad I got sick because, had I not, I would never have had the privilege of knowing them.

To my great regret it had taken my cancer to mobilize my appreciation of the wonderful work that all health workers do. Up to then if I came upon a health related topic on the radio I would have switched over to something else. It meant nothing to me. I had never been sick and was able to live my life as if the health industry did not exist.

When you enter a hospital as a patient all of that changes. In any society the people who directly look after and heal their fellow human beings must surely be the greatest of all. Everybody I came across in hospital from the porters and cleaners to the eminent surgeons were great. They all went about their duties with dedication and devotion. They were all working towards the same goal. That goal was ultimately to make me better. I felt guilty that I had so little knowledge of the work that they all did until then.

I began to think specifically about Simon Rogers and his team then. They had spent twelve hours working on me. Twelve hours in an extremely tense and stressful situation. But I had only been given a 5% chance of survival. This means they perform exactly the same intensive work on many people who don't make it. After twelve hours of the most pressurised work that anybody can do, your patient goes and dies on you.

In my case the situation was even worse. They did a perfect job and when I returned to the ward I got meningitis and nearly died. This had nothing to do with my surgical team. They had done their work brilliantly but as soon as their backs were turned I go and pick up some old bug that nearly killed me. If it had, all of their exceptional work would have been worthless.

The final outcome of what they do is not even within their control. A complete recovery also needs to rely on elements that are beyond them. If I design a house nobody is going to come along and mess it up by switching the bedroom with the kitchen. My surgical team however are not granted such a luxury. They perform incredible work but an unexpected setback or infection can just come along to cancel out everything they have done. These are surely the most important people that I will ever come across in my life.

No matter what the rest of us do, nothing compares to the work that takes place in operating theatres in hospitals around the world every day. Will my patient live or die. Can I restore them to the quality of life they enjoyed before they became ill. That is what real pressure is. And these people were all working in modern hospitals. What about surgical teams who have to work in war zones or third world countries with no equipment and few supplies.

I had an entirely new sense of awareness now. I could see so many things that I could never see before or had lost sight of. Ironically, now I only had one eye. How wonderful that I could see so much more with it than I did previously with two. I could see that I had a wonderful wife and family. I had never seen that I didn't have a wonderful wife and family but that, in itself, was the difference. I had turned a double negative into a positive.

Pam had been the most amazing woman through all of my illness. Her tenacity from the very beginning made sure that every possible opportunity for treatment was investigated and exhausted, even when it looked as if none was available. Her attention to detail ensured that my first bout of meningitis was not overlooked. She was a huge piece in my jigsaw. She was more than that. She was many, many pieces. Without her I would not be alive today.

Pam took her role way beyond that of the normal partner of a cancer patient. It wasn't just my cancer, it became hers too. She adopted my condition and recovery as her responsibility as well as mine. She became part of my medical team in her own right. While I was in the ring fighting, or trying to fight, she was going to be in my corner for every second until the final bell went.

But it wasn't just me she had to look after. She did all of this whilst also making sure that our three sons were always looked after too. Not only did she have a husband who looked as if he was going to die and three small children to cope with, she also had a stalled business and our future income to worry about. To complicate the mix you can throw in hospitals in three different countries and the fact that she had to organise six different places to live, whilst I was undergoing my treatment. Pam was a lot more than one piece in my jigsaw. She was more like half of all the pieces that were needed.

Not far behind her were my three great sisters, Carol, Dolores and Eleanor. A good family is a bit like an emergency break glass case. It is always there, on the wall, without drawing any attention to itself. As soon as you break it however it will immediately instigate whatever is required to deal with the emergency that has occurred.

My three girls literally stopped whatever they were doing for the duration of my illness. They donated their lives to me. They responded immediately, without question. All they needed was for the alarm to sound. It didn't matter where the call came from, they came straight away. If it was Liverpool or the Canary islands, all three of them were on the next flight.

With this new retrospective vision from the safe haven of the higher ground I could see my wonderful wife and family like I had never seen them before. I could also see the true value of my friends and my community. Just about everybody I have ever known re-entered my life at some stage during my treatment and recovery. They brought with them an entire kaleidoscope of good wishes and cherished memories. They came for only one purpose. They came to encourage me to keep living and not give up. They brought flowers and Mass cards. They organised hotel breaks and left cooked meals on our doorstep. They set up secret donation accounts and offered to fly me home in an air ambulance. They sent over an Irishman's Guinness survival cooler box disguised as a heart transplant kit. They had special Masses arranged, which they video taped and sent over to me. They all showed me how much they cared.

I have been blessed with a great wife and family. I live in the most wonderful community of Ballina and Killaloe. I have also collected up some of the greatest friends anybody could have from Horseleap, Liverpool and just about everywhere else I have ever been. I am not an unlucky man at all. I am a very, very lucky man.

56 – Is This the End

Throughout my recovery two big questions were asked of me. They tended to only be asked by people who either knew me well enough or whose curiosity was brave enough. The first was if I had got ready to die. The second was if I believed in God. My answer in both cases was yes.

I knew that as a human being I had probably come as close as I possibly could to death without actually dying. I always considered therefore that I would have been foolish to either ignore the possibility of my demise or to pretend it wasn't going to happen. I also knew that I was only going to be as strong as my weakest point. If I had one little corner that I was afraid of, my armour would have had a fatal flaw. My fight had to be total to survive. I couldn't afford to have a weakness in it. For that to happen I needed to be not afraid to die. If I could achieve that, I was then untouchable.

Death is something that is going to happen to us all. Yet we never really seem to want to talk about it. It is rarely covered in the media. We spend most of our lives acting as if it is never going to come. It is the dark corner that very few of us are prepared to shine a light into. But just as we live so too will we die. It is always a sad occasion of course. This is understandable. It is the end of a life. We are saddened by the loss of our relative or friend.

When somebody young dies it is often described as unexpected. We are shocked that somebody can die at such a young age. But why is this the case? We all know, deep down, that death can come at any age. Not a single one of us has ever been given a guarantee. Nobody has been promised a minimum of eighty or ninety years of life. Death is always sad but it can never be unexpected. That is the very essence of what it is. It has never pretended not to be part of our lives or that it can not strike at any time. It is only our desire to dictate when it should happen that makes it unexpected and transforms it into a shock.

These sentiments may appear harsh but if you need to address death you need to recognise it for what it is, not for what you would like it to be. You are then in a much better position to disarm it. Only when you look it in the eye can you remove all your fear of it. That is your first move. We are all going to die. That statement alone will completely immobilise the delusion that "it won't happen to me".

When you accept that your death is going to happen, the only question remaining is timing. Now you need to examine to the possibility that it might happen sooner rather than your preferred option of twenty or thirty years time. You are now on a level with your opponent for the first time. You are no longer denying that he exists. Now you are only arguing about the finer details.

Your next move is to start turning the tables. You need to have the strength to see, like you have never done before, that your glass is half full and not half empty. You need to use the possibility of your imminent death as an opportunity to recognise the wonderful gift of life you have already had. This line of reasoning will completely spook the Grim Reaper!

I felt as if I had sat at a poker table with my death when I cross examined myself in hospital. I believe I surprised my more fancied opponent that night. Every time he raised the stakes, I matched his bet. Every time he bluffed I called his bluff. He knew I had taken his trump card out of his hand. I could accept my death because I was happy with my life. He knew he had no hold on me after that. I faced him and told him I did not fear him anymore. He knew I was no longer afraid to die.

Had I not looked at my death I would not have seen my life as beautifully as I did. I could see things I had never seen before. I saw a young man who had lived a fine life. He had been born into a great family. He had a wonderful mother, father, grandmother and three great sisters. He lived in a lovely little Irish village with an unusual name. He had grown up where he had an old railway station and the Hill of Horseleap as the setting for his many boyhood adventures. He had lived when there were no world wars, no plague, no famine. He went to school and made good friends wherever he went. He decided he wanted to be an architect and got the chance to do so. He went to college. He didn't just go to college in any city, he went to college in Liverpool. He made more great friends there. He went to London and had a fantastic time. He collected more wonderful friends there.

He met a lovely girl called Pam Teese. They got married with a three day wedding. He lived in a lovely little house and had great neighbours. He got a job for eight years with a great architectural practice at the Albert Dock. He was at his wife's side when their first son, Christy, was born, as he was for two more, Lowell and Abe. He moved to Ireland with his family and discovered the idyllic setting of Ballina and Killaloe. He found a wonderful community waiting for him there. He set up an architectural practice with his wife and designed the new stadium for Athlone Town football club. This man had lived a wonderful life. This man was me. After living so well I had nothing to fear in death.

The next morning I read the newspaper again. I read it to find the people who would never be me. People who had not died. The child soldier in Africa, the child labourer in Asia, the child thief in South America. All of these could live to ninety and they would never have the life that I have had. They will never go to college and get whisked off to John O'Groats by Pete Morgan. They will never catch Neil Young's plectrum. They will never run a marathon. They will never meet Simon Rogers. They may all live a lot longer than me but I will have had ten times the life that they will have. I have lived a great and privileged life. How could I now start to complain when I see what others must face.

Perspective is the antidote to fear of death. Appreciating what we have had, compared to others, can make our death more palatable. Is it not better to live a short happy life than a long sad one. In our lives we have uncertainty every day. Death is just the greatest uncertainty of all. But it is the only uncertainty that we can be certain of. Until then our lives are an incredible gift to all of us. Until then the glass is always wonderfully half full. I was still able to see my glass was half full even when it looked as if it was empty. That was how strong I had become. Just as it was about to empty, it was half filled again. If it was half filled with water before, it is half filled with champagne now. By not fearing death, I am living all the more.

My death has knocked at my door. Before I could answer, it left again. One day it will return. When that day comes I will again not be afraid. I have already faced it and now it has no hold over me. I will not forget.

We have played poker already and I won. When it is his turn to win I will not be afraid to play my cards right to the end. He knows that and I know that. When that day comes it will neither be unexpected or a shock. I will smugly remind him that it took him two games of poker to get me. I will be ready. When that day comes it is not to be a sad day. It will be a day to celebrate the incredible life that I have had, rather than mourn the part of that life that was never to be.

57 - Faith

Death and faith tend to be located pretty close together in the human brain filing cabinet. All through my life I have observed people with faith. Without ever establishing what their particular brand of faith was, I always thought it was a good thing. I have seen older people especially, derive great strength and peace of mind from being able to believe in something greater than ourselves. I could see that without this it could be difficult to keep finding the reason to keep going. Their faith, even if by chance it was untrue, was doing them good. It was bringing hope and contentment into their lives when nothing else could. It was giving them the strength to carry on. Faith gives you the capability to deal with anything that life can throw at you because it is greater than life itself.

Faith, to me, is a very private matter. It is uniquely personal to every individual, as unique as your personality or your fingerprints. I can not and will not say what anybody should believe in. If people want to, they must find that for themselves. I do feel however that if you do believe in something it will become a great asset to dealing with a cancer fight or any crisis in your life. It gives you somewhere to go beyond where you now are. That can be a welcome refuge if all that surrounds you is hopelessness and despair. It can become your only beacon beyond discomfort, pain, disability and even death itself. Your faith therefore will always be there for you. It is untouchable by anything in the world you are in. It is the lighthouse beyond the stormy sea. The gale may blow or your boat may sink but it will always be there.

If you have faith you now need to use it to your advantage. It can be a powerful piece in your jigsaw. It can be a constant source of strength. It is also untouchable. It is beyond setbacks, time spans and the interference of others. You own it. It is part of you. It is yours.

Your faith will prompt you to assess the life you have lived. We have all been given a conscience. I believe this was for a reason. It was to give us the responsibility and the freedom to decide what we genuinely believe is right. If we do not then it is not simply a case obeying or breaking the rules of a state or a doctrine or a religion. We must answer to ourselves. You can hide from others but you can't hide from yourself.

If you have a faith it is entirely your decision whether it is part of a religious movement. Generally the essence of most religions is good. Be a good person. Try and be a better person. Bring as much love to this world as you can. Nobody can fault those aspirations. But we know they are aspirations rather than absolutes. We are not, and never will be, perfect. The goal therefore for most of us is surely to keep trying to reach those aspirations knowing we will sometimes fail.

For me your conscience is your gauge as to how hard you have tried and your faith is your inspiration to try again. These were the yardsticks I used for my life assessment. If this was to be the end, these would be the measures against which I would hold up everything I did or didn't do.

I go in to a church every day now. I intend to do this for every single day I have left in my life. I do it for two reasons. The first is that I believe in God. I believe he was also a major piece in my jigsaw. He was going to call me in but had a last minute change of heart. Perhaps he wasn't happy with the way I was going. He needed me to see that my glass was beautifully half full, rather than disappointingly half empty.

Maybe he felt he needed to redirect me. He had a new job for me. He decided to give me a new brief for my second chance at life. Maybe he was telling me to go back and encourage the cancer sufferers that were going to come after me.

The second reason I go in to a church is because I never want to let myself forget what has happened to me. I feel I need to make a space every day in which I can acknowledge how lucky I am to still be here. I have tried a variety of locations to achieve this. In the end the only place I found where you can make the world stand still for two minutes is a church. They are the only places where you can leave this mad cap planet of ours behind you at the door.

Churches, in Ireland anyway, are also very plentiful. No matter where I go, I can always find one to fit in to my day. These few quiet moments each day will ensure I never lose touch with what I have been through. They bring a pause to my life so that I can acknowledge and appreciate. Each new day is a little miracle in itself. It needs to be recognised as such. Another sunrise, another chance encounter, another evening run, another great day to be here. Each month brings yet another milestone or achievement. With each year that passes my second life begins to leave my first behind even more. God for me is infinitely good. It is only man in the two thousand intervening years that may have confused the issue. I like to take the time every day to thank him for being so good to me.

58 – Closure

I had now reached the point where I was effectively cured. When cancer comes back after the five year remission period it is regarded as a new version rather than a return of the old one. I was back working full-time again and leading a full life just as I had done before.

For the very first time I let myself believe I had successfully survived my ordeal. I had emerged from the forest. Now, at long last, I was in a position to begin to distinguish the wood from the trees. I could view my entire ordeal from the start to the finish. The realisation now was that my recovery had become an even bigger story than my survival ever was. Miracle number two had gone on to outdo miracle number one.

When I had completed my treatment I just wanted to be alive. The odds were so high against that possibility and the treatment I had to go through so destructive that nothing else was in the viewfinder. If I was alive it meant I had won, or at least I was winning. My cancer would only win when I was dead. I was prepared to pay any price to deny it that result.

I was so strong at that point that the prospects of blindness, deafness, loss of speech or reduced mobility made little impact on me. I just wanted to win and I didn't care how. My singlemindedness was so absolute that even if I had to go into a vegetative state in order to declare victory it wouldn't have mattered. With my life on the line, my mental focus was ensuring that nothing would distract from the desire to simply stay alive. I was right up against the wood then.

Now that I had reached open ground I could look back and see the forest was made up of many trees. Not only was I not just alive or a vegetable or blind or deaf or dumb, I was basically 95% of the person I had been before cancer struck. My survival, an amazing story in itself was turning out to be just the starter. My recovery had become the main course. If the starter was delicious the main course was sumptuous. It had become an unlimited platter of the finest food imaginable. I could see, hear, walk, talk, eat, drink, work, run, sleep, drive, swim, sing, cycle and even fly (in an airplane!). Apart from the eyepatch it was almost as if cancer had never happened.

Now that I had resumed every bit of the life I had before I got sick I wanted to draw a line in the sand. I wanted to make a clear distinction between cancer and post-cancer. I wanted to pick a point in time and be able to say that was the very last day of my ordeal.

I felt I needed to go somewhere for closure. Wherever I was to go, it would have to be somewhere special. A place that would receive me as a cancer patient and send me home as a free man. I wanted to make a journey to somewhere to mark the end of the journey itself.

I did not know where that place was going to be. I knew it could not be an extravagant destination like Las Vegas, Ibiza or Hong Kong. I knew it could not even be one of the more beautiful cities in the world like Paris or Sydney or Cape Town. It had to be somewhere very special, somewhere with meaning. It was going to be the place where I would close the book. The place where I would say "I have beaten cancer. I am still alive. It is over. Now I will get on with the rest of my life." I did not know where such a place was to be.

By now quite a few of my daily church visits had turned into going to morning Mass in Ballina. These weekday Masses were almost exclusively attended by a group of local women who hardly ever missed a day. Just about all of these wonderful women became devoted to my case. Without any invitation they had taken charge of the piece of my jigsaw that had "prayer" written on it. One of these women, Deirdre Griffin, approached me one morning as I was leaving Mass. She convinced me that the place I was looking for was Medjugorje.

I didn't know anything about Medjugorje. This was good. I liked the fact that it was a place I didn't know much about. It meant that I felt I was able to journey there on my own terms. I could make this a very personal pilgrimage, just for me, without any preconceived expectations of what Medjugorje was supposed to be.

I made a point of finding out very little more about it before I went. The little bit I did know however I liked. I knew that an apparition had occurred there. The only other thing I knew was that it had a mountain. That was good enough for me. I started with a mountain at Tountinna, so now I would finish with one too. Two small mountains were now going to bookend my entire cancer story, Tountinna in County Tipperary and Krizevac in Bosnia and Herzegovina.

Deirdre's sister-in-law, Rosemarie McKeogh organises a parish trip from Ballina to Medjugorje every year. She was only delighted to sign me up for the group going out in September. I too was glad to be travelling with a group of people I knew well but this was primarily a private mission. I was determined that I would isolate myself at the appropriate moments to make the personal closure I needed.

Within a week I also acquired two surprising but very welcome travel companions. My sister Dolores decided she would come. The joke was that she was coming to hail Pam and my two other sisters when the meningitis struck again. My recovery had now reached a point where such concerns, I'm glad to say, were unnecessary.

The other traveller was a bit more of a surprise. Geno was coming too. Deirdre had very cunningly played one of us off against the other for the previous few weeks. She told Geno that I was coming in a bid to secure his commitment. In turn she kept telling me that he was confirmed to finally convert my initial interest into signing on the dotted line.

Geno's presence gave the proposed trip a whole new complexion. A sense of intrigue began to break out. The lubricated tongues in every pub in the town began to wag. "Geno and Liam are going on a pilgrimage"! Surely this could not be as it seems. There must be some kind of cover up going on. Maybe they have discovered some new faraway paradise, full of beautiful women, who only desire men in their late forties from North Tipperary.

Other jokes were less kind. If you were ever thinking of going to Medjugorje you better go now. They are bound to close it after Geno has been.

The truth however was nothing so complicated. Geno, as it turns out, had a bit of soul searching to do like myself. After that he had simply fallen for the very persuasive charm of both Deirdre and Rosemarie, just like I had.

All three of us were glad the other two were coming. In the back of our minds it was our built in safety plan. If the trip turned out to be a disaster, for some reason, we could all bail out and head for the Croatian coast.

The first major impact of this trip happened before I even got out of Ireland. We were flying from Shannon to Dubrovnik. Our group of forty arrived at the airport shortly after nine in the morning. Shannon at that time was the major stop-over airport for the American troops flying to and from the Gulf war. On previous visits I had seen handfulls of soldiers in the duty free shops and the departure lounge but nothing prepared me for what I was now about to witness.

We arrived at the check-in desks full of good humoured holiday banter. This was my first pilgrimage. I was impressed with the collective bonhomie that a trip like this can generate. I suppose most people going on a pilgrimage are bringing a personal need of some kind. This becomes a great leveller. It created a sense of common social unity within the entire group, right from the off.

Pilgrims appear to set off full of optimism. We were all bonded by the hope that we would find something inspirational from our trip. This unilateral aspiration breaks down many of the barriers that a normal group of travelling strangers face. I found a warm sense of immediate absorption with travelling pilgrims that I had not experienced in previous travels.

So the first impressions were good. This looked as if it was going to be a memorable trip before I had even boarded the plane.

The departure lounge in Shannon is just one big long room. There is a small bar and cafeteria area in the middle with two huge seating areas at each end. When I entered this room on my trip to Medjugorje, I could not believe what I saw. The entire space was filled, as far as your eyes could see, with thousands of U.S. soldiers. The dramatic nature of the scene was amplified by the fact that everybody was dressed in exactly the same kaki coloured uniform and all had the same shaved head haircut. It was not just thousands of soldiers, but thousands of identical soldiers. I was in a hanger full of clones.

It was just like walking onto the set of a Steven Spielberg movie by accident. Dolores, Geno and I eventually manouvered our way, through the kaki maze, to reach the bar. I ordered my last pint of Irish Guinness for a week and as I sipped it I couldn't help but wonder about the young soldier beside me. What lay ahead of him in the weeks to come?

I took my chance to exchange a few words with him and enquired if they were going to war or returning home. He told me they were on their way to Baghdad. As I looked around the room I realised I needn't have asked. All of the faces I was seeing were sombre rather than cheery. We exchanged a few pleasantries and I wished him well. I told him that I hoped he would soon be back in Ireland again on his way home to his family.

This brief encounters allowed me, for the first time, to put a face on a story. For the previous few months I had watched the news every night. I was familiar with the many atrocities that were occurring on both sides in the Gulf war. These shocking stories unfortunately meant very little to me. I had nothing to relate them to. They were terrible stories, I knew that bit, but they were happening so far away they had little connection to my life.

Now I had a connection. I had just been talking to a young American soldier at a bar only twenty miles from where I live. Our life lines had crossed for a few seconds. He was part of those pictures I had seen on television.

I would now spend the rest of my life wondering how long more he was destined to live. He became just like the boy I sat beside on the bus in Mexico. Would this young soldier ever see Shannon airport again. Would he complete his tour of duty, return to his family and live until he was ninety. Or would he be killed in the coming months.

How quickly I had lost my ability to see. I had been watching the news without really taking in what the pictures were telling me. I knew nothing about hospitals until I got sick and now I knew nothing about the war in Iraq until I could look a young soldier in the eye and wonder about his future.

I started to look at all of them then. They were just kids really, seventeen, eighteen and nineteen years old. They were all just a few years older than Christy. How convenient this scene was I thought for the army generals of the world. They were able to sit in their plush offices in Washington, Baghdad, London or wherever and send out somebody else's children to do their dirty work for them.

The irony of the two trips then began to dawn on me. Our little group were going out in good spirits on a pilgrimage. We were going to a holy place. We were going to a gentle, kind place that would give people hope and belief. A good place. But in that huge room we were surrounded by an ocean of young men and women who were travelling in a polar opposite direction. They were going into battle. The sense of exuberance in our heart was only matched by the fear in theirs. Fear of the unknown. Fear that they were heading to the end of their young lives. There could not have been a greater contrast in the two journeys that were about to be called from that departure lounge. It was as if this huge room had become some kind of human sorting office. We were all being funnelled towards just two gates. The sign on one read "God and life". The sign on the other read "War and death".

Medjugorje is quite simply the most amazing place I have ever been. Most of my friends would not have been attracted to go somewhere like this so all week I was determined to play devil's advocate on their behalf. I wanted to make an assessment of the trip that was based on human experience rather than religious persuasion. It was almost as if I wanted to judge it from the starting point of needing to be convinced of its merits.

It is a small town. This was a good start. I liked the scale of the place. Through it's small size it created a reassuring sense of familiarity and comfort. It reminded me, in many ways, of the town I had just left, Ballina. They were both about the same size.

Medjugorje is also a town in its own right. It goes about its business, as any town would, regardless of the religious devotion taking place nearby. I liked this too.

The religious aspect of Medjugorje is nicely underplayed. It is not directed to meet you head-on as you arrive. You need to go and find it for yourself. There is no pomp and ceremony here. This is exactly what I was looking for. I wanted a place where I could be in control of my time there. I could go to it rather than it gushing to meet me. I didn't want a place where I was going to be herded around in a flock of sheep. I needed it to be a place where I could make my own closure, in my own way.

Medjugorje is the perfect host for each individual who goes there. It lays itself out for you like a passive smorgasbord of sights and activities. It is then entirely up to you to decide what you want to do and where you want to go. Some people just had a holiday. They only participated as if they were in any tourist town, eating in the restaurants, drinking in the bars and happily conversing with whoever happened to come within their company. They barely acknowledged the religious significance of this place. This was perfectly fine too. Medjugorje had room for everybody. It was an unconditional host.

This was a very special place. It seemed to have a unique ability to bring out the very best of the world we know and induce a profound consciousness of the one we don't. In the evenings especially, it was more than capable of dislocating itself from the surrounding gentile spirituality to socialise like any other town. This I liked too. You can't pray all day. This wonderful town showed us all that devotion and leisure need not be strangers. It was a beautiful stage where they could both be performed hand in hand. One minute you were sipping a glass of wine with friends and the next saying a quiet prayer for a friend. In Medjugorje, God, or whatever you defined as God, seemed to be just as present in the bar as it was in the church.

Some evenings I would just slip away from my company at the bar to light a candle for somebody I had forgotten earlier. Then I would just seamlessly resume my place as if I had been no further than the toilets.

Each day started with morning Mass. Geno, Dolores and I went on the first morning. We didn't expect we would go every day but these Masses were special. We never missed one all week after that, no matter how late we got to bed. There was something different going on here. You felt it at Mass. You felt it in the bars. You felt it when you were out walking. You couldn't put your finger on it but there was something very special about this place. Mass was the beginning of that sensation every day. This was not like anything we had ever seen before. The sense of being part of something very simple and fundamental but uniquely special was overwhelming. These Masses were a gathering of complete strangers and yet it was as if we all knew each other. We had all come together in this place to discover an acceptance of our flaws and an appreciation of our abilities like never before. It was an amazing way to start your day.

After that we visited the apparition sites and went to hear the visionaries address the crowds. We also attended some of the other religious ceremonies. Not one of these events disappointed. In their own way they all connected with each one of us. They all put their own stamp on the individual thoughts and reflections that were going through our heads. At other times we took time on our own to go for a walk, light candles, visit the church or just browse around the shops in the town. I found the experience of being in company and on my own equally rewarding in a place like this.

In the evening it was time to socialise and meet up with the others from the group, or indeed, people you had never met before. Medjugorje attracts visitors from all over the world but there are no strangers here. All week I had wonderful conversations with people I had just met. It was as if I had known them all my life.

Colombo's bar and restaurant was the epicentre of all our social interaction. It was the bar nearest the church itself. It became our second home and the place we were always to be found after the sun had gone down. If each day began with an amazing Mass, it ended with some of the most wonderful human interaction I have ever been privileged to experience, in Colombo's.

In between your day was filled with a serene sense of inner calm. You walked around with a genuine appreciation that the world was indeed a beautiful place to be. You knew that you were somewhere that could energize these emotions within you. This was a place that had the quality to bring out the very best in you. This place was very special and very rare. I will have very few days that will be greater than these.

No matter what the three of us did during the day we had one rule that had to be adhered to. You were not permitted to retire to bed before sharing a bottle of wine on the balcony with the other two. This became our own little forum to discuss all we had witnessed that day. Over a few glasses of wine we would analyse all the things we had seen and done, both collectively and independently. We viewed everything from all of the different angles. We purposely adopted the viewpoints of believers and non-believers. The discussions would range from looking for physical proof that God exists on one hand to rationalising the beauty and devotion of blind faith on the other.

There was something very rewarding about these late night conversations. We all spoke with a sense of freedom and honesty that rarely presents itself in normal life. We were not searching for results or conclusions. Nobody was trying to convince anybody else. We just made space to discuss things that are rarely discussed. The only conclusion that was made was that we were all delighted to be there. We all realised, irrespective of our own personal beliefs, that we were somewhere very different to anywhere else we had ever been before.

Medjugorje, above all, re-establishes a belief in the warmth of humanity. It does this, I believe, in a way that few other places can. All week you will find yourself just sitting down and having the most incredible conversations with complete strangers. There is no awkwardness here, no barriers, no pretentiousness. It is a place where everybody can be their own humble, flawed but beautiful selves for one week at least. Even without its religious aspect it is a wonderful place to be. It is a people place. A best of people place. Regardless of what you believe in, Medjugorje is one of the few places where you will see humanity at its very best.

The religious aspect was equally beautiful to me but that was just for me personally. Medjugorje does not impose itself on you. There was nobody to tell you what you should or shouldn't do. It is somewhere where every individual will find what they need for themselves. It knows you have brought more baggage with you than you put on the airplane. No matter who you are it will lift your spirits. It will put your faith back into the reassurance that this world is an incredible place to be. It will re-enlighten you to the fact that we are all gifted, wonderful people. It will ensure you are carrying less baggage home than what you brought with you.

We did two day trips while we were there. Dolores and I had a lovely day by the sea in

Split in Croatia. We just spent the day relaxing at those lovely al-fresco café tables that all Mediterranean cities do so well. We let the day pass by under the warm sun as we looked on.

Split is a beautiful city. Geno was to come too. Just as we were about to board the bus he realised he had forgotten his passport. He would need it to cross the border between Bosnia and Croatia so we had to go ahead without him.

Our other breakaway was a little more dramatic. On the Sunday, after Mass, we had assembled in Colombo's for breakfast as usual. Deirdre was with us and needing a seat a Norwegian man, Henning, joined our table. He was stationed in Bosnia as a U.N. diplomat and had come over to Medjugorje on his day off. He was curious to see some of the sights and find out what all the fuss was about. We got chatting to him when he sat down and he asked if we would be happy to show him around. In return he offered to take us in his car to show us the town of Mostar. He was very pleasant company and we were delighted to take up his offer.

For the next couple of hours we showed him the various religious sights around the church in Medjugorje. Then we all made the picturesque walk through the fields to Apparition Hill. Apparition Hill is where the Virgin Mary appeared to the four visionaries. It is a serenely beautiful place. From there you can see the entire town in the valley below with Krizevac, or Cross Mountain as it is also called, rising up beyond. The sense that you are overlooking a special part of this planet, is very strong. Henning was suitably impressed and on returning to Colombo's we all piled into his old Mercedes. We were heading for Mostar.

Mostar is less than an hour away from Medjugorje. If any place epitomises the conflict that has ravaged the Balkans throughout the early 1990's, this is it. When we arrived, over ten years later, the scars of war were still plain to be seen. We found it both breathtakingly beautiful and horribly desecrated in alternate images. The troops in Shannon were heading for the Middle East and we were going to Medjugorje. Little did we realise that just an hour from our destination we would find a scene just as horrific as the one they were destined for.

Before we got to Mostar we were stopped twice on the road at police checkpoints. Henning explained to us that these were normal in this part of the world. They were also not what they seemed. The police would inspect your papers and your car and make up some reason why an on-the-spot fine had to be paid. The driver then would have no choice but to pay up before making further progress. All U.N. diplomats were immune from these bribes. Henning smugly invited us to observe the disappointed expressions on the policemen's faces as soon as he showed them his identity card. Welcome to the Balkans!

Up to now our blinkered vista of Bosnia began and ended with the friendly little oasis that is Medjugorje. The wider context of the part of the world that we found ourselves in was now beginning to dawn on us. Having escaped our sanctuary we realised we had only scratched the surface of this uniquely complex region. This entire area was a delicate, simmering fusion of culture, race and religion. It was a part of the world that was an uneasy balance at the best of times and a horrific war zone at the worst.

The Balkans must be the biggest bottleneck in the history of the world. Just about every civilisation since time began has passed through here at some stage. The Goths and the Huns, the Greeks, the Romans, the Turks, the Arabs, the Germans, the Allies and the Russians have all stamped their footprint on this part of the globe. The modern day uncomfortable bedfellows are the Christians and Muslims. Having escaped beyond the sheltered boundaries of Medjugorje we were now receiving a virtual history lesson. And it was right on our doorstep. We had steered our train out of a sleepy siding, only to discover the biggest train station in the history of the world was just down the line.

The legacy of all of those uninvited visitors was that the country formerly known as Yugoslavia, that Tito had managed to gag with an iron fist for so long, had now shattered into seven distinctive regions. What used to be Yugoslavia is now Slovenia, Croatia, Serbia, Bosnia, Macedonia, Herzegovina and Montenegro. The differentials however don't even stop there. Further cross pollinization between the various sub-divisions has given us Bosnian Serbs, Serb Croats and Bosnian Croats. This is an impossible part of the world to get a handle on!

Mostar, both during and after the war, became an internationally recognised symbol of the two extremes of Balkan diversification. Geographically the town has always been split by the beautiful 16th century Stari Most bridge. It spanned the river Neretva in the centre of the town. The bridge was destroyed in 1993 as a clear message by the Croats that nothing was sacred in the bitter war between the two religious divides. The river, once a vein through the heart of the town suddenly became a chasm. It became the breach across which the Christians, on the west bank, were pitted against the Muslims, on the east. When the war eventually ended the bridge was rebuilt in 2004. It was beautifully re-constructed as an exact replica of the original and became a worldwide symbol of how reunification can prevail, no matter how bitter the division.

The new future of Mostar would start with a return to its past. It would begin with the rebuilding of a bridge that was five hundred years old. That bridge would restore a Mostar where Christians and Muslims where able to live and work again, side by side. To secure its future, Mostar needed to return to the beautiful market town it was in the past. It would once again be famed for its graceful bridge and lively, narrow streets rather than bombs, bullets and butchery.

This unexpected visit had now become an inherent part of our pilgrimage. Our detour to Mostar showed us that religion in this world can cause as many problems as it may solve. Our visit to this once desecrated town, just down the road, taught us that when you are sitting in the sun it is always raining somewhere not far away.

Mostar, in its own way, was even more inspirational than Medjugorje. It showed us that no matter how long it rains, the sun can always come out to shine again. On that day, in the middle of one of the most memorable weeks of my life, I had a humbling awareness of how delicate this world is. We are never far from either devastation or exhilaration. The lines are very fine.

The outskirts of Mostar have remained largely unchanged since the war. We drove through eerie streets of abandoned high rise, skeletal buildings. They have stood still in time since the day the shells stopped raining down. These buildings, by their stark presence on a barren urban landscape, have become monuments to the horror of what war is. They have become symbols of the destruction one man can do to another when he chooses to. We drove by in silence. We just stared at the bullet ridden concrete and shattered glass. It was as if we were put under some kind of macabre spell by these deathly still structures. Your introduction to Mostar starts with the past. A past that no civilization could be proud of.

We eventually emerged from the desolation to find the new Mostar. We had reached the vibrant, narrow streets that led to the Stari Most. All of these were filled with locals and tourists alike, all busy doing nothing of importance. Some were buying trinkets, others merely browsing from stall to stall. Every restaurant balcony was filled with smiling, happy customers. As we looked along the street they all looked like colourful human window boxes. People were talking, drinking coffee, enjoying this moment of their lives. Everybody seemed happy.

Inspiration surrounds us everywhere. Mostar is the proof of that. This world is for everyone and there is very little difference between us all. When we get it right there is no better place to be.

We all walked across the bridge together. It was beautiful. It had been rebuilt in precise detail and restored to its former glory. It was a special moment. Medjugorje had been inspirational but this simple structure was a monumental symbol that hope is never lost.

I waited until I was well settled in Medjugorje before planning my own secret mission. This was my personal reason for coming here in the first place. All week I was anxious to create the right opportunity to make it happen the way I wanted. This was to be the very last act of my story, the final closure. There were two days to go when I made my move. Krizavac was about a mile and a half outside of the town. In a nice twist, it was roughly the same height as Tountinna. That seemed symbolic even before I set out. The two bookends would match.

We were all advised not to climb in the middle of the day due to the intense heat. As a result, most of the pilgrims scheduled their visit for early morning, mainly in organised groups. This didn't appeal to me. Early mornings were not good after our late night balcony discussions. We were barely making ten o'clock morning Mass as it was.

I also wanted to climb it on my own. With everybody climbing in the morning I would have a much better chance of having the mountain to myself in the evening. I knew Geno and Dolores wanted to climb it too. That meant I would climb it twice but the sole reason that I was here was to go up that mountain alone. Now I needed to slip away to achieve this.

I bided my time as the afternoon wore on and took my chance to escape unnoticed. As it turned out I arrived at the foot of Krizevac a little later than I had intended. It was 5.00 p.m. There was still an hour of daylight left but I was a little wary of getting up and down a mountain I didn't know before darkness came.

The zig-zag pilgrims path to the top was clearly identified. The gradient was relatively steep but the ascent was no more than a difficult walk rather than an actual climb. Along the path the stations of the cross were recreated with life size statues like fourteen, thought provoking, displays for each climber. The first just as you set off and the last just before you reached the top.

Most groups ascending would stop at each station to recite specific prayers. That was one of the reasons I wanted to be alone. I wanted to travel this path and have it to myself. This journey was for me and me alone. It was my own little pilgrimage to end my long journey. I had Tountinna to myself when I ran. Now I wanted Krizevac to myself as I climbed.

I did stop at each station as I ascended. I began to use them to collect my thoughts and reflections as I made my way. It was only when I got to the third station that the correlation of what I was seeing and what I was thinking began to dawn on me. As we stood at the bottom of the mountain both Jesus Christ and I were condemned men. We were both going to die. On the journey that ensued he fell three times, and so did I. His first fall symbolised my first bout of meningitis, his second was my D.V.T. and his third was meningitis again. All of a sudden it was as if God had taken me to this place to re-enact my journey with me. He wanted to be beside me as I closed this chapter of my life. Whilst looking at his ordeal, I could see my own.

I was emotional now. This was what I had come for. This was my release. This was going to be the very end of my story.

With tears streaming down my face I climbed and climbed. At each station I could find some facet of my saga being reflected back to me. I was as if God was putting both our stories together. We would go up that mountain together. After each fall Jesus managed to get up and carry on. So did I. When we both got to the top the two of us were supposed to be dead. Neither of us were. He had risen from the dead and I had somehow managed to survive against all the odds. After that, as Paddy Hynes foretold, I would come down the mountain and get busy getting on with the rest of my life.

After the last station I made the short walk to the large cross that stands on top of Krizevac. We had been familiar with it all week because it can be seen for miles around. Now I was right beside it. I had not met anybody on the way up. I had, as I had wished, the entire mountain to myself. I went up to the cross and then beyond it to a large boulder. It dominated the flat plain that crowned the mountain. Dusk was just beginning to set. The twilight was casting its magic over the beautiful panorama that lay below.

One by one the twinkling lights of Medjugorje began to illuminate beneath me. They were like tiny candles venerating this great mountain that stands over them. The air was still and warm. The silence was only barely disturbed by the distant hum of a town getting ready for its evening festivities.

I just sat there and absorbed all the sights, smells and sounds of this little piece of heaven. It was as if I had been granted a vista to look down on the earth below. My emotions could be contained no longer. I began to cry. I cried and I cried and I cried. I sat on that rock for over an hour, probably crying most of the time. This was my final release. This was my exorcism. I went up that mountain as a cancer patient. I was going to go down it a free man. Any final remnants of my disease, either physical or emotional, were going to be left behind on that rock forever. My second life would be waiting for me when I got back down to the bottom.

This was one of the most incredible experiences of my life. If felt closer to God for that hour than I have ever done. It was as if he was physically there beside me. He was merely showing me he had been with me all the way. Krizevec was his mountain now he was showing me that it was mine too. It represented what we needed to do and we had conquered it together.

My climb had been a recreation of my cancer journey without me ever realising it would be. I had gone to Medjugorje for closure and my story was already waiting for me there. Now it was closed.

As I left the boulder I had one final act to do. I took out an eyepatch and buried it under the rocks. I was leaving the greatest symbol of my ordeal behind. The eyepatch is the greatest trademark of what I have been through. Now I was leaving it behind me. With that my story was complete. It was over.

It was dark now but I didn't care. It only seemed to make the mountain more intimate and views more spectacular. It was as if I knew every inch of Krizevac now. I had been with it in daylight, at dusk and now in darkness. There were no secrets between us anymore. It was my friend.

I slowly but safely made my way back down and rejoined the others in Colombo's. "Where have you been?" they all inquired. "Oh, I just went for a good long walk" I replied. I neglected to inform them that it had been the greatest walk of my entire life.

59 – Second Life Milestones

I had now reached an incredible place to be. I had taken on cancer and beaten it. It wasn't just any cancer. I had been given one of the worst versions available. It still couldn't take me down.

Survival, against the odds, came with plenty of bonuses. I now had a wonderful perspective view of how good it was to be alive. I had a great sense of balance in my life. I now considered myself to be tough and appreciative in the same heartbeat.

If I died, there and then, six years later, every second of my fight and recovery would had been worth it. Those six years had almost become the equal of the previous forty. I was on a high from simply being alive. But I wasn't going to die then. Or the next day or the day after that. Who is to say how long this wonderful recovery will now run.

This amazing story just keeps writing new chapters. What were once major milestones were now turning into minor statistics. My first 10K, post cancer, was a huge personal achievement. By 10K number twenty five, they had become routine. Our first, non-meningitis interrupted, family holiday, was a major landmark. In the following years we resumed holidaying like a normal family again and visited Spain, Turkey, Italy and America. I was now fully back to work again. Everything I had established in my first life had now been fully restored in my second.

I was quietly amazed to have come through all of this and be basically 95% of what I was before. Of the missing 5% at least 2% was down to being six years older, so that just left 3%. The man who was given a 5% chance to live, had now got back to 97% of the man he was before cancer struck.

I had lived to have seen my three boys grow from the ages of one, five and seven to seven, eleven and thirteen. That made everything worth it in itself. I had been granted the opportunity to get to know them. I was still present to watch them develop and see their personalities evolve. I was diagnosed just before Christy was about to make his First Holy Communion. I had now lived to see all three of them not just make their First Communions, but their Confirmations too. All of these family events have been huge milestones for me. They were all greatly appreciated and quietly acknowledged.

I had progressed from just being content to replace all of the foundation blocks of my previous life to now building a whole new structure on top of them. This was the greatest part of all of still being alive. I was living to enjoy the fruits of my recovery to the full.

No event or achievement is allowed to pass now without being logged. Everything I live to witness is gratefully appreciated. It was as if I had been spared just to see Munster win their first Heineken Cup in 2006 and my native county Westmeath win their first ever Leinster Senior Football title in 2004. I looked up to the sky again in appreciation the day my new home county, Tipperary won a hurling All-Ireland again in 2010. Who is to know how much more I should expect. I am holding out that perhaps an F.A.I. Cup and Champions League for Athlone Town and World Cups for Ireland in both soccer and rugby are pencilled in for me before I am finally called in. Why should the miracles stop now!

Some milestones stand out more than others. After the Canary Islands holiday saga we didn't dare fly anywhere again until I was well and truly recovered. That happened in 2006 when we went to Turkey. One day we took a boat trip from the harbour in Bitez. It was a lovely wooden ex-fishing boat. It had been converted to take about sixteen tourists out for the day. The itinerary was to see some local sights along the coast, visit an island and stop for a swim. Lunch on board was also included. As soon as we set off we quickly got to know the other tourists on board. There were two girls from Ireland, two couples from England and the rest were mainly Dutch. Everybody was all set for a day's sun worshipping, swimming and relaxing.

I was fully recovered by this but still a little self conscious on public outings. I was no match for the anatomical glamour that was being paraded elsewhere on board. I was also reluctant to swim because of my eyepatch. If I left it on it would get wet and I was still not comfortable exposing my damaged eye to complete strangers.

Just about everybody else on board was a good looking, well toned, specimen. They were all in their twenties or thirties. The girls were all wearing bikinis and the boys proudly displaying their bronzed, bare chests. I, in comparison, had a battle weary, pure white torso, complete with peg tube, tracheotomy and hip surgery scars. I opted to keep it under wraps. I stationed myself in a much less prominent part of the boat towards the rear.

I was quiet and fairly inconspicuous throughout most of the day and didn't take part in any of the activities. We just remained intact as a family unit, choosing to spectate rather than participate as the bikini clad girls and the bronze chested boys commandeered most of the attention.

It was now late afternoon and the boat was turning for home. We had one more stop to make. We were heading away from the shore towards an island a short distance away. As we approached we all began to search for the beach or castle or cafe that merited a stopping place of interest. All we could see however was a sheer cliff face. The nearer we got the bigger it became. At the base of the cliff we began to discern a large semi-circular shape of water that was a different colour to the rest of the sea. We were all familiar with the clean blue water of the Mediterranean but this was an exquisite pool of clear water. It was almost completely transparent. The clearest water I had ever seen.

The crew told us that a meteorite had hit this spot many years ago. The depth of the water in the semi-circle was fifty metres, hence the different colour. It was only then that we noticed the little winding path that made its way up the cliff. It emerged from a small landing area to the right of the pool and eventually reached a rocky ledge about half way up the cliff. The deep pool, the path, the ledge, at last we were beginning to work out the puzzle. Now we knew why we had stopped here. This was a place where you could take a big jump into the sea.

Two of the crew members immediately changed into their swimwear and dived in. They come here every day we all thought. They are going to show us how it is done. But no, they swam around in the crystal clear water for a while and returned to the boat. The two Irish girls and all of the heavenly Dutch bodies were next. Surely one of them will go for it we assumed. They certainly had the physique for it. But again, no matter how much they all swam and frolicked, nobody ventured over towards the little landing steps.

After about twenty minutes everybody began to climb back on board. The crew began to make preparations for our return to the harbour. We can't just go, I thought. Somebody has to do the big jump.

The crew were now calling the last of the swimmers in. That was my cue. Our boat had some unfinished business that needed to be attended to. We were not going to be the boat that let the side down. At that moment I stood up, took off my eyepatch and gave it to Pam. "Here, hold that for me please. I'll be back in a minute" I said. Then I jumped into the water and began to swim towards the steps that led to the path.

This was new territory for me. For the first time in four years I had cast away the safety harness of guarding my gentle recovery. Up to then it was a case of think at least four times before deciding on any action. This was the most impulsive, even reckless, thing I had done for ten years. But my stubborn pride had taken over now. Somebody had to do the jump. An impulsive uprising had taken over my brain and unplugged its cautious medical protective system.

It was a long walk to the top of the path. This gave me plenty of time for the realisation of what I was about to do to sink in. I began to think of the very complex revised bone structure I now had in my right cheek. Would it be okay when I hit the water? Images of John Fenton and Simon Rogers began to appear in front of me. What would they think of what I was now about to do. Would they approve?

But it was too late now. Everybody on the boat was now cheering me on. I was well past the point of no return. I couldn't walk back down the path now with my tail between my legs. Somebody had to do the jump and the only volunteer was me.

When I got to the ledge I went to the very edge to check the distance to the water below. It was about twenty metres. It looked more like a mile. It was a view that I decided I couldn't afford to see again. If I did I wouldn't have jumped.

I went to the back of the ledge. I knew the only way I would get over the edge was to start to run. That way it would be too late to change my mind when I would see the drop to the sea again. My mental uprising knew it had to opt for the "try to put the brakes on a charging elephant" policy. I also knew that this was going to be the best way to prevent snagging my back on the rocks I had seen protruding just below the ledge.

I went back as far as I could and turned to face the sea. The longer I delayed the more time I was allowing for doubts to prevail. I just took a deep breath and ran. My mind suddenly flooded with uncertainty but it was too late. For once the legs had taken control from the head. The edge came and went before I could register it. Then I was only running on fresh air. It was as if I had left the planet for a few seconds and was now hurtling into the unknown.

All of the doubts that had been suppressed earlier, suddenly sprang forth. Had I made a terrible mistake? As I raced to the edge my body was pumping adrenalin but now it had all congealed into pure fear. That fear now made me question if my bout of spontaneity had been wise.

Before any of these thoughts crystallized I was crashing through the wonderfully clear waters of the deep pool. First adrenalin, then fear, now sensation. I was falling gently through the water. I had escaped from gravity. It was like being on the moon. Eventually my gentle descent came to a halt. I looked up and through the clear blue water I could see the even clearer blue sky. I swam back towards it. The two Irish girls were quite near me when I broke through the plain between water and sky. "I'd love to be able to do that" I overheard one say to the other. I felt proud then.

I swam back to the boat, where a great reception was waiting for me. I was the man who did the big jump. They all considered me to be brave. The bronzed Dutch hunks didn't look so cool anymore. The bikini clad girls were starting to look my direction now. I wasn't just a withered old man after all. There was no need to hide myself away anymore. It was a different journey all the way home.

This was a very small event but it was a major milestone. I may have had cancer but I was the only person on the boat who would do the big jump. That jump meant a lot to me. I have it down as one of the greatest achievement of my second life!

Many cancer patients make big statements after surviving their ordeal. Phrases like "It was one of the best things that ever happened to me" or "It has completely changed my life" are not uncommon. These sentiments are not entirely pure because nobody wishes to get cancer in the first place but I can fully understand their origin. Just like the old saying that you will never miss your mother until she is gone, nothing makes you appreciate your life more than the possibility of losing it. Without some kind of a wake up call most of us tend to trip through our lives speedily, taking most of it for granted as we go along. We can develop an inherent blindness to pitfalls, believing they are for others rather than ourselves. We can begin to believe that we control our lives, rather than they controlling us. We start to assume that every time we toss up the coin it will come down on the side we want.

This sense of expectation can sometimes spawn a lack of tolerance for things not going to plan. Issues like traffic jambs, bad weather or having to wait can suddenly become huge, if they are the only problems we have. They can breed as much annoyance and despair as something far bigger. Unchecked, they may cause as much stress or unhappiness to us as something as profound as an illness, a family death or serious financial concerns.

Cancer is very good at punching through all of this. It gives you a proper yardstick. Now you can judge all of the disadvantages in your life on their actual merits. It will allow you to see what you could not see before. A traffic jamb or waiting for somebody who is late or a rainy day when you want to have a barbeque is not a problem. They are all merely mild inconveniences. The man on the news in Afghanistan on the other hand, whose wife and four children have just been blown up, has a real problem.

Everybody has a bag of troubles. One person's cancer is another person's bankruptcy. Our lives have been designed in such a way that we will never be trouble free. Some people's greatest worries are that they can't change their car this year. Others that they can't afford to holiday in the Seychelles this summer. They may have to go to Portugal instead.

Other people are told that they have only months to live or that their son has just been murdered.

Our individualism governs how these troubles affect us. We all grade them differently. Each bag of troubles is not strictly comparable. They are all uniquely personal. Who is to say a cancer diagnosis is worse than a prison sentence. The person who has to holiday in Portugal may be suicidal as a result of not being able to keep up with their peers. The person with three months to live may have calmly accepted it. If so the first person is arguably in a worse situation than the second. Which of us can judge?

We can only live the lives that are put in front of us. The unhappiness we feel is our own unhappiness, no matter what its source. We can disconnect ourselves from the devastation of a tsunami on the other side of the world but we cannot blank out the bad neighbour or the difficult boss. We can feel sympathy for the victims of the flood or the earthquake. Their troubles are huge compared to ours but we can only really feel the impact of our own. It is only the issues in our own lives that generally make us unhappy.

One of the greatest benefits of a cancer diagnosis is that it allows you to put all of your grumbles in order. As soon as this is done you see that many of them are not grumbles at all. Cancer empowers you to do this because it threatens you with the greatest grumble of all. There is no problem in this world bigger than dying.

Everybody who gets cancer should address, even if only momentarily, the possibility that it could lead to their death. This is an area very few of us want to confront but it can have surprising benefits if we do. You can end up finding positivity in an area you believed was exclusively negative.

One of the best things about contemplating your death is that it will make you look at your life. Only now you will look at it like you have never looked at it before. It is only from the standpoint of knowing that it will end, that you will truly begin to recognise and treasure what a blessing it is to have lived at all.

This thought process will allow you to take a vacuum cleaner to much of what clutters up your daily world. You will begin to see that the morning traffic jamb only lasts twenty minutes. The car that you are so desperate to replace is actually still running quite well. The exam you have just failed can be repeated. All of your concerns can be addressed in some way, or simply ignored. There is generally another road available even if it is not the one you set out to take. Cancer however puts a problem in front of you that has no alternative. If you die then you are just dead.

You have entered forbidding territory now but if you are not daunted by it you can reap great dividends. You are taking on cancer on at its own game. By standing up to it you are already starting to beat it. All it has on you is fear of death and if you disarm that, it has nothing left. Now you have the upper hand. Cancer, believing it was going to weaken you, is actually making you stronger. You have taken away its ultimate weapon, the fear of dying.

You can now use all of this newly discovered strength to underpin your battle. If you are not afraid to die you have called cancers bluff. It has no armour against you now. My fight really took off from this point. I was indestructible once I could look my cancer in the eye. There were no dark corners, no Achilles heels, nowhere I was afraid to go anymore.

My opponent in the boxing ring was twice my height and twice my weight but now he knew he was in a fight. I had just caught him with a stunning blow to his solar plexus. There would be no early knockout. I was like a mean boxer with a towel over my head. It was there to make sure I was only focussed on one thing. All I wanted to see now was my opponent in front of me. This fight was going all the way. It was going all the way to the final bell. I just didn't care about anything else now.

That final bell sounds on the last day of remission. The fight is over and the winner is about to be declared. If you are still standing, it is you. The sense of achievement on that day is very personal to all cancer patients. This is your victory. This is the day you have been striving for since the day you were told you had cancer. This is the day when all of your determination pays off. Against all odds, your opponent lies vanquished before you. He picked the wrong person to invite into the ring. Now he can only slump out of that ring in defeat. You can turn to the crowd with your fists in the air. You won this fight because you never stopped fighting. You won because you were not afraid. You won because nothing was going to stop you. Without that spirit you will not win but with it, you are practically unbeatable. It will take an extraordinary opponent to get the better of you.

One of the nicest rewards of victory is that the focus that carried your fight to stay alive can now be re-directed to enjoy the spoils of your triumph. Up to now you have been monopolised with survival. Now you can immerse yourself exclusively in just how good it is to be alive.

This is one of the unforeseen delights of your recovery. You have been given a renewed opportunity to both recognise and celebrate how wonderful your life actually is. You should grasp that opportunity with both hands. Life is an amazing gift. It should never be taken for granted again.

As survivors, we need to now have a permanent appreciation of how fortunate we have been. We should enjoy and treasure the fact that we are alive like never before. We have now become the lucky ones. Often it is difficult to recognise how good life is until you have been presented with this second chance. We now have that gift of perspective. We should never lose it again. We have defied the odds. Every day we live to be able to re-tell our story, is a great day.

With this new sense of realisation I began to enjoy my life like never before. After the first few years of remission I developed what I call a state of "pleasant recklessness". If I wanted to do something, something that had no detrimental impact on anybody else, I just did it. If I fancied another desert after my meal, I just ordered it. If the three boys wanted to go to a match that previously I would have been too busy for, we just went. If we all needed to take a few days break the buckets and spades were packed into the car and the work commitments were re-shuffled. Now that I could see the true value of life again I was determined to enjoy it to the fullest.

My long dormant music interest was a major benefactor of this reinvigorated outlook on life. I started going to concerts again, both big and small. Pre-cancer I wouldn't have even known they were on. Christy was a catalyst in this too. He was now just entering his early teens and was developing similar music tastes to my own. Selective brainwashing by my careful control of the car CD player for the previous ten years had something to do with this. Rock music had been through a barren spell since I was just a little older than he was. Now it was back in vogue. A whole new genre of rock bands had emerged and we began to trade. I passed on many of my old hero's like Neil Young, Rory Gallagher, AC/DC and The Cure. He gave me back a whole host of exciting new ones like The Killers, Greenday, Queens of the Stone Age and Foo Fighters.

U2 came to Croke Park in Dublin in 2005 as part of their world tour. The whole country appeared to be going to see them. I had seen U2 many times by then, both in big and small venues. I was happy to let this tour pass me by. As the concerts approached however I had a change of heart. I decided I wanted to bring Christy to see them. It would be his first really big concert. He wouldn't make a better debut than U2 in front of their home crowd. By now all of the tickets on general sale were sold out but Ireland is a small place. I was confident I had enough contacts to shake a couple of tickets from somewhere. I immediately put out the feelers that I was looking for two seats for any of the three nights.

The weeks started to go by without anything turning up. U2 had not been to Ireland for over four years and the demand was phenomenal. Eventually it came to the week of the concerts and I was beginning to admit defeat. I had tried but nothing had come back so that was that. I had built Christy up in the expectation of getting a ticket so he was a little despondent, but he was still young. His day would come.

On the Friday, the night of the first concert, I went down to Liam O'Riains. Inside I was expecting to find many of my friends who were reliably there on Friday nights. What I found instead was that the pub was almost deserted. Liam himself was behind the counter. "Any sign of Ian Connolly tonight Liam" I inquired as he handed me my drink. "Oh, he's gone to Dublin to see U2" he replied. "What about Bob Noonan" I continued. "Yes, he's gone too" came the reply. "Piers Devereux ?" the tone of my voice getting more desperate. "Piers up there too apparently".

At this I felt that if the next person I selected was Piers Devereux's great grandmother I was only leaving myself open to being told that yes, she too had gone to Croke Park to see U2. This concert was now becoming a bigger problem than I had anticipated. The whole country seemed to be at it but not me. Not only was I not there but now it was also impinging on my night out. It had taken all of my friends away from me. This concert was now choosing to antagonise me. The more I had tried to ignore it the more it seemed to be forcing itself into my life.

Eventually a few people I did know came in. By then however the possibility of salvaging my night out was gone. No matter who came or how many drinks I had, the frustration continued to grow inside me. Thousands of adoring fans were in front of U2 at that very moment and Christy and I were not among them.

I managed to keep a lid on this inner turmoil until I left the pub. On the walk home however, an emotive eruption of renouncement, fuelled by the mix of alcohol and disappointment, could be contained no longer. This was just not acceptable! Everybody I knew was at U2 and I was not able to bring my eleven year old son. Something had to be done. It was time to stop this concert dragging me back past zero. It was time to take it on!

The newspaper that morning had carried stories about concert tickets being returned due to credit card fraud. As I arrived at the house I had a thought. Perhaps the ticketmaster staff put these tickets back up for sale just before they go to bed. If I log on now I might just be lucky. I might find some freshly released tickets.

I went straight upstairs to my computer. I was on the hunt for a run of last minute returned tickets and hoping to be one of the first to avail of them. The screen began to illuminate the information before me. I scrolled down with excited anticipation.

U2 AT CROKE PARK. FRIDAY, SATURDAY & MONDAY.

Surely I would find something

...............…………NO TICKETS AVAILABLE!

I slumped back in my chair. My plan had been dashed. That was that. The door had finally been closed.

I sat there momentarily gazing at the screen. I had not become accustomed to admitting defeat. I had overturned much bigger opponents than this one. But this time I seemed to have little choice but to accept it.

I was tired. It had been a long day. It was time to go to bed.

Just then I noticed a little box at the bottom of the screen.

It read OTHER CONCERTS POSSIBLY AVAILABLE.

I clicked the box. The instruction to do so, from my brain to my finger, was sent out of curiosity rather than intent. I was only wondering where U2 were heading after Dublin. At that point I had no idea where this simple action could lead.

MILLENIUM STADIUM CARDIFF, WEDNESDAY NIGHT - TICKETS AVAILABLE.

"Mmmm……….well, it's not as if I'm going to go but I'll just have a look."

The website told me that some last minute seats had become available. The best two of these were in the middle of the stand overlooking the front of the stage.

"Tell you what, I'll just have a look at the ferries for the hell of it".

I clicked into the Irish Ferries website. They had space available to take a car from Rosslare to Pembroke and back at a very good rate. All of a sudden this bit of idle curiosity had transformed into something very enticing. U2 for Christy and I was sitting there right in front of me, just two clicks away.

At that point the switch tripped. We were just going to go! Pam was too asleep to run it by her and if I left it until the morning the opportunity would be lost. It was just like what I had said to Simon Rogers four years earlier

"There is no need to leave the room. The decision is already made."

The decision was that if my son Christy wanted to see U2, then that was what was going to happen. All of my normal cautionary mechanisms had been tranquilized. I was on auto pilot now. The plane was being powered by second life adrenalin.

With two simple clicks I booked the necessary tickets, the two seats at the concert first and then the ferry. It was the most outrageous act of spontaneous expenditure I had done in years. But I was alive. I was beautifully alive. I was alive enough to be able to make sure Christy and I were going to see U2.

I came out of my office on a complete high. As I passed Christy's door I couldn't resist. I slipped into his room, leaned over him and gently began shaking him. "We're going to U2! We're going to U2!"

The next morning when he came down for breakfast he revealed that he had a strange dream the previous night. He said some mad eegit was shaking him and telling him he was going to see U2. I was delighted to be able to tell him that his dream had come true. The mad eegit in his dream was actually sitting across the table from him!

Christy and I had a memorable trip. We did Cardiff and back in 36 hours. Father and son on tour. It was like making our own road movie. The time we spent together on route was just as rewarding as the concert itself. We left home at 4.00 am on the Wednesday morning to catch the 8.00 am ferry from Rosslare. We reached Cardiff at 3.00 pm, giving us plenty of time to collect our tickets, get something to eat and soak up the pre-concert atmosphere.

I had never been to Cardiff before and was amazed to discover that the Millenium Stadium is right in the middle of the city centre. As a consequence any event taking place there becomes an integral part of the city itself. The streets were pulsating with a vibrant fusion of excited U2 fans and enthusiastic locals who were only too happy to be part of the great sense of occasion. This direct link between the heart of the city and the magnificent stadium it contains generates an atmosphere in Cardiff for big events, that few other cities can match.

We went in to the concert at seven o'clock. The American band, the Killers, were the support act and this was an added bonus for us. The roof was closed, eliminating the daylight and ensuring the light show and the sense of anticipation were at the maximum level from the very start.

U2 came on stage shortly after nine. As usual, they didn't disappoint. It was a great show. One great song after another was unleashed, each one rapturously received by the adoring hoards in front of them. The audience were entranced in a manner that often only live music can achieve. For two hours the rest of the world was forgotten as both band and fans cocooned themselves in a fortress of ecstatic connection. It was a rare sensation, something of true beauty.

The 44 year old cancer survivor, standing in the south stand with his eleven year old son beside him, was very proud that night. Proud to have been there. Proud to be still alive to have been there. Proud to have his son standing beside him.

I was also proud to be Irish. These four men on stage, who had the world at their feet, were from the same country as me.

After the concert we made our way back to Pembroke. Our return ferry to Rosslare was at 3 in the morning. We were still on a high as we drove on to the ship but eventually tiredness caught up with us. We managed to get a few hours sleep on board soon after we pulled away. It would tide us over until we got home to a proper bed and a proper bedtime.

We broke the drive home for a cooked breakfast in Waterford city. This was going to be the last scene of our real-time movie. The credits were about to roll. Soon we would be back in the world we had left behind. The real world.

These are the moments that it is great to be alive for. The adventurous trip, Cardiff city centre, the concert, father and son having breakfast together, the little bit of devil may care that made it all happen. This was my second life at its very best.

The following Friday night I went back to Liam O'Riains. This time I found all of my friends inside as usual. "How did the concert go last weekend" I enquired. "Fantastic" they all replied. "It was an unbelievable show". In the course of the conversation they revealed that the only minor hiccup was that a small amount of rain fell during one of the concerts.

"And what about you" they enquired in return. "What did you get up to"? "Well" I replied, "I was going to go to Croke Park but didn't like the look of the weather forecast so I popped over to Cardiff on Wednesday night instead. The roof was closed. It was an unbelievable concert and nobody got wet"!

I have told this story many times in recent years to demonstrate the difference between my first and second lives. This concert trip just would not have happened had I not got cancer. I would simply have tried to get tickets for Dublin and having failed would then have given up. I would have been too busy and too blinkered to ever contemplate that a possible plan B might have existed.

I had now turned the mental focus I had used to stay alive to make sure a way was found for Christy and I to see U2. I wasn't prepared to take no for an answer, until it was the only answer. If Dublin wasn't possible then it was going to be Cardiff. If Cardiff wasn't possible who knows where we could have ended up.

I was turning negatives into positives again. I was prepared to go down every road, just as I had done when I was diagnosed. If there was a way, I was going to find it.

This is one of the greatest attributes of your second life. It will let you throw caution to the wind. It encourages you to live for today. It has already shown you that tomorrow can not be guaranteed.

I now had identified three very specific milestones that I wanted to put in place in my post cancer life. The first of these was to get back working to a serious level again. The second was to start running to a serious level again. The third, more bizarrely, was to go and see the Smashing Pumpkins. This was the band that I had formed a personal alliance with all through my illness. Every night, as I lay in my hospital bed, the Pumpkins was the only music I could listen to. They were the only band who knew how I was feeling. Only their music could provide a refuge for the places I needed to go.

Their angst was as loud as mine. Their hope as strong as mine. Their despair as black as mine. Their fight as tough as mine. Billy Corgan and Co., without ever knowing it, had become a little piece of my jigsaw. As I lay there with an uncertain future ahead of me, my wish was that maybe one day I would live to get to see this wonderful band. One day I would get to replace the headphones with the real thing.

It was a wish however, that was even beyond the miracle needed on my side of the bargain. The Smashing Pumpkins had broken up in 2000. The dream to see them play needed not just me to survive, but they also needed to come back from oblivion. A double miracle was required!

If this could ever happen, it would surely be one of the greatest milestones of all. It looked as if my bond with the Smashing Pumpkins would remain forever as a memory of those emotional hospital nights of my early recovery.

On January 27th 2007 Christy and I took to the road again. This time our journey was a lot shorter. We were going to Dublin. We were setting out for another eagerly anticipated concert. If our U2 trip was primarily for him this one was definitely for me. We were going to see the Smashing Pumpkins!

The Pumpkins had reformed in 2006. My double dream of living long enough to see them and they getting back together had come true. I was going to get to see the musical piece of my survival jigsaw after all. I feel as if I have had many divine moments at this stage but this was surely one of them. Somebody, greater than me, had a hand in this. What a beautiful twist this was towards the end of the story. Not just one but two unlikely events were coinciding. The Smashing Pumpkins and I had come back from the dead to make this happen.

To most of the audience in the R.D.S. that night it was a good concert. To me, with tears in my eyes, it was amazing just to be there. I had lived to be there. At some point, during every song, I was transported back five years to ward 29 in Aintree University Hospital. I was singing along again but this time I was free. I was free from bed and tracheotomy and peg tube and pain. I was free and I was here. Once again I sang "LET ME OUT" but now I had been let out. I sang "DESPITE ALL MY RAGE I AM STILL JUST A RAT IN A CAGE" but now I had no rage. But the greatest line of all remained unchanged "TODAY IS THE GREATEST DAY OF MY LIFE".

Now I could appreciate these great songs at their very best. They were not being fed to me through a pair of ear phones as I lay in anguish and torment. This time everything was for real. The Smashing Pumpkins had come to me and I had gone to them. We had both survived. We had both managed to come through and finish what we had started.

That night was the closing of a very special chapter for me. The Smashing Pumpkins and I shared the same space for a couple of hours. This was my music. These were my songs. This was my night.

The music that night recreated the most vivid memories of my treatment I had since leaving hospital. These were the only songs that could tackle what I needed at that time. The only songs I could listen to when my life was dangling in front of me. Now they brought me right back to that time. I was emotional all through the night.

But now I had come from there to here. I had come from lying on a bed of painful uncertainty to standing in front of this incredible band. I had lived to turn hope into reality. This night was a huge testament to how miraculously I had survived. A huge milestone to how incredible my recovery had become. This night was closure all by itself.

All of these social and family achievements were big building blocks in the return of Liam Ryan to the real world. Any final doubts that life number two had now completely caught up with life number one were finally extinguished in 2008. That year the final two missing corner stones were to be put back in place.

All through my recovery I felt I owed a debt to my running. It had been there for me when I needed it most. Now was not the time to turn my back on it. I owed it for what it had done for me. The mental toughness it gave me was an essential piece of my own part of the jigsaw. I owed it because I loved it. I promised my body that I would, if at all possible, get it back to the condition it had enjoyed before my surgery. I was determined to run again.

This was a huge building block. If I could run my recovery would have gone past the point where it could be called a recovery anymore. Running would be an incontestable attestation that I was back to leading a normal life again. It would be more than that. To run seriously again would be confirmation that my normal first life had now been surpassed by my extraordinary second. The man given a 5% chance of life was a lot more than just alive. He was back running again in his late forties.

This was a great new area to shift my, now increasingly frustrated, mental determination into. It was looking for a new challenge. Now it had something new to get its teeth into. My recovery had reached the stage where it was not content just to have won. It wanted to show cancer that it had come and gone without being able to change a single aspect of my life. I had always run. My disease was not going to prevent me running again. Lance Armstrong had got back on his bike, now it was my time to run again.

For the early years of remission running was the furthest thing from my mind. I was in a permanent state of exhaustion. I used to go to bed tired and seemed to wake up just as tired the next morning. If running was to be incorporated as an essential building block of my second life, it would have to be one of the very last. It would have to wait until just about everything else was in place. That, by itself, would make it one of the most conclusive of all.

In the final years of remission I was still too tired to run. I began to worry that I had lost it forever. I could not imagine my life without running, in some form, being part of it. By the summer of 2008, however, I at last began to feel I had sufficient strength to consider it again. I was ready to take my first tentative strides since Ian Connolly ran with me in the weeks before my operation.

We live beside the hurling field in Ballina. It was the ideal location to see what, if anything, I was capable of. A hurling pitch is much bigger than a soccer pitch. A full lap would be a similar distance to a running track with four laps roughly equivalent to a mile. I had always only run on the roads but the pitch allowed me to run as much or as little as I was able to without going anywhere. It was much less daunting than tackling a road run.

The Ballina hurling field provided me with exactly what I needed to start running again. It allowed me to assess exactly what my capabilities were. I could run privately, at my own pace and slowly begin to build up my leg muscles again. I wouldn't return to the roads until I was strong enough to do so.

I managed to persist, on and off, with the hurling field for the remainder of the year. By the spring of 2009 it had served me well. My legs were strong again and the roads of Ballina and Killaloe were waiting for me to return to them once more.

That summer I ran four 10K races. Those runs were huge personal achievements. They were the proof of how far my recovery had now come. The finishing time in each case was nothing of note but the T-shirt and medal collected were earned by a body that had been ravaged by cancer, surgery and radiotherapy. Consequently they were just as treasured as anything received previously, for much better times.

Those four races were great milestones to me privately. I had become my own biggest critic when it came to adjudicating when the end of my recovery had been reached. My own doubts were the greatest of all.

Now there could be no doubt. Most men of my age were not capable of running a 10K and they never had cancer. My recovery had now taken me past where many of my non-cancer suffering peers now stood. It was complete. Lance Armstrong went back to winning the Tour de France. I'm no Lance Armstrong but I was more than happy to be running slow 10K races again. These were the final marker. They drew the line. On one side was a recovering cancer patient. On the other was a man, busy getting on with the rest of his life.

Those 10K runs in 2009 might have been the start but the greatest race of my second life was still to come. I attended a head and neck cancer conference in Liverpool in November that year. It was a lovely trip for me. I was effectively there as a demonstration model. I was on display to show what was possible.

I spent more time with Simon Rogers in those two days than I had ever done previously. We both swopped some of the finer details of my case that neither of us had been aware of before. He asked me to accompany him when he was due to give his annual lecture to the dental students at Liverpool University. As we entered the building he turned to me. "Liam I want you to give this lecture this year." "I can't give a lecture" I replied alarmingly "Just sit down in front of them and tell them your story".

I went in and sat down in front of the students and did as he asked. I was honoured. I was able to tell them that this great man was a lot more than just their lecturer. I let them know that this incredible man did a lot more work than they may have known about. I told them how lucky we all were to have him in the room with us.

I was not expecting "Gave a lecture at Liverpool University" to be a box that my second life would tick. This was further proof that life number two was beginning to overtake life number one. My first life was now beginning to grow envious.

After the lecture Simon graciously said to me, to underline the calibre of the man he is, "They will never remember any of the lectures I have given them but they will always remember yours".

During one of our conversations on this visit I mentioned to him that I was running again. Simon had also been a runner in a previous life. He too had never lost the bug. The head and neck department were looking for a major fundraising event. We discussed between us the possibility of a sponsored 10K run that we could both run together. What an end to an already incredible story this would be. A less than five percent chance to live, a twelve hour operation, two bouts of meningitis, a deep vein thrombosis, a long and difficult recovery and now, after eight years, the surgeon and patient were going to run a 10K together.

On Saturday May 29th 2010 I was once again travelling to Liverpool by ferry. This seemed to be appropriate. I had not been on a ship since making the same journey to begin my treatment in 2002. This time however the reason for travelling could not have been further removed from that original crossing.

The ferry brought back evocative flashbacks of that first voyage, eight years previously. I remembered coming out on deck and looking at all of the people around me. I was wondering where they were going. Were they going over to visit friends or relatives. Perhaps they were about to start a university course or go to a football match. Maybe they were they going over to buy a car or even a greyhound.

I wondered if they, in return, had any inkling as to why I was travelling. I wondered if they knew that I may have been looking back at Ireland for the last time as it disappeared on the horizon. I almost wanted to tell them why I was there. I wanted to tell them that worrying about finding a flat or finding the right greyhound was not a problem. I wanted them to know that of all the passengers on board, I was making the biggest journey of all.

Now I was out on deck looking at them all again. This time however my quizzical analysis was much less burdensome. I wondered if any of them were going over to run the Liverpool 10K. I wondered, perhaps smugly, how many of them were capable of running a 10K. This time I wanted to tell them all that I was going to run a 10K with my surgeon.

I was glad to be on the ferry. It has always been the best way to arrive in Liverpool. I was glad that I now would have two memories of this journey. This trip was the closing of another circle. On the first trip I wanted to tell the passengers that it was likely that I could die. Now I wanted to tell them all that I was a runner.

The Liverpool 10K 2010 began in the city centre. Then it went through the Mersey tunnel and finished in New Brighton on the Wirral. This route itself was hugely significant to me. It linked the two locations where I had my treatment, Aintree on the Liverpool side and Clatterbridge on the Wirral. The darkness of the tunnel inbetween symbolised the black days of the numerous setbacks between treatments.

This was always going to be an emotional day for everybody. The field of runners included surgeons, doctors, nurses, patients, survivors, carers, relatives and friends. The link between us all was cancer. Vivid memories of what everybody had endured, both good and bad, were going to be revived. There were tears and cheers, sadness and jubilation. We all had a great sense of presence that day. An awareness that for one more day all of our lives had been brought together again.

Simon and I started off together, just like we promised each other six months earlier. The surgeon and his patient. The patient and his surgeon. But today we were equals, the runner and the runner. He also had his young son, Matthew, running beside him so that day it was Simon the family man rather than Simon the surgeon. I was carrying a calf strain into the race so soon after we entered the tunnel I had to let them go. It seemed fitting. This wonderful man had saved my life, it just wouldn't have seemed right if I could now run faster than him. I couldn't anyway.

My calf eventually snapped with two miles to go and ruined any chance I had of finishing in a reasonable time. It was a pity. Nothing disappoints a runner more than having to walk and that day I was there as a runner, not a surviving cancer patient. Nonetheless, I was determined to finish. In a strange way, this seemed appropriate too. To hobble along for the last two miles with an unshakable resolve to cross the line was exactly the kind of spirit I had needed eight years previously. The situation had changed but it was nice to see the determination was still there. It had merely shifted from "I'm going to stay alive" to "I'm going to finish this race".

Simon was waiting for me at the finish line. We embraced and I felt so proud to have lived long enough to have shared that moment with him. Just before my surgery he wanted to give me hope that I would be able to return to some kind of sporting activity. He told me that he had a patient who had undergone surgery somewhat like mine and he was now able to play an occasional game of squash. If I did survive, that was the extent of his expectation for me.

I was now able to joke with him that I had come a lot further than an occasional game of squash. I had survived and now, eight years on, had partially run 6 miles beside him. He told me that he never really believed this day could happen. I had taken his less than 5% chance and turned into something incredible for both of us. This day was tribute to his magnificent work and to my spirit to beat cancer. Surgeon and patient together at the finish line.

For that instant I seemed to have the whole world at my feet. If Medjugorje was the closure of my treatment for my heart and soul, this was it for my head, my legs and the remainder of my wonderful body. The merger of the first and second life capabilities was now complete. There now could be no doubt that I was now physically back to where I had been before my cancer arrived.

The final cornerstone of my recovery was put in place in November 2008. Pam spotted an advertisement for the position of construction manager for the new Ecovillage in Cloughjordan. This was a wonderful new project. It was the first development of its kind in Ireland, a completely new village that was to be integrated into the existing village of Cloughjordan in Tipperary. It was only 20 miles from where we lived.

On completion it would comprise 130 new residential units, both houses and apartments and was to include shops, studio spaces, offices, a market square, three community buildings, a district heating system, a riverside boardwalk, a hostel, allotments, playgrounds, performance spaces, an amphitheatre and playing fields. Our own work was beginning to slow down and she prompted me to go for the job.

I went over to see the site and immediately liked what I saw. About €5 million had already been spent. All of the roads, paths and services had been put in place with the individual residential sites just waiting for the building work to begin. I liked the very essence of this project. It was community shaping environment rather than environment creating community. This was a non-profit making development where the future residents had come together to create the place they wanted to live in. It was a development without a developer. This was a building project wholly inspired by the desire to create a nice place to live rather than the profits it could generate for a development company. I wanted to become part of this project. I wanted to help it turn the dream into reality.

I was called for an interview two weeks later. This was my first job interview in twelve years. I had to borrow a suit from my neighbour Brian Commins. The interviews were being held in an upmarket office building in Dublin. I caught sight of a couple of the other candidates in the reception. They were all about half my age and none of them wore an eyepatch. This was the real world.

Across the table in the interview room were five of the most prominent people behind this project. Gregg Allen was one of the founders who came up with the original concept. Aidan O'Brien was one of the main builders on the site. Eamon Ceannt was the director of capital investment at U.C.D., Deirdre O'Brolchain was an I.T. Consultant and Mick Canney was a director of drama at Trinity College. Four of the five would be future residents.

I did a good interview. I based my presentation on the fact that as an architect, as well as an experienced site manager, I had more strings to my bow. I could perhaps offer a more versatile service which I believed they would need.

I also explained my eyepatch. I told them I was already familiar with uphill battles. I would bring not just experience but determination and perspective too. I would commit all of my energies to help every resident and every builder in any way I could to get this project on the move. The focus that had served me so well before would now be aimed at steering the Cloughjordan Ecovillage towards the finish line. I would give everything I had to help achieve that goal.

As I climbed back down the stairs I saw the next person going up for his interview. He looked young and confident. Now I had a reality check. I was 47. All of the others were younger, had their own suits and two, perfectly functioning, eyes. These were strange surroundings for Postman Pat the architect. It was still a long shot.

A week later the phone rang. It was Aidan O'Brien. I had got the job. I was going to be the new construction manager in one of the most exciting projects to be built in Ireland for many years. They had assessed all of the competition and assessed me. Then they picked me. All of this had taken place in the real world of 2008. If I had any lingering doubts up to that point that my recovery was not complete, they were now well and truly quashed. I had jumped into the sea in Turkey, I had run a 10K with my surgeon and now I had landed one of the best jobs in Ireland. My second life was now beginning to act as if it had never known my first.

60 – The Rest of my Life

No matter how long I live now the realisation that I should no longer be here will never be lost on me. There appears to be little logical reason why I did not die in 2002. If a stage 4 cancer did not manage to get me then meningitis and deep vein thrombosis surely should have. The fact that I am still here to write these words, ten years later, is indeed, to me, a miracle. The rest of my life, as a result, will always be treasured as an unexpected gift. My daily church visit is just one of the mechanisms I have to ensure that this appreciation will never be lost.

Everything is a bonus from here. Every day is one more day that I really shouldn't be here. I now need to keep my head in that space. I need to retain a permanent sense of gratitude for how lucky I am to be alive.

My survival was the first miracle. The odds I was given were just to achieve that alone with no promise of how good that survival might be. Then I recovered only for my recovery to become an even bigger miracle than my survival ever was. I watched my body start from scratch again. It had to learn to talk, walk, see, eat, drink and sleep again. Then it started to run, swim, cycle, drive and work again, just as it did before. Now it can run a marathon again. This story is not just one miracle. It is an entire procession of miracles. This story is the proof that the expected outcome is never for certain. It shows that what can happen in life will always be a step ahead of what we believe will happen.

Nothing fazes me now. Not bad weather, or traffic, or being late, or missing a flight. None of them are important compared to what was important to me ten years ago as I lay in intensive care. Perspective is the wonderful gift I have been given by my ordeal. It is a pity that most of us seem to need a crisis before we can find it. I have perspective in spades now and feel privileged to do so. My cancer has done that for me.

Before I got sick my life was a conveyor belt of expectation. There was no time for appreciation or recognition. As soon as one demand was met another was lining up and insisting it was attended to. Expectation brings anxiety that goals will be met. Anxiety brings disappointment when objectives are not achieved. Our lives should not be an endless over-reach. They are not there to be put upon. To just become a series of demands. We need to cherish them. Every moment and every ability should be treasured for the rare gifts that they truly are.

Ten years later I am leading a normal life again. I can do everything I did before only now I do it with a sense of privilege. Everything is done with a realisation of how lucky I am to be able to do it. The end product is no less than before, everything still gets done. The awareness and appreciation of the ability to do it is the difference.

Now as I look over my life, I am blinded by the good in it. I have a wonderful wife. She played an incredible role in keeping me alive. I have been blessed with three fine sons. They will go on and take up their own challenges as their lives unfold. I have three great sisters. They showed me what a great family really is.

I love to work. I know how much I would miss it if it wasn't there. I don't ever want to retire. I live in a lovely place. I live in the midst of a wonderful community. I have incredible friends who I value more than ever before. There is very little wrong in my life. In fact there never was. I just couldn't see it clearly until now.

But I have come so much further than just re-appreciating my life and everybody in it. Cancer has taken a duster to everything I do. On the mantlepiece of my life it has not only dusted off the existing ornaments, allowing me to see them again, it has also added many new ones. I now have so many new aspects to my life that were never there before. I know what the value of my health really is. I now have a tremendous appreciation for the incredible work that all health workers do. They ultimately keep the rest of us alive. In John Fenton, Carmel O'Sullivan, Simon Rogers and David Husband I have four of the finest people in the world embedded forever into the remainder of my life. I will always be indebted to them and their wonderful staff for all their great work.

For these new attributes I can thank my cancer. The jigsaw may be complete but none of the individual pieces will ever be forgotten. My ordeal has gifted me an awareness and an appreciation that I never had before. It has taught me how to value the truly important things in life. None of this would have come to me without getting cancer.

With this sense of new enlightenment the victory is absolute. My cancer is even denied the satisfaction of regretting that I got it in the first place. It will never be acclaimed as a frightening disease that nearly caused my death. Instead it has become just another chapter of my life. One that helped me rediscover the true meaning of what being alive really is. Now, well beyond recovery and long after the fight is over it still can't drag me back towards zero. It will never be credited as the fearsome invader that it craves. Instead it will always just be regarded as a lifetime experience in a lifetime of many experiences. That experience, as it turns out, has brought more that is positive, than negative, to me. My cancer has made me a stronger, happier, more contented individual. For that, ironically, I will always be grateful to it.

I believe in God. I therefore also believe that God had a hand in my survival too. In fact I believe he had the ultimate hand of all. If his piece wasn't in the jigsaw then none of the others would really have mattered. If God has granted me a second chance in life then I also believe it was not without obligation. He didn't just send me back to carry on as before. Equipped with a fresh appreciation of what the value of life truly is I feel a renewed sense of duty to use it well. God has reinvested in me. I don't want to disappoint him. I need to try and eradicate mistakes I was making before. I need to try and be the best person I can be. I need to show it was the right decision to give me a second chance.

My second life has now become an inspiration for all those who are following behind. I am an ambassador now. An ambassador for cancer survivors everywhere. I need to fulfill that role. I want to show that there is always hope. I want to show that nothing is for certain. My survival is the proof of that. I want to use that survival to help anybody facing similar odds to mine. That is the attribute I have now been given.

My second life, under these new terms, was never going to be like my first. It was always going to be better. It is my job to keep making it better. I will not always succeed of course but I need to keep trying. Just like the stations of the cross on Krizevac, I need to keep getting up after I fall. These are the conditions that I believe have been incorporated into my license to continue to be part of this planet. They need to become the basis for everything I try and do from now on. Otherwise the grant of a second life to me has been wasted.

All of these objectives, by a beautiful coincidence, make my life much more fulfilling to lead. I see wonder and beauty where I never saw it before. I try to ensure I continually recognise the little treasures that come along every day. I make myself see the morning sunshine or the gentle rain or a bird in flight or the night sky. Things I was too preoccupied to see before. Simple but beautiful things. Essential elements of life that are around us everyday but we no longer see them. I will never take them for granted again.

And these are just the little things. It is the people in it that make this world truly amazing. I am continuing to meet incredible people. People like Roger and Jean Downer, Aine O'Meara, Richard O'Donnell and Paddy McCaul. At times of despair when you want to see how exceptional this world is, just look around you. We are surrounded by wonder.

Life is a wonderful thing. There is good in every one of us. A lot more good than bad. We just sometimes lose our ability to be able to see it. When you look for it, there it is. I have been blessed in all areas of my life with the best people I could wish to meet. This is not unique to me. We all have great people around us. We just don't recognise them often enough.

In the midst of chaotic, high-speed lives we often lose the ability to appreciate the simple but extraordinary things we can do every day. We can also lose sight of the wonderful humanity that is all around us. I do not intend to lose that vision ever again. I aim to squeeze every delightful drop of being alive for every day that I now live. One year of my new life has become the equivalent of five of my old one. If my second life has been given to me as an unexpected gift, I intend to keep unwrapping it forever.

Who is to say now when my death will come. My natural life has been significantly shortened. I am closer to my death than I would had cancer not come along. Many of the staff in Liverpool are amazed I have lived this long. The radiotherapy that I have undergone has been incredibly destructive to my body. It is also a certainty that one day my cancer will return.

When my death does come it will not be a stranger. I have prepared for it once already. I will recognise it when it comes again. The break glass case that was put away is still on the wall. It will be there for me when I need it for real. None of this is difficult to accept as long as I never lose sight of how lucky I am to still be alive. Every day is a bonus and will be treasured accordingly. My shorter life will be a stronger life as a result. I am immune to the vast majority of everyday worries and stresses. I have a protective shield. It is called perspective.

I will never again be afraid to die. I wasn't afraid before so I won't be afraid again. The miracle of my second life will run until then. Every day is another great day to still be here.

The great advantage of this mindset is that it frees me to spend the remainder of my time being busy living rather than in fear of dying. Whatever I do is tackled because I want to achieve it. When it is completed it is gratefully recorded and privately appreciated. My second life, as a result, has become a procession of milestones. A procession that had to return to cornerstones of my first life to begin. Now it has gone way beyond that. I am registering milestones every day, both big and small. The smallest can be a new encounter on the street or an unexpected sunny day. The greatest are major personal, family or sporting achievements. I have become the ultimate human scrapbook and new pages just keep filling up.

If I was to die today, every second of my life since my surgery would have been worth it. I have been granted ten years that were not predicted. I treasure every moment of them. I have watched my young family grow up. I have been on holidays with them and been with them at memorable matches and concerts. I have run a 10K with Simon Rogers. I became the construction manager of the Cloughjordan Ecovillage. In my three years it grew from no houses to nearly sixty. I have been back to the Millenium Stadium in Cardiff to a Heineken Cup final with Eddie Rooney. I have been to Medjugorje. I have enjoyed memorable evenings in Seamus Malone's pub enthralled by the hilarious stories that only Jim Nihill can tell. I have worked with great men like Jim Egan from Puckane and Pat Burke from Bodyke. I have seen the Smashing Pumpkins!

But the greatest part of this story is still to come. I still have one outstanding milestone before I am done. 2012 is the tenth anniversary of the year I was told I had cancer. I was forty then. Now I am fifty. This is going to be my year. My time to give something back.

The biggest challenge of all remains unfulfilled. Now it is in my sights. The greatest milestone of my second life was always going to be my first marathon, post cancer. With it came an incredible opportunity. The opportunity to turn my story on its head to help other cancer sufferers follow where I have led.

I have been handed a torch and now I have the opportunity to run that torch to an incredible destination. I was a runner first, then a cancer survivor and now I am a runner again. Now I can run so that others will survive.

My first marathon since my cancer struck is an opportunity to let my disease know the fight goes on. It will come back one day so I am going to fight it until then. This is my opportunity to raise the funds that will save the lives of many like me. This is my chance to give this already amazing story a truly incredible ending.

Cancer selected me as its victim. Now I am selecting it. I am going to dedicate the rest of my life to continuing the fight. It chose me for one of its worst cases. But it made one big mistake. It did not take away my ability to run. It has left me with a platform to exact revenge. Now the fight is on my terms.

In 2012 I am going to run my first marathon post cancer. My first marathon in twelve years. For this run and many more in the coming years my aim is to raise €3 million to fight cancer. The money I raise may one day lead to a cure being found for this incredible disease. By selecting me, cancer may have ultimately led to its own eventual downfall. This is my mission now. My fight had never gone away. It was only looking for its next target.

My inspiration for this is a wonderful girl from England called Jane Tomlinson. Jane Tomlinson was an extraordinary woman. She sadly died in 2007 after her cancer returned to her in 2001. At that point she was told she had twelve months to live. Over the next six years, in spite of terminal cancer, Jane ran four marathons, as well as other grueling pursuits and raised £1.85 million for cancer charities. She knew she had the C.V. to do this. She dedicated the remainder of her life to raising money to fight her disease for the benefit of others who would come after her. I know I am one of the very few with that C.V. too. Jane carried that torch for as long as she could. Now I believe I have a duty to pick it up for her carry it again. I am honoured to be able to even try to follow where she has led. This is what my second life is for.

So this story is really only beginning. It will not end until I can run no more. By then I hope to have raised millions to have continued to carry the fight to cancer. On that day I hope God will decide that he was right to send me back.

Who knows how many more days I will live to enjoy. Who knows how many more milestones are on their way. Who knows how far I have yet to run. Who knows how many more pages of the scrapbook are to be filled in.

Only one person knows. When he decides my time is up then this story will be over. Until that day comes there are many more adventures ahead. There is a family to be treasured and friends to be appreciated. There are roads to be run. There is money to be raised. There are lives to be saved and a disease to be beaten.

Until that day comes my life will be lived every day and cherished every second. I will try to acknowledge every step that is taken, every place that is visited, every person that is met. I will be grateful for every beat of my heart, every drop of my blood, every hair on my head, every breath to my lungs. I will try to make sure my eye appreciates everything it sees, my ears everything they hear, my tongue everything it tastes. I will continue to run what I see until the day I can run and see no more.

Life is a wonderful gift. It is a gift that is sadly denied to many of us far too soon. Those of us still fortunate enough to be enjoying it should never lose sight of how wonderful it is. If it has taken cancer for me to fully appreciate that then yes, it probably is one of the best things that ever happened to me!

POST SCRIPT

And so, after ten years, the book has finally been written. The yoke of this story has been taken from my shoulders. I have written it down and now it can be passed on without me.

I hope you found something in it. Something to inspire you, something to encourage you, even just something to make you smile. I hope it has given you renewed strength as you face your mountain, whatever that mountain may be. I hope it has provided you with an appetite for the climb. There are many beautiful things in this life. Many wonderful things that we lose sight of and take for granted. One of those things is that hope is never lost. Nothing is for certain. Don't ever give up.

And now that it is written maybe one day somebody will decide this book would make a good film. If so I already have a suggestion for what the title of that film could be. It could be called "Saving Ryan's Privates"!

LIAM RYAN CANCER APPEAL

Bank A/C No. 83457312, Bank of Ireland, Nenagh, Co. Tipperary

Please help me with my new mountain – to raise €3 million for cancer patients who must follow behind me – Thank you.

Liam can be contacted at
liamryan5cancer4@gmail.com